OTHER
SOLITUDES

OTHER SOLITUDES

CANADIAN MULTICULTURAL FICTIONS

EDITED BY
LINDA HUTCHEON
& MARION RICHMOND

Toronto
OXFORD UNIVERSITY PRESS

Oxford University Press, 70 Wynford Drive, Don Mills, Ontario M3C 1J9

Toronto   Oxford   New York
Delhi   Bombay   Calcutta   Madras   Karachi   Kuala Lumpur
Singapore   Hong Kong   Tokyo   Nairobi   Dar es Salaam
Cape Town   Melbourne   Auckland   Madrid

and associated companies in
Berlin   Ibadan

To the Rossi and Bortolotti families—L.H.
To my father, Lawrence Tapper, who helped to build the
Canadian North—M.R.

The publisher gratefully acknowledges support for this project from the Multiculturalism Sector, Department of the Secretary of State of Canada, and the Canadian Publishing Foundation.

Canadian Cataloguing in Publication Data

Main entry under title:

Other solitudes : Canadian multicultural fictions

Includes bibliographical references.
ISBN 0-19-540756-3

1. Multiculturalism – Canada – Literary
collections.*   2. Immigrants – Canada – Literary
collections.   3. Minorities – Canada – Literary
collections.   4. Canadian fiction (English) – 20th
century.*   5. Authors, Canadian – 20th century –
Interviews.   I. Hutcheon, Linda, 1947–
II. Richmond, Marion.

PS8323.M8074 1990   C810'.08355   C90-095046-3
PR9197.35.M8074 1990

OXFORD is a trademark of Oxford University Press
3 4 5 6 7 – 97 96 95 94 93
Printed in Canada by D.W. Friesen & Sons Ltd.

CONTENTS

PREFACE

Fifty years ago the term multiculturalism — as we understand it in Canada today — was unknown, and a book such as this would not have been considered an important literary endeavour. Although from early times Canada has been a cultural mosaic, and early writers such as Frederick Philip Grove and Susanna Moodie before him have had a profound influence, our literature did not reflect this mosaic until the late 1940s, when, beginning with Jewish writers such as A.M. Klein, a new generation of writers looked to their cultural roots for inspiration. At that time Canada still consisted *officially* of only two separate peoples — the French (mostly in Quebec) and the English (everywhere else); people of other ethnic and racial origins, however important their role in building this country, had to conform to the two official cultures. The Canadian Multiculturalism Act, declaring as its goal the preservation and enhancement of Canada's multicultural heritage, was passed only recently, in July 1988.

Over the last four decades, literature dealing with the immigrant experience, racism, and ethnic diversity in this country has gained an audience. The aim of this book is to explore the nature of our cultural diversity in the fiction of eighteen contemporary writers and in conversations with them. These writers and their interviewers, themselves immigrants or the children of immigrants, are particularly qualified to probe, to analyse, and to evaluate the experience of the 'other solitudes'. To explore the impact of multiculturalism further, it was considered important to include interviews with writers from our first and founding nations. As Margaret Atwood wrote in *The Journals of Susanna Moodie*, 'we are all immigrants to this place even if we were born here.' This awareness is a fundamental part of the Canadian sensibility.

Marion Richmond
February 1990

ACKNOWLEDGEMENTS

We would like to thank the Department of the Secretary of State, Multiculturalism and the Canadian Publishing Foundation for their assistance in funding this volume.

For their invaluable assistance, we would also like to thank the Honourable Gerry Weiner, Minister of State, Multiculturalism and Citizenship; Edward Richmond, QC; Richard Teleky, our editor at the press.

Marion Richmond
Linda Hutcheon

HIMANI BANNERJI 'The Other Family' is used by permission of the author. NEIL BISSOONDATH 'Dancing' from *Digging Up the Mountains* by Neil Bissoondath © 1984. Reprinted by permission of Macmillan of Canada, A Division of Canada Publishing Corporation. DIONNE BRAND 'Blossom: Priestess of Oya, Goddess of winds, storms and waterfalls' from *Sans Souci*. Reprinted by permission of Williams-Wallace Publishers. AUSTIN CLARKE 'Canadian Experience' from *Nine Men Who Laughed* by Austin Clarke. Copyright © Austin Clarke, 1986. Reprinted by permission of Penguin Books Canada Limited. MATT COHEN 'Racial Memories' from *Living on Water* is used by permission of the author. JANICE KULYK KEEFER 'Mrs Mucharski and the Princess' is reprinted from *The Paris-Napoli Express* by permission of Oberon Press. JOY KOGAWA 'Obasan' is used by permission of the author. MARILU MALLET 'How Are You' from *Voyage to the Other Extreme* translated by Alan Brown. Used by permission of Vehicule Press. ROHINTON MISTRY 'Swimming Lessons' from *Tales of Firozsha Baag* by Rohinton Mistry. Copyright © Rohinton Mistry, 1987. Reprinted by permission of Penguin Books Canada Limited. MICHAEL ONDAATJE 'The Bridge' from *In the Skin of a Lion* by Michael Ondaatje. Used by permission of the Canadian Publishers, McClelland and Stewart, Toronto. FRANK PACI 'The Stone Garden' is used by permission of the author. MORDECAI RICHLER From *The Street* by Mordecai Richler. Used by permission of the Canadian Publishers, McClelland and Stewart, Toronto. JOSEF SKVORECKY From *The Engineer of Human Souls* by Josef Skvorecky, © 1979. English translation © Paul Wilson, 1984. Reprinted by permission of Lester & Orpen Dennys Publishers Ltd, Canada. YESHIM TERNAR 'Ajax là-bas' is used by permission of the author. W.D. VALGARDSON 'The Man from Snaefellsness' from *What Can't Be Changed Shouldn't be Mourned*. Used by permission of the author and The Bukowski Agency. KATHERINE VLASSIE 'A Proper Goodbye' from *Children of Byzantium*. Used by permission of Cormorant Books. RUDY WIEBE 'Sailing to Danzig' is used by permission of the author. PAUL YEE 'Prairie Widow' is used by permission of the author.

LINDA HUTCHEON

Introduction

I — 'A Spell of Language':
Introducing Other Solitudes

'But it was a spell of language that brought Nicholas here, arriving
in Canada without a passport in 1914, a great journey made in
silence. Hanging under the bridge, he describes the adventure to
himself, just as he was told a fairy tale of Upper America by those
who returned to the Macedonian villages . . .'

Michael Ondaatje, 'The Bridge'

The initial purpose of *Other Solitudes* was to break through what
one commentator has called 'the protective shell of Canadian-style
tolerance: acceptance without concern'.[1] Its articulation of *concern* — through questions about multicultural identity posed to and
by writers of fiction — explores both the *lived* experience and the
literary expression of multiculturalism in Canada at this particular
historical moment. For this reason you will find here both fiction
and interviews. The conversations frequently address crucial issues,
such as racism and cultural confusions and tensions, in a direct, even
confrontational manner, and no attempt has been made either to
direct or to censor them. The stories raise similar issues, but they
also clearly point to the important role played by the images we
create and the stories we tell in our sense of identity and self-worth.
In Himani Bannerji's story 'The Other Family', a young East Indian
child's drawing of a clichéd, textbook 'Canadian' family provokes this
response:

> Listen, said the mother, this is not your family. I, you and your
> father are dark-skinned, dark-haired. I don't have a blond wig
> hidden in my closet, my eyes are black, not blue, and your father's
> beard is black, not red, and you, do you have a white skin, a button
> nose with freckles, blue eyes and blond hair tied into a pony tail?
> You said you drew our family. This is not it, is it?

The power of such images and stories is what this collection explores.
     As two women with manifestly 'Anglo' marital surnames that mask
Eastern European/Jewish and Italian backgrounds, we have deliberately entitled this book *Other Solitudes* in order to recall and revise

Hugh MacLennan's earlier designation of Canada as 'two solitudes'. In 1945, perhaps, French and English were still the dominant ethno-cultural groups in Canada; certainly the only people who could con-test their historical claim to founding status were the indigenous native populations. Almost half a century later, however, the multira-cial, pluri-ethnic nature of Canada is an undeniable reality. And one of the consequences of this change is that MacLennan's idealistic optimism has to be reconsidered, for his title alluded to a poem by Rainer Maria Rilke: 'Love consists in this / that two solitudes protect, / and touch, and greet each other'. With the cultural diversity that twentieth-century immigration has brought to Canada have come both cultural riches and social tensions that move far beyond those of bilingualism and biculturalism. When, on 12 July 1988, the House of Commons passed Bill C-93, 'An Act for the preservation and enhancement of multiculturalism in Canada', it enshrined both an ideal and an ideology. This book investigates the intersection of the tensions and the riches, the ideal and the ideology.

In using the term 'multicultural' in our subtitle, we rather pointedly avoid the term 'ethnic'. The two historical strands that weave the meaning of the latter are as problematic for us as for many others, as shown in this book by the conversations between Frank Paci and Joseph Pivato and between Mordecai Richler and Marlene Kadar. The first strand—from the Greek root *ethnos*, meaning 'nation' or 'people'—should suggest that *all* Canadians are ethnic, including French and British; the fact that the word is *not* so used points to a hierarchy of social and cultural privilege that this collection wants to challenge. The second strand of meaning is derived from usage: whether in its earlier associations with 'pagan' and 'heathen' or in its more recent ones with 'foreign', the word 'ethnic' always has to do with the social positioning of the 'other', and is thus never free of relations of power and value. Yet these are the very issues raised by the structure of this book, as well as by the individual voices within it.

In selecting the writers and interviewers as well as the works to be included, we were guided by a number of both choices and inherent limitations. The latter are perhaps obvious: of the great number of ethnocultural and language groups that have active writers residing and working in Canada, we could include only a small frac-tion. The authors included here have their roots in Czechoslovakia, Barbados, Russia, Japan, Iceland-Ireland, Bangladesh, Sri Lanka, Chile, Italy, Greece, India, the Ukraine, Trinidad, Turkey, and China.

Some have their primary social and cultural roots in religious group-ings, especially Jewish and Mennonite. The fact that almost half the writers are members of what are now called 'visible minorities' marks a significant new development in Canadian immigration patterns. The interviewers' backgrounds are similarly diverse: Polish, Hungar-ian, Turkish-East European, Italian, Mennonite, Scots-Irish, Indian, British, Czech, Ukrainian, Scots-Indian, Finnish, and Jewish. Despite this variety, the list is obviously not complete. Some groups are not represented at all, and others have multiple representation. There are, for instance, three West Indian writers because important differ-ences of gender, race, age, and time of arrival in Canada seemed worth exploring in one sample group, even if we could not do so for all. There are also a number of Jewish writers—again, of differing ages and backgrounds—representing the diversity within the cultural group that has produced so many Canadian writers, in both the past and the present. The most obvious omission might well be someone originally from the United States, but the political and cultural ambi-guities of Canada's relations with her powerful southern neighbour are the topic of conversation in over half the interviews here.

Following these interviews and stories, a section entitled 'The First and Founding Nations Respond' adds another layer of historical complexity to the various questions raised. Robertson Davies' essen-tially positive, perhaps complacent, faith in the notion of something 'Canadian' at the heart of multiculturalism is challenged by what Jacques Godbout sees as overshadowing both: 'I am still fighting for the presence of the French language,' he says. The first voice, that of native playwright Tomson Highway, poses new questions and suggests interesting, perhaps unexpected, resolutions which under-line the historical fact that what we now call Canada has always been multicultural, that it has always negotiated the space between social tension and cultural richness.

Within the restrictions of availability and of the necessity of selec-tion, then, we have attempted to present a range of ages and genera-tions, as well as races and ethnicities, in both authors and interviewers. Approximately half are Canadian-born; half have immi-grated to Canada as either children or adults. We have selected a mixture of well-known, 'mainstream' writers and younger or less familiar ones, and have ordered them by chronological age. Some interviews are very personal, while others are didactic, teaching us about the more public experience of multiculturalism; some conver-sations are literary in their emphasis, while others are more social, even sociological. This range could not have been planned, but the variety should ensure that all readers find something of interest here. We have not removed the unexpected and often ironic points of unintended dialogue: at one point, Frank Paci asks how Michael Ondaatje and Joy Kogawa feel about their status as 'other', for instance, and elsewhere in the book you can indeed read how they do feel; Matt Cohen asks where the Greek, Italian, or West Indian writers of Canadian cities are—and one answer is: on these pages.

One point must be emphasized, however: this book is an exploration of the meeting-ground of experience and literary expression in individual writers. These writers are not necessarily meant to speak for any group as a whole; indeed, as several interviews show, both the individuals and the groups in question might well reject such a role, however straightforward it may seem. Each writer has a special agenda; each is working out his or her relations with a particular group and with the nation in individual ways. Having said that, I should add that there is also a sense in which their very appearance in this volume unavoidably grants them all representative roles. Yet the fiction and the conversations you will read show that even writers within the same racial or ethnic grouping often disagree on the function or success of multiculturalism as both policy and reality. Nevertheless, some—such as Paul Yee and Himani Bannerji—clearly feel they want to speak *to*, if not *for*, a particular cultural community. Others, however—such as Yeshim Ternar, Mordecai Richler, and Michael Ondaatje—seem to see their audience as much broader, perhaps because of a fear of parochialism or of becoming a 'professional immigrant'. In his story 'Swimming Lessons', Rohinton Mistry uses gentle but pointed irony to express his fears about this last danger. As the protagonist's parents in India read his first published stories, we are told:

> The last story they liked best of all because it had the most in it about Canada . . . and Father said if he continues to write about such things he will become popular because I am sure they are interested there in reading about life through the eyes of an immigrant, it provides a different viewpoint; the only danger is if he changes and becomes so much like them that he will write like one of them and lose the important difference.

Multiculturalism, for all the extremes of 'hype' and cynicism, is real and immediate for Canadians. As many others have noted, this is not just because most of us can quite easily trace our origins or perhaps

even our arrival from elsewhere. Nor is it simply because the media
are quick to present racial and ethnic tensions or to show us Chinese,
Tamil, Polish, or Armenian Canadians responding to events in their
homelands on the streets of Canada. The multiracial and multi-
ethnic nature of this country is made real to us — is written into our
consciousness of what it means to be Canadian — by Canadian writers.
To read their writing here in a multicultural context is not to homoge-
nize differences, nor to forget that the French and British are themselves 'ethnic' and different. It is to recognize that literature depends
on the whole of culture, of history and social traditions, without
reducing diversity to ethnocultural enclaves. It is, in the end, to help
ourselves understand that there are ways of seeing the world, and of
writing in and about it, that may be different from our own ways —
whatever they might be — and valuable because of that difference.
Dutch Canadian novelist Aritha Van Herk evokes well the challenges
not only of writing in a multicultural context but of reading as well:

> Imagine a country as this country is, peopled by characters who
> have abandoned their setting and who seek to plot their own story
> in a new way. They choose to displace themselves, to surrender
> the familiar. . . . Curiously enough, bcause they make the choices,
> they are happy, if not always satisfied with their story, and the
> effects of displacement only begin to appear in the children or
> grandchildren. Some people would say that it is only a matter of
> adapting to a new environment, or adjusting to custom, of learning
> a language. I maintain that it is much more profound, a displace-
> ment so far-reaching that it only vanishes after several generations.
> At least it was for me. I learned that the world was fiction and
> fiction was refuge.[2]

II — The Dilemmas of Diversity

'. . . a Canadian is a hyphen . . . we're diplomats by birth.'

Joy Kogawa, in conversation with Magdalene Redekop

There is no obvious place to start any investigation of the ethnocult-
ural diversity that has created what we call 'multiculturalism' in
Canada today — or, indeed, what we call 'Canada' today. The tempta-
tion is to resort to lists: for example, lists of ethnicities, races, or
religions represented in the country. The latter alone would yield:
Christian (in all its various forms), Jewish, Rastafarian, Muslim,
Hindu, Buddhist, Sikh . . . But could even this list ever be exhaustive?-
And would it account for the cultural differences among Mennonites,

Hutterites, Doukhobors, and other Christian-based social groupings? Even listing by the broader category of ethnicity — in the sense of shared cultural, linguistic, racial, national, or religious background — risks oversimplifying. For example, as many have pointed out, both the census category of 'British' and the politically loaded, colloquial 'WASP' mask significant differences: Celtic vs. English, types of Protestantism, historical enmities. Could we even generalize by local region? Is the story of the Canadian West really the tale of Ukrainian immigrants as told by fiction writers such as Maara Haas, Myrna Kostash, and, before them, Vera Lysenko and Illya Kiriak? If so, what do we do with Laura Goodman Salverson's *The Viking Heart*, Adele Wiseman's *The Sacrifice*, or even Margaret Laurence's Scottish/Métis Manawaka stories?

I have deliberately shifted ground here from history to novels, because the purpose of this collection of fiction and conversations is to investigate not only how multiculturalism is *lived* but how it is *written into* Canadian life. The cultural richness that immigration has brought to this country has changed forever our concept of what constitutes 'Canadian literature'. Let me take just one example, but a typical one: to talk of South Asian writing in Canada today is to talk of writers like Himani Bannerji, Rohinton Mistry, Michael Ondaatje, and Neil Bissoondath — who all appear in this volume — but there are other writers whose names you may not yet know as well, but who are writing and publishing in Canada: Krisantha Sri Bhaggiyadatta, Rienzi Crusz, Cyril Dabydeen, Lakshmi Gill, Reshart Gool, Suniti Namjoshi, Uma Parameswaran, Asoka Weerasinghe, S. Padmanab, and many others. What even this partial listing hides, however, is that South Asian writers come from India, Pakistan, Bangladesh, Sri Lanka, Nepal, Afghanistan, the Maldive Islands — often via East or South Africa, the West Indies, Guyana, Fiji, Mauritius, or the Malay Peninsula, not to mention Europe and elsewhere in North America. This historical and cultural complexity is emblematic of the difficulties facing any attempt to generalize about the consequences of multiculturalism for any group of writers.

The difficulties do not stop there, however. Both the lived experience and the literary impact of multiculturalism in Canada vary according to an intricate set of variables in the lives of both authors and the characters they create: the time and conditions of immigration, age, gender, class, religion, race. Even education can be a factor: not all immigrants feel as superior to Canadians as does Josef Skvorecky's protagonist in *The Engineer of Human Souls*. And, as is seen in the stories by Joy Kogawa and Rohinton Mistry, and in the conversations between Frank Paci and Joseph Pivato or Janice Kulyk Keefer and Jars Balan, time and place of education can make for rifts between family generations that are not easily bridged, that create what Mordecai Richler in *The Street* calls 'the familiar and agonizing process of alienation between immigrant parents and Canadian-born children'. It seems to make a difference, too, if one has emigrated by free choice or through economic or political necessity. Sometimes, an immigrant such as Nicholas Temelcoff in Ondaatje's 'The Bridge' finds Canada a refuge, however difficult the uprooting; even more frequently, however, as the story by Austin Clarke shows, what immigrants have found upon arrival has not been an easy life, for some not even an improved one, at least in material terms. Learning a new language, as Marilú Mallet's story illustrates, is often part of the difficulty: being able to speak English or French is potentially a sign of belonging. Yeshim Ternar's 'Ajax là-bas' addresses the blocks to that sense of belonging: 'We come here to speak like them, she thinks; but it will be a long time before they let us practice.' For writers language is bound to be a central issue, as both Rudy Wiebe and Josef Skvorecky explore in very different ways in the interviews here. And for women (even beyond their specific social groups), the old structures of patriarchal society seem to die hard, even in the New World, even at the end of the twentieth century. The stories in this book by Katherine Vlassie, Paul Yee, Janice Kulyk Keefer, Neil Bissoondath, and W.D. Valgardson all deal with various gender-related problems, as does the conversation between Himani Bannerji and Arun Mukherjee.

The other thing that resists change, as the fiction and interviews here sadly show, is that the single most significant factor in the response to multiculturalism in Canada today appears to be race. It would be naïve to think that the various waves of European immigration did not create social tensions in Canada: the very existence of abusive terms such as 'wop' or 'bohunk' or 'kraut' bears witness to the contrary. Not even those groups that seemed to fit Canada's unofficial self-image as a northern nation ('the true north strong and free') — such as the Scandinavians and Germans — have escaped. Canada does not have an unblemished past with regard to racism, but with increasing numbers of immigrants who, as Jacques Godbout here puts it, are 'visibly different, have different religions, different attitudes toward women' and different political histories, racism is once again a concern that cannot be ignored. The often subtle signs of social or employment discrimination today are explored in Austin Clarke's 'Canadian Experience' and in the Mistry/Novak and Ternar/Leith dialogues. But Mordecai Richler's selection from *The Street* recalls that even wartime Canada was already seen as a place that was 'flawed and hostile' to Jews, and the interviews with Paul Yee and Austin Clarke remind us of a longer history of racism in this country, a history whose colonial legacy is further investigated in the Bannerji/Mukherjee and Bissoondath/Srivastava conversations. The prejudice may be subtle or blatant, but few non-white — or Jewish — writers will deny that it can exist, masked behind the rhetoric of tolerance that is an intrinsic part of multiculturalism.

Yet not only white Canadians are guilty of this. Rohinton Mistry talks to Dagmar Novak about the racism he has found in India; Magdalene Redekop tells Joy Kogawa of finding the same in Japan. And, as Yeshim Ternar explains, racism is often hard to pinpoint: 'But what is prejudice, and what is curiosity, and what is tactless questioning?' she asks. And, both Paul Yee and Austin Clarke ask, what is racist stereotyping? And on what grounds does such thinking become exclusive, alienating those of other races and religions? asks Matt Cohen's story 'Racial Memories'. In his novella *Intelligence*, Lebanese Canadian writer Marwan Hassan's protagonist expresses his irritation at being asked why the West, especially its press, does not see Arabs in a positive light: 'I long ago gave up trying to understand why Arabs are disliked. . . . The average Canadian has never even so much as met one of us, there are too few of us.'[3] In a recent article, Neil Bissoondath puts such Canadian racial intolerance in context: 'racism is as Canadian as maple syrup,' he writes, but 'it is also as American as apple pie, as French as croissants, as Jamaican as ackee, as Indian as aloo, as Chinese as chow mein.'[4] His story 'Dancing' deals with what might be called 'reverse racism' — of blacks against whites — and it should likely be read in the light of the twist that Bissoondath is not black himself, but of Indian descent.

Racism extends not only to relatively new arrivals to Canada but to those who were here well before any European colonizers; yet this is something that Canada's idealistic multicultural ideology has not really addressed. Canada is not a new country; it is old, in both physical and cultural terms; it has been lived in by our native peoples for longer than it has been colonized. Yet our Euro-centric concepts of history more often than not fail to note this fact and thus condemn to silence the past of the land and its peoples. And for those silenced by this Euro-centrism, the cultural stakes are high. Canadian novelist and playwright George Ryga often commented that in the Alberta in which he grew up, Ukrainians and natives were considered equally inferior.[5] Métis writer Maria Campbell has said that she didn't understand her own people's history of injustice until she had read about the Mennonite and other communities' histories.[6] Rudy Wiebe reverses this, claiming that his Mennonite background has helped him understand the dispossession and displacement of native peoples.

I do not mean to suggest either that all Canadians are racist or that the response to being non-white in Canada is a single, monolithic one. Nor is race the only factor, especially for writers, for whom language always plays such a crucial role. This is the case not only for those who must learn English or French, as we have seen, but also for those who speak either as their native tongue. Austin Clarke's novel *The Bigger Light* illustrates, through its portrayal of a Barbadian couple in Toronto, the difficulties of generalizing: the husband, aware that language is power and embarrassed by his West Indian-ness, seeks a new way to speak; his wife too represses her accent and idiom at work, but revels in them when she is with Island friends. For her, they do not represent all that was left behind; rather, they become the symbol of the living link with that past. This split response, of course, may well be typical of the kind of tension felt by any immigrants to any new place. Doubleness, as many commentators have pointed out, is the essence of the immigrant experience. Caught between two worlds, the immigrant negotiates a new social space; caught between two cultures and often languages, the writer negotiates a new literary space. That this can be a difficult process is perhaps obvious; that it is shared by our native people is perhaps less so. Meeks Uniuqsaraq, an Inuit high-school student, writes: 'Language is one of our most important traditions; if we lose our language to French and English, we lose ourselves.'[7]

But we should not lose sight of the positive possibilities. In Suwanda Sugunasiri's words, 'Canadian literature is an ocean fed by many a river in which flow the tears and joys of our 70 or so cultural groups,'[8] and the merging of those rivers has not left any of the waters unchanged. When a Toronto Jewish photographer like Robert Minden and a Malaysian/Anglo immigrant poet like Daphne Marlatt choose to represent in images and words a Japanese Canadian fishing town, the result is *Steveston* — a book that could be called postmodern, or even post-colonial. I introduce those two 'post-' words here because the literary products of Canada's multicultural ideology can be seen to partake of both cultural phenomena. Their common valuing of the 'different' and what has been considered marginal over what is deemed central has marked a major shift in cultural thinking; their common use of rhetorical strategies such as irony and allegory — in order to confront dominant literary forms and traditions — has marked much Canadian writing. History leaves its mark on our literature; it always has.

III — *Canadian History* as *Multicultural*

'You come telling me you going to Canada as a' immigrant? To be a stranger? Where Canada is? What is Canada?'

West Indian father to son, in Austin Clarke's 'Canadian Experience'

The history of Canada, as it was taught to most of us, is the history of immigration. It also happens to be the history of European colonialism and of native displacement and cultural erasure: whether, as Susanna Moodie felt, emigration from Britain in the last century was a 'matter of necessity, not of choice' — 'an act of severe duty' — or whether it marked the imperial usurpation of lands already occupied depends on whose history is being written — and read. Whichever way the story is told, what we today call 'multiculturalism' figures prominently: all Canadians of other than native stock are originally immigrants from somewhere, and even the native peoples are and were plural — in other words, multicultural. Whether the Europeans came as explorers, fishermen, missionaries, fur traders, or homesteaders, they came from elsewhere. The Canadian West, for example, was settled by a mixture of British, American, German, Scandinavian, Russian, Polish, and, especially, Ukrainian immigrants, who brought with them not only different languages and customs, but different religions. According to Canadian geographer Cole Harris's 'archipelago' theory of Canadian regionalism,[9] the historical settlement pattern — island by island, across the country — created socially and culturally disparate groupings that were internally linked by networks of local and kinship traditions. Our country, in other words, was set up — historically and demographically — in such a way that the eventual formulation of something like multiculturalism might seem to have been inevitable. While many immigrants have thought of Canada as a 'new' society in a New World — or in what today one might call, along with Skvorecky's narrator in *The Engineer of Human Souls*, a 'country of cities with no past' — the multicultural history of Canada is not a recent one. And the traces of that longer history can be seen literally in the marks left by many immigrants on the face of the cities and farms where they lived and worked.

The Loyalist migration following American independence in the last quarter of the eighteenth century had injected a rich racial and ethnic mix into early Canadian society: Highland Scots, French Huguenots, Swiss Germans, Dutch, Joseph Brant's natives, black Loyalists. African blacks had, of course, arrived in Canada as early as the beginning of the seventeenth century—as slaves at Louisbourg and Halifax auctions—and in the mid-1800s, the Underground Railroad brought still others. Earlier in that century, the Irish famine, the unemployment following the Napoleonic wars, and the Scottish enclosure laws had already provided more immigrants and perhaps entrenched the image of Canada as a refuge for what Hugh MacLennan once somewhat disparagingly called 'the flotsam and jetsam of defeated racial and political groups'.[10] Europeans left homeless by this century's wars have found Canada a safe haven, as have other victims of foreign political strife: Hungarians, Czechs, Ugandan Asians, Haitians, Lebanese, Tamils, Chileans, Vietnamese. For still others, Canada—though often a second choice to the United States— has seemed to offer economic opportunities for a better life: Italians, Portuguese, Greeks, Koreans, Chinese, South Asians, West Indians. As various stories in this book suggest by their settings, many (though by no means all) settled in Canada's largest cities—Montreal, Toronto, Vancouver, Winnipeg.

While the view of Canada as a tolerant, welcoming nation is to some extent valid, the fiction and dialogues here suggest that it must not be accepted without acknowledging an equally compelling history of intolerance: from the extermination of the Beothuk in Newfoundland to the restriction of the other native peoples to reserves; from the deportation of the Acadians to the cultural denigration of French Canada in Lord Durham's Report; from the head tax collected only on Chinese immigrants to the displacement and internment of all Japanese Canadians during the last war; from the deportation of the sick, poor, unemployed, or politically radical in the first decades of this century to the refusal to accept European Jews before the Holocaust. In 1988 the Canadian government did grant $300-million compensation to the interned Japanese Canadians, but the Chinese National Council is still seeking redress for the injustice of both the head tax and the Chinese Immigration (Exclusion) Act that for twenty-four years represented the only such racially and nationally specific exclusion in Canadian law.

There is another fear felt by many Canadians who are not of French or English heritage, a fear that seems to contradict this historical memory of prejudice based on difference: this is the fear of assimilation. The tension between wanting to belong to the new society and yet wanting to retain the culture of the old one obviously varies from person to person in intensity and emotional weight. But it is rarely absent. Himani Bannerji, both in conversation with Arun Mukherjee and in her story 'The Other Family', voices her concern that the next generation (by choice or by indoctrination) may not want to retain the cultural links with the past. As Skvorecky ironically puts it, they would become 'Anglo-Saxons with names like Bellissimmo, Hakim, Svensson'. Paci's Italian-born boys in 'The Stone Garden' have differing memories of an Italy now left behind. Yet the tensions exist there too, as they try to exclude from their Italian group a Scottish Canadian girl — as much for reasons of ethnicity as because she is female. Yet other writers, as Joy Kogawa reveals at the end of her talk with Magdalene Redekop, feel that the mixing of races and ethnicities — both in general cultural terms and through intermarriage — is part of the Canadian identity and need not be deplored. Indeed, she may be demographically correct: Statistics Canada reports that, according to the 1986 census, 28 per cent of Canadians are descended from more than one ethnic group.

Despite the fact that fully 100 per cent of non-native Canadians are immigrants or from immigrant backgrounds, a CBC television report stated that 64 per cent of those polled by Environics in 1988 felt that too many immigrants were being allowed into Canada. What can this discrepancy mean? Historical amnesia might account for some part, but ethnocentrism and xenophobia cannot be discounted, even in a country that, since 1971, has been officially multicultural.

IV — Multicultural Policy and its Discontents

'Canadians have begun to come into their own — no longer colonial, no longer defined in negatives only, no longer a huge blank on the map of humanity, but empowered, mature, and free at last to aspire to that multiracial democracy that a few of our number once glimpsed in dreams of the future.'   William Kilbourn[11]

One of those who 'glimpsed' the possibilities of a different Canada was Pierre Elliott Trudeau. For years, bilingualism and biculturalism carried the weight of defining what 'Canadian' meant (thanks to a silent ignoring of the First Nations). In 1970 the Royal Commission on Bilingualism and Biculturalism offered for general consideration what, in the fourth volume of its report, it called *The Cultural Contribution of the Other Ethnic Groups*, and in 1971 Trudeau acknowledged that contribution in the form of a policy statement about Canada's multicultural identity. The subsequent decades have seen attempts, not always happy, to define how much difference can actually be accommodated within a federal system of centralized cultural and political authority. The passing of Bill C-93, the 'Act for the preservation and enhancement of multiculturalism in Canada', in 1988 enshrined in law the recognition and promotion of cultural and racial diversity that is intended to result in a mutually enriching meeting of cultures. Even if some people remain unconvinced that this act is not just paying lip-service to an undeniable social fact, or concealing assimilationist impulses behind a mask of tolerance, few would deny that its ideal is a worthy one.

The fiction and interviews in this collection explore the territory that lies between that ideal and its reality, between intention and achievement. That this space has sometimes been perceived by writers as a figurative 'no man's land' is a clear sign of some disappointment. One of the most bitterly ironic evaluations has, sadly, been that of someone who was intimately involved with the academic and political debates on the topic: Robert Harney, founder of the Multicultural History Society of Ontario and University Professor of Ethnic, Immigration and Pluralism Studies at the University of Toronto. For Harney, multiculturalism was 'an idea en route to an ideology fashioned from the rhetoric of ethnocultural impresarios huckstering for the folkloric and visiting British royalty searching for a way to describe the colorfulness of the colonies (no doubt after countless onslaughts by Cree, Blackfoot, and Ukrainians in full ethnic battle dress, herded by red-tunicked guardians of "the Canadian way")'.[12] The authors in this book are rarely so caustic, but their views of the stereotyping and ghettoizing tendencies inherent in multicultural policy and its implementation are testaments to the power of fear, ignorance, and prejudice that even the most idealistic of official ideologies cannot eradicate.

The pluralism that Jacques Godbout refers to here as a 'cultural shopping centre' is now guaranteed by Canadian law, but this has not managed to upset fundamentally the hierarchy (based on class and ethnicity) in our social structures of power that John Porter once called 'the vertical mosaic'. Though the board rooms (as well as the

House of Commons) of Canada do look somewhat different than they did in the mid-1960s, when Porter first wrote about continuing British dominance in terms of prestige and influence, the basic metaphor would appear to hold for the economy, if not the society at large. The lowest-paying work, once undertaken by Slavs, Italians, Portuguese, and Greek immigrants, is now being done by Filipino, Caribbean, East African, Latin American, and Korean immigrants — often women. The titles of books and articles on multiculturalism and immigration in Canada are revealing — and disturbing — in their negativity, titles such as *Double Standard: The Secret History of Canadian Immigration* or *'Dangerous Foreigners': European Immigration Workers and Labour Radicalism in Canada, 1896-1932* or *None Is Too Many: Canada and the Jews of Europe.*

Immigration to this country has been both the result and the cause of major changes. The Multiculturalism Act is one of those changes, and its effects are felt in very obvious things like the various 'ethnic' heritage festivals it supports. This kind of event — and funding — comes under considerable scrutiny in this volume and, typically, there is little agreement on their worth: Toronto's colourful West Indian parade and festival inspire one West Indian writer with pride, while another is embarrassed. In W.D. Valgardson's 'The Man from Snaefellsness' a woman collects 'ethnic' boyfriends, just as she does ethnic foods and dress. Many of the stories and conversations in this book articulate other worries: worries about stereotyping, about fossilizing cultures into unchanging folk memories, about reducing 'otherness' to singing and dancing or exotic food, about relegating non-Anglo and non-French to the margins of Canadian culture where they are prey to tokenism as much as to ghettoizing.

But there are also more positive changes as a result of the Act, and these changes go beyond the multilingual media and services now available and even beyond the heritage language programs in the schools. Beyond and including all these important developments, what has been created is an entire 'discourse' about multiculturalism — a way of thinking and talking about ethnicity and race — that is gradually working to change how Canadians define themselves. Now the National Ethnic Archives in Ottawa, the Multicultural History Society of Ontario in Toronto, and the 'Generations' series of government-sponsored historical accounts of Canada's major ethnocultural groups give us access to other versions of Canada's past. There is an increasing academic interest in Canada's diversity, not only in formal ethnic studies programs, either particular or general, but in English, sociology, and history departments. In 1973, a Canadian Ethnic Studies Association was founded, and in any given year numerous conferences on topics related to our multicultural identity are held. The publication of journals, articles, and books on the topic has increased dramatically: in 1990 John Miska published his *Minority Literatures in Canada, 1850-1988: A Bibliography of Primary and Secondary Material* — including 5497 references in 65 languages.

Inevitably, this institutionalization of multiculturalism in Canadian society has extended to its literature: writers with names like Ondaatje, Richler, Kogawa, and Wiebe are today as much part of the literary mainstream as are those named Atwood, Munro, Laurence, Findley, Davies, or Hodgins. What we may have become more aware of is that for a Hodgins, for instance, a certain Irish element cannot be ignored, nor can the Irish-Scots for a Munro. Various issues of the *Canadian Fiction Magazine* have brought Canadian black, Asian, Latin American, and other writing to general attention, as have the many particular anthologies of writing from Canadians of Italian, Dutch, Mennonite, and other descents. This expansion of what is published — and thus, taught and read — as 'Canadian' is one of the most exciting and productive results of multiculturalism as both an ideal and a reality in Canada today.

I am not unaware that there are Canadians who see multiculturalism as a sign of the collective historical guilt (or even hypocrisy) resulting from Canada's earlier immigration policies, or who interpret it as a federal stratagem to divert attention from questions about Québécois identity or discontent within Confederation, or the Americanization of Canadian culture and resources. However, as writers as diverse as Rohinton Mistry, Janice Kulyk Keefer, Neil Bissoondath, and, perhaps most interestingly, Tomson Highway suggest, multiculturalism has the more positive possibility — if not yet completely realized — of being an innovative model for civic tolerance and the acceptance of diversity that is appropriate for our democratic pluralist society. In other words, the cynical response is just too easy, and may not be fair. While many of the writers and interviewers in this book do speak to the failures, the limitations, the inadequacies of multiculturalism, they often end up acknowledging at least the potential it holds to allow room for the aspirations of those who do not happen to be of British or French heritage. In the 1960s, when Canadians said they wanted Canada to stay 'Canadian', they usually meant 'not American'. Today, some seem to think that 'Canadian' means French- or (more likely) English-speaking and white. To keep multiculturalism from becoming just a complacent cliché, we must work to grant everyone access to the material and cultural conditions that will enable the many voices of contemporary Canada, to speak — and be heard — for themselves. That is the purpose of this collection.

NOTES

[1]Raymond August, 'Babeling Beaver Hunts for Home Fire: The Place of Ethnic Literature in Canada Culture', *Canadian Forum*, August 1974, p. 8.

[2]'Placing Truth or Fiction', in *Displaced Persons*, eds Kirsten Holst Petersen and Anna Rutherford (Mundelstrup, Denmark: Dangeroo Press, 1988), p. 156.

[3]Marwan Hassan, *The Confusion of Stones: Two Novellas* (Dunvegan, Ont.: Cormorant Books, 1989), p. 115.

[4]*Toronto Star, Saturday Magazine*, 11 February 1989, p. M13.

[5]In Jars Balan, ' "A Word in a Foreign Language": Ukrainian Influences in George Ryga's Work,' in Jars Balan, ed., *Identifications: Ethnicity and the Writer in Canada* (Edmonton: University of Alberta, Canadian Institute of Ukrainian Studies, 1982), p. 50.

[6]In 'Ethnicity and Identity: The Question of One's Literary Passport', panel discussion in Balan, ed., *Identifications*, p. 80. Canadian actress and playwright Linda Griffiths claims that Campbell's awareness of history forced her to rethink her own relation to power and oppression in terms of her Scots heritage. See the many discussions on this topic in *The Book of Jessica: A Theatrical Transformation* (Toronto: Coach House, 1989).

[7]In Jane A. Shapiro, ed., *Voices: From the Eastern Arctic* (Yellowknife: Outcrop Press, 1987), p. 4.

[8]*Toronto Star, Saturday Magazine*, 7 January 1989, p. M24.

[9]'Regionalism and the Canadian Archipelago' in *Heartland and Hinterland: A Geography of Canada*, ed. L.D. McCann (Scarborough, Ont.: Prentice-Hall, 1982), pp. 459-84. My thanks to Germaine Warkentin for bringing this to my attention.

[10]'After 300 Years Our Neurosis Is Relevant', in William Kilbourn, ed., *Canada: A Guide to the Peaceable Kingdom* (Toronto: Macmillan, 1971), p. 10.

[11]'The Peaceable Kingdom Still', special issue, 'In Search of Canada', *Daedalus*, 117, 4 (Fall 1988), p. 27.

[12]' "So Great a Heritage Is Ours": Immigration and the Survival of the Canadian Polity', in *Daedalus*, 117, 4 (Fall 1988), p. 66.

JOSEF SKVORECKY b. 1924

FROM

The Engineer of Human Souls

The skies they were ashen and sober;
  The leaves they were crispèd and sere —
  The leaves they were withering and sere;
It was night in the lonesome October. . . .

EDGAR ALLAN POE, 'Ulalume'

The whole range of thought and feeling, yet all in organic
relation to a ridiculous little waltz tune.

ALDOUS HUXLEY

Outside the window, which is high, narrow and gothic, the cold
Canadian wind blends two whitenesses: snowflakes sifting down
from lowering clouds and snowdust lifted and whirled by the wind
from the land stretching southwards to Lake Ontario. The snow
swirls through a white wasteland broken only by a few bare, black-
ened trees.

Edenvale College stands in a wilderness. In a few years the nearby
town of Mississauga is expected to swell and envelop the campus
with more variety and colour, but for the time being the college
stands in a wilderness, two and a half miles from the nearest housing
development. The houses there are no longer all alike: people have
learned something since George F. Babbitt's time. Perhaps it was
literature that taught them. Now there are at least four different
kinds of bungalow spaced at irregular intervals so that the housing
development looks like a Swiss village in one of those highly stylized
paintings. It is pretty to look at.

But I see it only in my mind's eye, as I look out on the white, cold,
windy Canadian landscape. Often, as my thoughts flow, I conjure up
again the many wonderful things I have seen in this country of cities
with no past. Like the Toronto skyline with its black and white
skyscrapers, some plated with golden mirrors, thrusting their peaks
into the haze, glowing like burnished chessboards against the eve-

ning twilight above the flat Ontario landscape, and beyond them a sun as large as Jupiter and as red as an aniline ruby sinking into the green dusk. God knows why it's so green, but it is. The Toronto skyline is more beautiful to me than the familiar silhouette of Prague Castle. There is beauty everywhere on earth, but there is greater beauty in those places where one feels that sense of ease which comes from no longer having to put off one's dreams until some improbable future—a future inexorably shrinking away; where the fear which has pervaded one's life suddenly vanishes because there is nothing to be afraid of. Gone are the fears I shared with my fellows, for although the Party exists here, it has no power as yet. And my personal fears are gone too, for no professional literary critics in Canada will confine me in arbitrary scales of greatness. My novels, published here in Czech by Mrs Santner's shoestring operation, are widely read by my fellow Czechs but hardly ever reviewed, because there is no one to review them. There are those two or three grateful laymen who lavish praises on them in the émigré press, their flatteries sandwiched between harvest home announcements and ads for Bohemian tripe soup; they are literate, but they do not understand literature. Then there is Professor Koupelna in Saskatchewan. Every once in a while Passer's mail-order firm in Chicago sends him one of my books as a free gift along with his order of homemade jelly and Prague ham. The book arouses a savage and instinctive outrage in the good professor which he mistakes for the spirit of criticism and he fires off a broadside to the journal of the Czechoslovak Society for Arts and Sciences in America. Fortunately, his attack is launched from such a pinnacle of erudition that most Society members find it repellent. And his erudition has so many gaps in it that even those who are not repelled remain unconvinced.

I feel wonderful. I feel utterly and dangerously wonderful in this wilderness land.

Sharon McCaffrey, the Irish girl from Burnham Lake Settlement, with the stunning red hair and the sweet, creamy complexion, is rattling off an oral paper behind me on *The Narrative of Arthur Gordon Pym* by Edgar Allan Poe. She is in a hurry to get it over with, while I'm hoping she will spin it out to save me from having to talk too long myself. I know the book she has copied her material from, and at least it's not Coles Notes. As a matter of fact, it's a rather worthy book by Professor Quinn, and she has reproduced his argument faithfully, omitting nothing. Right now, although I didn't ask her to (but it is in Quinn), she is comparing *Pym* to *Moby Dick*. 'The introductory sentences are practically the same: "My name is Arthur Gordon Pym" and "Call me Ishmael". Both talk about the town of Nantucket. Some of the characters in both novels concern themselves with hidden meanings: Pym and Peters try to decipher the hieroglyphics carved into the rocks on the island of Ts . . .' — she stumbles over the word with its Slavonic cluster of consonants — '. . . Tsalal. The crew of the *Pequod* puzzle over the golden doubloon Ahab has nailed to the mast. Pym and Augustus, at the beginning of the story, almost perish on the sea. Ishmael visits a whalers' chapel and studies the memorial plaque bearing the names of sailors lost at sea. . . .'

I peer into the white vortexes outside the window and, in the warmth of the room, I know how inhumanly icy they are. The howling wind is barely audible inside and I can hear again in my mind the sounds of the Russian poetry I once read to my students. Poe, I'm afraid, bores them. The horror films on television are far more horrifying. So I try to enliven him as best I can, which was one reason I recited the Russian version to them. The other reason was that I had again succumbed to my foolish but probably irrepressible desire to explain the inexplicable. And I had succumbed because Irene Svensson, with her graceful and supercilious face, had stood up to declare 'The Raven' a worthless, sentimental piece of tripe. It was an act of revenge, for she had noticed how my voice broke (I can't help it, I'm sentimental) whenever I read the lines:

Tell this his soul with sorrow laden if, within the distant Aidenn,
It shall clasp a sainted maiden whom the angels name Lenore . . .

and she thought it would be a clever way to get back at me in front of the others for having tortured her, last term, in the privacy of my office, where I had donned my professional mask and browbeaten her like a drill sergeant. But I hadn't reported her plagiarism to the Dean. I cannot bring myself to be genuinely nasty to anyone called Irene. It is one of my ancient inhibitions. Irene Svensson therefore produced a new paper and she thought, this time, she had put one over on me. But luck was against her. Having first underestimated my scholarship, she now failed to reckon with Murphy's Law. She bought a ready-written essay from a shady operation calling itself Term Papers Inc. Two years before, they had sold the same paper to a pretty Chinese student from Trinidad by the name of Priscilla Wong Sim, who had turned to Term Papers Inc. at my indirect suggestion —

to pass her with a clear conscience I had to have at least one essay from her in which every second word was not misspelled and there were no such oriental mysteries as 'This novel is a novel. It is a great work, for it is written in the form of a book.'

Irene ended up in my office again. This time she confessed in tears and it was a delight to see that proud, sophisticated face with its smug mouth dissolve gently into the face of an uncertain little girl from Oshawa, Ontario. But where, I wondered, was her feminine instinct? Didn't this Swedish girl smelling of deodorant and lavender realize that I could never ever have brought myself to report her to the Dean?

It was not, of course, her lack of instinct; it was her inability to understand my kind of experience. She had no way of knowing, even if her name had not been Irene, that life had long since immunized me against the temptation to inform on anyone, regardless of what authority demanded it. My reluctance is as impregnable as the Iron Curtain. I lived too long in a country where even the most pristine truth, once reported to the authorities, becomes a lie.

I commanded Irene Svensson to write her essay in my presence. She took her Parker Silver Ballpoint and one of those lined notepads students use and for the next two hours she fabricated a paper on 'The Function of Colour in Hawthorne's *The Scarlet Letter*'. She was perspiring so heavily I could detect the faint aroma of a girls' gymnasium through the lavender, and as she gnawed on the end of her Parker the indelible ink stained her mouth. For the next two weeks she came to lectures with lips like the dead Ligeia's.

And so, in the face of her revenge, I had succumbed to the preposterous desire to square the circle, to demonstrate that something written well, as Hemingway once said, can have many meanings: I brought Yesenin-Volpin's Russian adaptation of 'The Raven' along to one of my lectures on Poe.

The swirling white whirlwind outside the window is now creating a hissing filigree of sound on the glass, and I can hear the sound of Poe in Russian:

Kak-to noch'yu v chas terrora,
Ya chital vpervye Mora. . . .

The hard Russian *r*'s rolled through the drowsy lecture room. It was winter then too, with a gale blowing outside, a week before the Christmas holidays. 'Cheap, mechanical inner rhymes,' Irene had said, her mouth curling into a shorthand of disdain. 'The contemporary critics didn't call him a jingle man for nothing.' Clearly she had prepared for her revenge. 'In reality his monotonous poetry is only a weak, watered-down version of English romantic poetry and has scarcely anything at all to contribute to modern sen . . .' — she hesitated — '. . . sensibility.' She had destroyed the effect. No one in the class appeared to have noticed but she knew I had and she flushed with anger.

I v somneni i v pechali
ya sheptal: 'To drug edvali,
Vsekh druzey davno uslali. . . .

Tears rose to my eyes. I wanted to strike back at Irene but I could not. I had to stop reading for a moment until my Pavlovian reaction to poetry, conditioned by my own experiences — national and international, fascist and communist — had subsided. Irene had the advantage because, as far as she was concerned, my hesitation was further evidence of my ridiculous sentimentality. My eyes slipped over the Cyrillic script:

O Prorok, ne prosto ptitsa!
Est'li nyne zagranitsa,
Gde svodobny ob iskusstve
ne opasen razgovor?
Esli est', to dobegu li
ya v tot kray, ne vstretiv puli?
V Niderlandakh li, v Peru li
ya reshil by staryy spor —
Romantizma s realizmom
do sikh por ne konchen spor!
Karknul Voron: Nevermore!

Sharon chirrups on. Soon she'll be over and done with it. 'There has never existed a writer who concentrated more on utterly personal experience. He was the first and greatest artist of abnormal psychology. He displayed a tendency to immerse himself in problems, the solution to which assumed an almost brilliant perspicacity without demanding any actual experience of life whatsoever.' She has switched her unacknowledged sources and is now parroting Krutch. I look into the flurrying snow and a well-fed raven (or simply a black bird) stalks circumspectly through a corridor of white vortexes, and the phantom ship of Captain Guy looms up out of the white fog.

> *'Nikagda!' — skazala ptitsa. . . .*
> *Za moryami zagranitsa. . . .*
> *Tut vlomilis'dva soldata,*
> *sonnyy dvornik i mayor. . . .*

Irene sat down, pleased with her ambiguous victory — the mechanical internal rhymes of a drunken jingle man — and I angrily fought back the tears. Her revenge for my exposing her twice and humiliating her thrice (her lips were still a shade of aquamarine) was achieved.

> *Pered nimi ya ne sharknul,*
> *odnomu v litso lish' kharknul,*
> *No zato kak prosto garknul*
> *chernyy voron:* Nevermore!
> *I vazhu, vazhu ya tachku,*
> *Povtoryaya:* Nevermore . . .
> *Ne podnyat'sya . . .* Nevermore!

I had to pretend to blow my nose, long and hard. The disrespectful eyes of the young of this young and innocent country looked at me with curiosity. I read them my own English translation of the Russian.

> Once at night in time of terror
> I first was reading Thomas More. . . .

> Racked with doubt and sorrow
> Whispered: 'It could hardly be a friend
> All my friends have been imprisoned. . . .

> O Prophet, plainly no mere bird
> Is there no foreign country
> Where to argue freely about art
> Portends no peril sore?
> Shall I ever reach that region
> If such be, and not be shot?
> In Peru or Netherlands
> I'd settle that old contentious score
> Of the realist and romantic
> Still disputing as before
> Croaked the raven: 'Nevermore!'. . . .

'Never, never!' quoth the bird. . . .
That foreign land's beyond the sea. . . .
Whereupon in burst two soldiers
A drowsy porter and a major. . . .

I did not click my heels before them
merely spat into a face,
But the Raven, sombre Raven
simply croaked out: 'Nevermore!'
Now I push a wheelbarrow
keep repeating, 'Nevermore . . .'
There's no rising. . . . Nevermore.

The translation murdered everything, the rumbling Russian *r*'s, Poe's
'O', the saddest of all vowels, far, far sadder in Russian than in the
language of the Stratford genius, that court lickspittle, but I could
still hear the Russian verses rumbling in my ears, interpreting E.A.P.
with immeasurably greater understanding than the literary critics
possess, despite a long century and a great ocean between them,
displaying a knowledge of life that Poe, through some secret twist of
fate and despite what Krutch said, did have—a knowledge that
Joseph Wood Krutch does not possess.

Ya boyus'drugoy puchiny
v tsarstve, gryaznom s davnikh por. . . .
Karknul Voron: Nevermore!

For I have feared since time of yore
Yet another such abyss
in realms corrupted heretofore. . . .
Croaked the Raven: 'Nevermore!'

'If Pym's pilgrimage is not interpreted as a voyage of Mind, then
it is nothing more than one of the many quite ordinary accounts of
sea adventures.' And Sharon stops as though someone had cut her
off. I turn around. She stares at me with her green Irish eyes, somewhat sheepish, not on my account but because she is ashamed for
having put on such a display of intellectuality in front of her class-
mates. Premature cynicism is not a characteristic of young Canadians.
She has finished reciting her plagiarized paper, and there is only one
unpleasantness left to endure: my questions—assuming, of course,
that I'm curious about anything.

I look around. Ted Higgins, who plays tight end for the Varsity Blues, is crouched down behind Davidson's edition of Poe, eating his lunch. Irene Svensson (and this too is a part of her revenge, this ostentatious lack of interest) is provocatively painting her nails with something that looks like stovepipe silvering. Vicky Heatherington, who plays trombone in the school jazz band, is flirting with a shaggy fellow called William Wilson Bellissimmo, his hair as bristly as his Americanized triple-double-consonanted surname. They are struggling over something in Vicky's right hand and Bellissimmo has his arm round her shoulders. Her trombone-enlarged breasts swell under a T-shirt sporting the garish picture of a man. Once, when I asked her who it was, she told me it was a self-portrait of Van Cock. Behind these dallying lovers the sad eyes of Veronika Prst peer at me and through me. She is a moody girl from the Vinohrady district of Prague. On her way back from a tour of Cuba she defected to Canada, and in her first week in class she fought bitterly with Larry Hakim, who had once gone to Cuba to help with the sugar-cane harvest.

'Do you really believe that?' I ask Sharon. 'I mean, that *Pym* is either a pilgrimage of the soul or else just an ordinary thriller?'

Sharon stiffens. She can't admit she has no opinion of her own, so she responds with an obstinate 'yes', and my unfettered thoughts carry me back to the wooden cabin on the wooden schooner of Captain Guy, to a distant time of primal terror, a time when each night before falling asleep I sailed with Jules Verne over a blue-black sea, through a cleft in the giant glaciers, the alabaster gateway of the southern passage, towards a lukewarm sun glowing low over the horizon, while before the ship stretched a tranquil, gently rippled sea, and in the distance, land, and immensely far away, wild purple mountains. Why and how they came to be purple I did not yet know. Arctic swallows swooped through the air, I saw Poe in a hovel in Baltimore scratching away with a goose-feather pen in a cold winter room, just like me in that bed, in that wooden cabin, held captive by the impenetrable curtain hung around the protectorate of Böhmen und Mähren, completely cut off from all avenues to the beautiful Antarctic, Poe a captive of poverty, dreaming on paper of the Wilkes expedition that had left Jeremiah Reynolds behind and sighing Reynolds' name on his deathbed — why? Because he might have lived Reynolds' life? In the beautiful and ghastly freedom of the purple mountains of madness? But Reynolds' life was not his: Poe's life ebbed away in a grim prison of poverty, in the airless stench of a New England hovel. A pilgrimage of the soul? A pilgrimage *in* the soul. A magnificent boyhood adventure. Only the rich, the successful, the important, the powerful ever cease to be boys and girls.

Those tears. Perhaps they were a disgrace—Anglo-Saxons are, it is popularly believed, unsentimental. Anglo-Saxons with names like Bellissimmo, Hakim, Svensson. But now Irene is silent. Perhaps she at least had appreciated the exotic, guttural rumbling of *Kak-to noch'yu v chas terrora, ya chital vpervye Mora*. Her grey, northern eyes observed me unprotestingly, thoughtfully. To my surprise, for I had given her a c minus in the freshman course, she enrolled this year in my sophomore course, which was partly intended to reiterate in depth (that, at least, was the theory) the same material covered in the freshman course. Poe, therefore, is on the course again, and this year Irene's papers are excellent. Perhaps she has hired a teaching assistant to help her, or perhaps she has actually begun to study. Generally she keeps silent, observing me. . . . *Kak-to noch'yu v chas terrora*. . . . Once at night in time of terror. . . . We have always been surrounded by terror and by the beauty that is an inseparable part of it.   *Translated by Paul Wilson*

◆ ◆ ◆

JOSEF SKVORECKY was born in 1924 in the town of Nachod in northern Czechoslovakia. He was already a very successful novelist and translator when he and his wife Zdena Salivarova immigrated to Canada in January 1969 in the wake of the Soviet-led invasion of Czechoslovakia in August 1968. After brief stays at Cornell University and the University of California (Berkeley), Skvorecky accepted a position in the English department of the University of Toronto. Since 1972 he and his wife have run 68 Publishers, considered by many to be the most important Czech publishing house anywhere, since they published authors once banned in Czechoslovakia. Among his publications in English are *The Cowards* (trans. Jeanne Nemcova; Harmondsworth: Penguin, 1972); *The Bass Saxophone* (trans. Kaca Polackova; Toronto: Lester and Orpen Dennys, 1980); *Miss Silver's Past* (trans. Peter Kussi; London: Picador, 1980); *The Swell Season* (trans. Paul Wilson; Toronto: Lester and Orpen Dennys, 1982); *The Engineer of Human Souls* (trans. Paul Wilson; Toronto: Lester and Orpen Dennys, 1984); *Dvorak in Love* (trans. Paul Wilson; Toronto: Lester and Orpen Dennys, 1986).

SAM SOLECKI is a professor of English literature at the University of Toronto. A former editor of *The Canadian Forum*, he has written extensively on English, Canadian, and Czech literatures. He has edited *Spider Blues: Essays on Michael Ondaatje* (1985), and Josef Skvorecky's *Talkin' Moscow Blues: Essays about Literature, Politics, Movies and Jazz* (1988). His *Prague Blues: The Fiction of Josef Skvorecky* is forthcoming.

I spent nearly the first ten years of my life living in a camp for Polish refugees in the English midlands, and one of the most magical of English words for all of us was 'America'. Looking back I realize that for many of us the word came from the same group as 'Oz' or 'the promised land'. Canada, on the other hand, was only mentioned if someone had relatives there or as an adjunct of the United States. Did you know much about Canada when living in Czechoslovakia?

I had a vague and probably unrealistic image based on some youthful reading of James Oliver Curwood, who I believe to be a Canadian though some say he's an American. He wrote boys' novels about mounties and trappers and Indians and Indian girls — so my image of Canada included mounties and deep woods and grizzly bears and a few other romantic details. Also as a boy I loved to read Ernest Thomson Seton. So I had an image of a pretty wild country and knew nothing about Canadian cities, for example. On the other hand, I knew something of the famous American cities like New York and Chicago because I had seen them or heard about them in American films. Canada was hazy and my picture of it was pretty romantic.

All emigration involves anxiety, but leaving Czechoslovakia in January 1969 must have been particularly anxious for you since you were a writer. You were forty-four and had achieved a substantial reputation as a novelist, a script writer, an editor, even a cabaret writer. But this was all in Czech, a language you once described as 'that unknown, useless and difficult language of the Western Slavs'. Suddenly you were in a country where the demand for Czech writing and writers was minimal.

I had no idea what I would be doing. If I had known Russian I could have hoped for a job at a university in a department of Slavic studies. But actually I felt quite good because I knew things would have been even worse had I stayed in Prague. I also knew that if I had stayed I would have had three choices: I could recant and say that I had been wrong and that I would mend my ways; I could go back into the underground of which I had been a member in the early fifties, but then I had been a young man and had been willing to write for the desk-drawer; or I could stop writing and do something completely different. In comparison to these, anything was better.

Like Milosz and Kundera, you tend to think of most North Americans as relatively naïve about foreign affairs or, more precisely those foreign affairs related in some way to the Soviet Union. My impression is that one of the consequences of your essentially 'conservative' stance on foreign affairs is that many critics fail to look beyond this to attitudes and views on other issues. After two decades you must be tired of this whole topic.

You're right, but it's important, very important. One of the inevitable consequences of being an emigrant or exile is that one remains tied to the old country and concerned with the fate of that country. And, since in my case and in Czechoslovakia's case, that fate is tied up with totalitarianism and communism, and communism has a world importance, then it's inevitable that my interest, what you call my politics, should be primarily concerned with foreign affairs.

One of the results of this seems to be that you have little interest in domestic Canadian or American politics.

You could say I'm interested but not as interested as I am in the other politics which are so obviously more important or urgent. Don't forget that for my generation, at least since Hitler, politics, real politics, always involved danger. You could die for saying or writing something. You could also be in danger simply because of what or who you were. From that extreme perspective, Canada and the United States and most of Western Europe don't have politics; life in these societies is free of politics. On the other hand, Czechoslovakia is still political in the old sense, and I'm still a Czech. So *glasnost* and *perestroika* and their effect on Czechoslovakia are more important to me than the Liberal and Progressive Conservative parties. This is probably true for most immigrants who come to Canada as adults. Those who come as children will grow up to be a hundred per cent Canadians and they will be more concerned about whether to vote for the Liberals or the Conservatives than whether Jakes is the head of the Czechoslovak government. Their politics will be mainly national politics. I came too late to be like that. It all depends on the age when you emigrate.

I first saw Canada as a child from a ship, the ss Captain Cook, *sailing up the St Lawrence, so that the first cities I saw were Quebec City and Montreal. I still remember being disappointed by Ontario's towns and cities because they seemed so much less interesting than Quebec's. It was as if Quebec had a history and Ontario didn't. Only in school and even then only gradually did I start to see Ontario as 'historical' in its own way, though I must admit it still doesn't excite my imagination in the way that Quebec's history does.*

You could say that I lived in history for the first forty-five years of my life, so that I take castles and châteaux and medieval and baroque churches for granted. Prague is, after all, as full of history as any city. But to me the general conditions of life, the general intellectual conditions of life, are much more important. Beautiful medieval churches are interesting, but they don't compensate for the fact that intellectual and cultural life are lived under conditions that, from one point of view, are also medieval. You know, whenever I go to Europe now, and I only go on business or to give readings, I always look forward to coming home, coming to Toronto. This is home and I feel more at ease here than I do in Germany or anywhere else in Europe. The only exception to this is England which I like very much, perhaps because of the language or because I always remember it as very green, very beautiful. The language is very important because Czech and English are now my main languages. Like many Czechs I used to speak German very well, but I haven't really spoken it since the war, which is almost half a century ago. I read it well, but when speaking I feel rusty.

I want to return to what we were just saying about Canada and history. When I came here, Canada struck me as so much younger than the United States. You can see this when you compare the Czech communities in the two countries. The Canadian one is really quite recent; most of the people came either before the Second World War or immediately after in 1948. Then there was the final group that came, as I did, after 1968. But the American Czechs — and I wrote about this in *Dvorak in Love* and it is also a topic in the novel I am now writing about Czechs in the American Civil War — the American Czech community is much older. Many Czechs settled in America after the revolutions of 1848, and there was continuing immigration after that. There are now many fourth- and fifth-generation Czechs in America. Toronto has about 14,000 Czechs and about 8,000 of them came as a result of 1968. One of the results of this is that the Canadian Czech community tends to be more intensely interested in what is happening in Czechoslovakia because they have come from there much more recently. Most American Czechs, on the other hand, have little direct knowledge of the old country. Still, I want to say that I admire the American Czechs very much because of their perseverance. Without any multicultural grants and official encouragement they remained Czechs. I was at a conference in Texas a few years ago where there were about ten mixed choirs all singing Czech songs, even though many of the singers obviously didn't understand the language. It was very impressive. There were people there in the old national costumes which they made themselves, but the ornaments on the costumes were Bohemian and Texan. And all this was done without any kind of official governmental support or encouragement.

In your account there doesn't seem to be much difference between the American 'melting pot' and the Canadian 'mosaic'.

I don't think there is, except that the Canadian government certainly talks about ethnic groups and multiculturalism more than the Americans do.

I've always thought much of this is just political, a jockeying among parties for influence and votes with various groups. In fact, my own response to official multiculturalism is that it is ultimately divisive, in that it creates nearly countless small interest groups which see the country primarily if not exclusively from their own limited ethnic perspective.

I wonder if one of the results of all this is that many Canadians think that European immigrants are sort of old-fashioned, simple people who do cute dances in outlandish costumes and sing in funny languages. I think that, if an ethnic culture is going to survive beyond the second or third generation, it will do so whether or not it is officially supported. But usually immigrants become assimilated. I think that's inevitable whether in Canada or the United States. It's ironic, by the way, that most of the folk dances and songs that the ethnic dance groups do at officially sponsored events are no longer done in the hills of Bohemia or Poland or wherever. The teenagers there dance to rock and roll, and those dances haven't really been performed spontaneously for years.

Do you think of your writing as directed at a Czech readership?

Not really. I just assume that, if what you write is any good, then it will always find some readers — Czech, English, French, whoever. After all, there isn't such a great difference between the readers in one country and another. If what I write is not entirely bad, then the work will find its own readers, no matter in what country or in what language. I should point out, though, that some of my stories and parts of *The Engineer of Human Souls* and *Dvorak in Love* are probably incomprehensible for readers in Czechoslovakia because they are written in a Czech heavily influenced by North American English. Other than that, I believe that people are essentially the same everywhere, and if a writer manages to write well about some aspect of life, people will read him.

Would it be valid to call the Czechoslovakia of your youth multicultural? Prague, after all, was a German, a Czech, and a Jewish city, and Czechoslovakia had many national or ethnic or linguistic minorities within it during the First Republic.

The society was certainly multicultural, but not in the way that Canada or America are multicultural. There was certainly a lively German culture in the country, but the Germans lived only in the Sudeten and in Prague. Similarly the Hungarians lived in the south-east in Slovakia, while the Ukrainians lived in the Carpathians. The various groups were fairly separate. So as a result there was a greater homogeneity in the country's culture than the term 'multiculturalism' suggests. We didn't have the mixture that a city like Toronto has. My own home town of Nachod, for example, was a Czech town and only had about seven German families in it. That's out of a population of about 14,000 people. By the way, the fact that the town was almost completely Czech prevented it from being annexed after the Munich Agreement in 1938.

Do you ever worry about your own Czech language? You left Czechoslovakia over twenty years ago and have lived since then in an English-speaking world. The language must have changed over that period of time.

Oh yes. There are always new terms, slang words, idioms and so on. But the core of the language seems to me to have remained the same, and when I write I write in it and from it. But, you know, when I speak Czech, I have noticed that I use American or Canadian Czech. I think of it as a dialect of the mother tongue. And it is over a century old. Rosie's letters in *Dvorak in Love*, for example, which are written in that dialect, are based on a series of letters published in the 1890s in a Chicago Czech humorous weekly. They are supposedly written by a servant named Rosie. The folks back home write back that they can't understand her. She responds by telling them that they should learn English. But this situation, in which the immigrant's first language is influenced by English, is common to all immigrants and you can find it in every ethnic community. Henry Mencken writes about this in his appendix to *The American Language* where he shows how European languages become corrupted by American English. My own attitude to this is fairly liberal. I see it as an interesting linguistic phenomenon with great humorous potential which, as you know, I try to make use of in my fiction, although it is very difficult to translate into English. It needs a reader who knows both languages and can see and hear the humour that comes out of the meeting of the two.

Since coming to Canada you have written essays and articles in English for The Canadian Forum, The New Republic, *and* The New York Review of Books, *but you have never written any fiction in English. Why not?*

Well, fiction involves playing with language in a way that non-fiction doesn't. I use slang, various idioms, make jokes, and play with dialects. I find that difficult enough to do in the language I have spoken all my life, the one I feel at home in. I don't think I could do it in English — there I'm just a visitor who arrived late. It would certainly change my style, but I'm not sure that I could really write in it. I enjoy writing essays and reviews in English, partly because it's a challenge, though a smaller one than trying to write fiction in an acquired language. I would even say that I prefer writing non-fiction in English because, when I write in Czech, I find it very easy to slip into clichés and platitudes and predictable expressions. An acquired language makes me think harder and often I somehow get better ideas.

Perhaps it would be appropriate to end by dealing with a theme that is particularly prominent in The Engineer of Human Souls — *the return home. Was this ever a possibility for you in the 1970s and 1980s?*

'You Can't Go Home Again' — Thomas Wolfe.

What about now — now that your friend Vaclav Havel is president and Czechoslovakia is on the verge of gaining nearly complete political independence? Are you and you wife tempted to return?

We are not. Believe it or not, we have become Canadians. My Bohemia is now strictly a Bohemia of the soul, not a geographical entity. We are happy here, also because this country does not forbid you anything, not even remaining a Czech novelist who gets Canadian literary prizes. We both will always remain Czechs in the sense of caring for the old country very, very much. But we have become Canadians, caring for this sweet new country as well. Thinking about it, we are typical nineteenth-century phenomena.

MORDECAI RICHLER b. 1931

FROM

The Street

Two streets below our own came the Main. Rich in delights, but also squalid, filthy, and hollering with stores whose wares, whether furniture or fruit, were ugly or damaged. The signs still say FANTASTIC DISCOUNTS or FORCED TO SELL PRICES HERE, but the bargains so bitterly sought after are illusory — and perhaps they always were.

The Main, with something for all our appetites, was dedicated to pinching pennies from the poor, but it was there to entertain, educate and comfort us too. Across the street from the synagogue you could see THE PICTURE THEY CLAIMED COULD NEVER BE MADE. A little further down the street was the Workman's Circle and, if you liked, a strip show. Peaches, Margo, Lili St Cyr. Around the corner there was the ritual baths, the *shvitz* or *mikva*, where my grandfather and his cronies went before the High Holidays, emerging boiling red from the highest reaches of the steam rooms to happily flog each other with brushes fashioned of pine tree branches. Where supremely orthodox women went once a month to purify themselves.

It was to the Main, once a year before the High Holidays, that I was taken for a new suit (the itch of the cheap tweed was excruciating) and shoes (with a built-in squeak). We also shopped for fruit on the Main, meat and fish, and here the important thing was to watch the man at the scales. On the Main, too, was the Chinese laundry — 'Have you ever seen such hard workers?' — the Italian hatblocker — 'Tony's a good goy, you know. Against Mussolini from the very first.' — and strolling French Canadian priests — 'Some of them speak Hebrew now.' 'Well, if you ask me, it's none of their business. Enough's enough, you know.' Kids like myself were dragged along on shopping expeditions to carry parcels. Old men gave us snuff, at the delicatessens we were allowed salami butts, card players pushed candies on us for luck, and everywhere we were poked and pinched by the mothers. Absolutely the best that could be said of us was, 'He eats well, knock wood,' and later, as we went off to school, 'He's a rank-one boy'.

After the shopping, once our errands had been done, we returned to the Main once more, either for part-time jobs or to study with our *melamud*. Jobs going on the Main included spotting pins in a bowling alley, collecting butcher bills and, best of all, working at a news-stand, where you could devour the *Police Gazette* free and pick up a little extra short-changing strangers during the rush hour. Work was supposed to be good for our character development and the fact that we were paid was incidental. To qualify for a job we were supposed to be 'bright, ambitious, and willing to learn'. An ad I once saw in a shoe store window read:

PART-TIME BOY WANTED FOR EXPANDING BUSINESS
EXPERIENCE ABSOLUTELY NECESSARY, BUT NOT ESSENTIAL

Our jobs and lessons finished, we would wander the streets in small groups smoking Turret cigarettes and telling jokes.

'Hey, *shmo-hawk*, what's the difference between a mail box and an elephant's ass?'

'I dunno.'

'Well, I wouldn't send *you* to mail my letters.'

As the French Canadian factory girls passed arm-in-arm we would call out, 'I've got the time, if you've got the place.'

Shabus it was back to the Main again and the original Young Israel synagogue. While our grandfathers and fathers prayed and gossiped and speculated about the war in Europe in the musty room below, we played chin the bar in the upstairs attic and told jokes that began, 'Confucius say. . . .' or, 'Once there was an Englishman, an Irishman, and a Hebe . . .'

We would return to the Main once more when we wanted a fight with the pea-soups. Winter, as I recall it, was best for this type of sport. We could throw snowballs packed with ice or frozen horse buns and, with darkness falling early, it was easier to elude pursuers. Soon, however, we developed a technique of battle that served us well even in the spring. Three of us would hide under an outside staircase while the fourth member of our group, a kid named Eddy, would idle provocatively on the sidewalk. Eddy was a good head-and-a-half shorter than the rest of us. (For this, it was rumoured, his mother was to blame. She wouldn't let Eddy have his tonsils removed and that's why he was such a runt. It was not that Eddy's mother feared surgery, but Eddy sang in the choir of a rich synagogue, bringing in some thirty dollars a month, and if his tonsils were removed it was feared that his voice would go too.) Anyway, Eddy would stand out there alone and when the first solitary pea-soup passed he would kick him in the shins. 'Your mother fucks,' he'd say.

The pea-soup, looking down on little Eddy, would naturally knock him one on the head. Then, and only then, would we emerge from under the staircase.

'Hey, that's my kid brother you just slugged.'

And before the bewildered pea-soup could protest, we were scrambling all over him.

These and other fights, however, sprang more out of boredom than from racial hatred, not that there were no racial problems on the Main.

If the Main was a poor man's street, it was also a dividing line. Below, the French Canadians. Above, some distance above, the dreaded WASPs. On the Main itself there were some Italians, Yugoslavs, and Ukrainians, but they did not count as true Gentiles. Even the French Canadians, who were our enemies, were not entirely unloved. Like us, they were poor and coarse with large families and spoke English badly.

Looking back, it's easy to see that the real trouble was there was no dialogue between us and the French Canadians, each elbowing the other, striving for WASP acceptance. We fought the French Canadians stereotype for stereotype. If many of them believed that the St Urbain Street Jews were secretly rich, manipulating the black market, then my typical French Canadian was a moronic gum-chewer. He wore his greasy black hair parted down the middle and also affected an eyebrow moustache. His zoot trousers were belted just under the breastbone and ended in a peg hugging his ankles. He was the dolt who held up your uncle endlessly at the liquor commission while he tried unsuccessfully to add three figures or, if he was employed at the customs office, never knew which form to give you. Furthermore, he only held his liquor commission or customs or any other government job because he was the second cousin of a backwoods notary who had delivered the village vote to the *Union Nationale* for a generation. Other French Canadians were speed cops, and if any of these ever stopped you on the highway you made sure to hand him a folded two dollar bill with your licence.

Wartime shortages, the admirable Protestant spirit of making-do,

benefited both Jews and French Canadians. Jews with clean fingernails were allowed to teach within the Protestant School system and
French Canadians off the Atwater League and provincial sandlots
broke into the International Baseball League. Jean-Pierre Roy won
twenty-five games for the Montreal Royals one year and a young man
named Stan Breard enjoyed a season as a stylish but no-hit shortstop.
Come to think of it, the only French Canadians I heard of were
athletes. Of course there was Maurice Richard, the superb hockey
player, but there was also Dave Castiloux, a cunning welterweight,
and, above all, the wrestler-hero, Yvon Robert, who week after week
gave the blond Anglo-Saxon wrestlers what for at the Forum.

Aside from boyhood street fights and what I read on the sports
pages, all I knew of French Canadians was that they were clearly
hilarious. Our Scots schoolmaster would always raise a laugh in class
by reading us the atrocious Uncle Tom-like dialect verse of William
Henry Drummond: *Little Baptiste & Co.*

On wan dark night on Lac St Pierre,
De win' she blow, blow, blow,
An'de crew of de wood scow 'Julie Plant'
Got scar't and' run below—
Bimeby she blow some more,
An'de scow bus' up on Lac St Pierre
Wan arpent from de shore.

Actually, it was only the WASPS who were truly hated and feared.
'Among them,' I heard it said, 'with those porridge faces, who can
tell what they're thinking?' It was, we felt, their country, and given
sufficient liquor who knew when they would make trouble?

We were a rude, aggressive bunch round the Main. Cocky too.
But bring down the most insignificant, pinched WASP fire insurance
inspector and even the most arrogant merchant on the street would
dip into the drawer for a ten spot or a bottle and bow and say, 'Sir'.

After school we used to race down to the Main to play snooker at
the Rachel or the Mount Royal. Other days, when we chose to avoid
school altogether, we would take the No. 55 streetcar as far as St
Catherine Street, where there was a variety of amusements offered.
We could play the pinball machines and watch archaic strip-tease
movies for a nickel at the Silver Gameland. At the Midway or the
Crystal Palace we could see a double feature and a girlie show for as
little as thirty-five cents. The Main, at this juncture, was thick with

drifters, panhandlers and whores. Available on both sides of the street were 'Tourist Rooms by Day and Night', and everywhere there was the smell of french fried potatoes cooking in stale oil. Tough, unshaven men in checked shirts stood in knots outside the taverns and cheap cafés. There was the promise of violence.

As I recall it, we were always being warned about the Main. Our-grandparents and parents had come there by steerage from Rumania or by cattleboat from Poland by way of Liverpool. No sooner had they unpacked their bundles and cardboard suitcases than they were planning a better, brighter life for us, the Canadian-born children. The Main, good enough for them, was not to be for us, and that they told us again and again was what the struggle was for. The Main was for *bummers*, drinkers, and (heaven forbid) failures.

During the years leading up to the war, the ideal of the ghetto, no different from any other in America, was the doctor. This, mistakenly, was taken to be the very apogee of learning and refinement. In those days there also began the familiar and agonizing process of alienation between immigrant parents and Canadian-born children. Our older brothers and cousins, off to university, came home to realize that our parents spoke with embarrassing accents. Even the younger boys, like myself, were going to 'their' schools. According to them, the priests had made a tremendous contribution to the exploration and development of this country. Some were heroes. But our parents had other memories, different ideas, about the priesthood. At school we were taught about the glory of the Crusades and at home we were instructed in the bloodier side of the story. Though we wished Lord Tweedsmuir, the Governor-General, a long life each Saturday morning in the synagogue, there were those among us who knew him as John Buchan. From the very beginning there was their history, and ours. Our heroes, and theirs.

Our parents used to apply a special standard to all men and events. 'Is it good for the Jews?' By this test they interpreted the policies of Mackenzie King and the Stanley Cup play-offs and earthquakes in Japan. To take one example—if the Montreal *Canadiens* won the Stanley Cup it would infuriate the WASPs in Toronto, and as long as the English and French were going at each other they left us alone: *ergo*, it was good for the Jews if the *Canadiens* won the Stanley Cup.

We were convinced that we gained from dissension between Cana-da's two cultures, the English and the French, and we looked neither to England nor France for guidance. We turned to the United States. The real America.

America was Roosevelt, the Yeshiva College, Max Baer, Mickey Katz records, Danny Kaye, a Jew in the Supreme Court, the *Jewish Daily Forward*, Dubinsky, Mrs Nussbaum of Allen's Alley, and Gregory Peck looking so cute in *Gentleman's Agreement*. Why, in the United States a Jew even wrote speeches for the president. Returning cousins swore they had heard a cop speak Yiddish in Brooklyn. There were the Catskill hotels, Jewish soap operas on the radio and, above all earthly pleasure grounds, Florida. Miami. No manufacturer had quite made it in Montreal until he was able to spend a month each winter in Miami.

We were governed by Ottawa, we were also British subjects, but our true capital was certainly New York. Success was (and still is) acceptance by the United States. For a boxer this meant a main bout at Madison Square Garden, for a writer or an artist, praise from New York critics, for a businessman, a Miami tan and, today, for comics, an appearance on the Ed Sullivan Show or for actors, not an important part at the Stratford Festival, but Broadway, or the lead in a Hollywood TV series (Lorne Green in *Bonanza*). The outside world, 'their' Canada, only concerned us insofar as it affected our living conditions. All the same, we liked to impress the *goyim*. A knock on the knuckles from time to time wouldn't hurt them. So, while we secretly believed that the baseball field or the prize-fighting ring was no place for a Jewish boy, we took enormous pleasure in the accomplishments of, say, Kermit Kitman, the Montreal Royals outfielder, and Maxie Berger, the welterweight.

Streets such as ours and Outremont, where the emergent middle-class and the rich lived, comprised an almost self-contained world. Outside of business there was a minimal contact with the Gentiles. This was hardly petulant clannishness or naïve fear. In the years leading up to the war neo-fascist groups were extremely active in Canada. In the United States there was Father Coughlin, Lindberg, and others. We had Adrian Arcand. The upshot was almost the same. So I can recall seeing swastikas and 'A bas les Juifs' painted on the Laurentian highway. There were suburbs and hotels in the mountains and country clubs where we were not wanted, beaches with signs that read GENTILES ONLY, quotas at the universities, and occasional racial altercations on Park Avenue. The democracy we were being invited to defend was flawed and hostile to us. Without question it was better for us in Canada than in Europe, but this was still their country, not ours.

I was only a boy during the war. I can remember signs in cigar stores that warned us THE WALLS HAVE EARS and THE ENEMY IS EVERYWHERE. I can also recall my parents, uncles and aunts, cracking peanuts on a Friday night and waiting for those two unequalled friends of the Jews, Roosevelt and Walter Winchell, to come off it and get into the war. We admired the British, they were gutsy, but we had more confidence in the United States Marines. Educated by Hollywood, we could see the likes of John Wayne, Gable, and Robert Taylor making minced meat out of the Panzers, while Noel Coward, Laurence Olivier, and others, seen in a spate of British war films, looked all too humanly vulnerable to us. Briefly, then, Pearl Harbour was a day of jubilation, but the war itself made for some confusions. In another country, relatives recalled by my grandparents were being murdered. But on the street in our air cadet uniforms, we FFHS boys were more interested in seeking out the fabulously wicked v-girls ('They go the limit with guys in uniform, see.') we had read about in the *Herald*. True, we made some sacrifices. American comic books were banned for the duration due, I think, to a shortage of US funds. So we had to put up a quarter on the black market for copies of the *Batman* and *Tip-Top Comics*. But at the same newsstand we bought a page on which four pigs had been printed. When we folded the paper together, as directed, the four pigs' behinds made up Hitler's hateful face. Outside Cooperman's Superior Provisions, where if you were a regular customer you could get sugar without ration coupons, we would chant 'Black-market Cooperman! Black-market Cooperman!' until the old man came out, wielding his broom, and sent us flying down the street.

   The war in Europe brought about considerable changes within the Jewish community in Montreal. To begin with, there was the coming of the refugees. These men, interned in England as enemy aliens and sent to Canada where they were eventually released, were to make a profound impact on us. I think we had conjured up a picture of the refugees as penurious *hassidim* with packs on their backs. We were eager to be helpful, our gestures were large, but in return we expected more than a little gratitude. As it turned out, the refugees, mostly German and Austrian Jews, were far more sophisticated and better educated than we were. They had not, like our immigrant grandparents, come from *shtetls* in Galicia or Russia. Neither did they despise Europe. On the contrary, they found our culture thin, the city provincial, and the Jews narrow. This bewildered and stung us. But what cut deepest, I suppose, was that the refugees spoke English better than many of us did and, among themselves, had the effrontery to talk in the abhorred German language. Many of them also made it clear that Canada was no more than a frozen place to stop over until a US visa was forthcoming. So for a while we real Canadians were hostile.

For our grandparents who remembered those left behind in Rumania and Poland the war was a time of unspeakable grief. Parents watched their sons grow up too quickly and stood by helplessly as the boys went off to the fighting one by one. They didn't have to go, either, for until the last days of the war Canadians could only be drafted for service within Canada. A boy had to volunteer before he could be sent overseas.

For those of my age the war was something else. I cannot remember it as a black time, and I think it must be so for most boys of my generation. The truth is that for many of us to look back on the war is to recall the first time our fathers earned a good living. Even as the bombs fell and the ships went down, always elsewhere, our country was bursting out of a depression into a period of hitherto unknown prosperity. For my generation the war was hearing of death and sacrifice but seeing with our own eyes the departure from cold-water flats to apartments in Outremont, duplexes and split-levels in the suburbs. It was when we read of the uprising in the Warsaw ghetto and saw, in Montreal, the changeover from poky little *shuls* to big synagogue-cum-parochial schools with stained glass windows and mosaics outside. During the war some of us lost brothers and cousins but in Canada we had never had it so good, and we began the run from rented summer shacks with outhouses in Shawbridge to Colonial-style summer houses of our own and speedboats on the lake in Ste Agathe.

MORDECAI RICHLER was born in 1931, and raised 'to manhood in a hairier, more earthy Montreal' — as he puts it — on St Urbain Street. His grandfather came to Canada from a Galician *shtetl* in 1904 to be

a pedlar on the Main, what came to be known as the Jewish ghetto —
in between Canada's two cultures, and 'still their country, not ours'.
Richler was educated at Sir George Williams College (now Concordia
University) where he was also writer-in-residence in 1968. At that
time he had been living with his family for eleven years in London,
England, where he returned when the position ended. In 1972 he
returned to Montreal and he now lives in the Eastern Townships of
Quebec, close enough to the city of Montreal to drive in occasionally.
He and his wife have raised five children. His works include *The
Acrobats* (London: Andre Deutsch, 1954); *Son of a Smaller Hero*
(London: Andre Deutsch, 1955); *A Choice of Enemies* (London:
Andre Deutsch, 1957); *The Apprenticeship of Duddy Kravitz* (Lon-
don: Andre Deutsch, 1959); *The Incomparable Atuk* (Toronto:
McClelland and Stewart, 1963); *Cocksure* (Toronto: McClelland and
Stewart, 1968); *St Urbain's Horseman* (Toronto: McClelland and
Stewart-Bantam, 1971); *Jacob Two-Two Meets the Hooded Fang*
(Toronto: McClelland and Stewart, 1975); *Joshua Then and Now*
(Toronto: McClelland and Stewart-Bantam, 1980); *Solomon Gursky
Was Here* (London: Viking, Penguin, 1989).

MARLENE KADAR is a Canada Research Fellow and Assistant Professor
at York University, affiliated to both the Robarts Centre for Canadian
Studies and the Humanities Division. She is currently working on
two books: a reader in 'life writing' (Oxford University Press) and a
collection of essays on the same topic (University of Toronto Press).
She has recently published her first piece of fiction in *Tessera*, 'A
Postscript for Maria, Parts 1 and 2', and is preparing an annotated
volume of Earle Birney's correspondence for publication. She has
edited translations of Frida Kahlo's letters to Ella and Bert Wolfe, one
of which has been published in *DATA and ACTA: Aspects of Life
Writing*, edited by Evelyn Hinz (1987). Her dissertation in comparative literature was published in condensed form in the *Canadian
Review of Comparative Literature* as 'Partisan Culture in the Thirties:
Partisan Review, the Surrealists and Leon Trotsky' (1986).

*When someone like me comes along and asks you what you think
of ethnicity, what's your response?*

My initial response is anger because I find the term tiresome and
pejorative. What is 'ethnic' writing, and why is a Scots Canadian

'ethnic'? Or why is Jewish 'ethnic'? Or Ukrainian? This is a country made up of many people, thirty per cent of whom are neither English nor French. And within twenty years the majority will not be English or French. It's a pejorative WASP term. If you look up the Oxford Dictionary definition, 'ethnic' is very insulting.

As a first-generation Canadian, I feel uncomfortable asking you about ethnicity. As far as I can tell an ethnic is a pagan. The word comes from the Greek adjective for 'heathen' nations, says the OED, not Christian or Jewish. In the world of multiculturalism, however, ethnics are the quaint, the different. The question is, different from what? So what about the fact that scholars want to say that Mordecai Richler is an ethnic writer? Or exploits the theme of ethnicity and the Jewish immigrants of his boyhood Montreal?

Well, they're mostly not scholars, they're busybodies. The writer's job is to bring in the meat; I don't care whether people stamp it. I write about the society I know. I don't only write about Jews; I write about all kinds of people. I write more about Jews because I was brought up Jewish. I don't read most of these essays; I don't really care about them. I think this Canadiana stuff is a self-perpetuating small-time industry. Professors publish for promotion and for each other, and most academic critics can't write very well – with very few exceptions. They write to be promoted within their own departments. And that's a misunderstanding because a man who is a gifted teacher is not necessarily a writer, any more than I could teach.

You wrote in 'Why I Write' that it is the critic's job to 'eviscerate bad [books], lying ones'. What is a lying book?

What I really want is to be an honest witness to my time and place. And that's what I've set out to do. Now, my own vision may be limited or prejudiced, or may not be something everyone would agree with, but I'm stuck with it. So I don't write to ingratiate myself to anyone. I'm not thin-skinned and I'm fair game. I'm very critical; I don't mind if people criticize what I do.

It sounds like you don't think 'ethnicity' is really an appropriate issue in fiction. But there are some writers who write because they think their particular ethnic vision should be highlighted.

No writer ever thinks about whether he's ethnic or not ethnic. He writes about what he knows.

You don't think some writers think about whether they are ethnic first? The way feminists may think of themselves as feminists first?

Then that's bad writing. I find some feminists as tiresome as the left-wing writing we had in the thirties. People are moved around like ciphers in order to prove points. And that's not the way you write fiction. You don't manipulate characters to prove theories. I think, on the one hand, some of the best writing models we've had have been written by women. I'm going back to George Eliot, Jane Austen and today I mean people like Anne Tyler, Toni Morrison; they're really wonderful novelists, but they're novelists first, not feminists. If you want to write about feminism or ethnicity you write an essay. But you can't do that in a novel. Like Gertrude Stein once told Hemingway many years ago—it may have been Fitzgerald—novels aren't opinions. So you save that stuff for a broadside, or an essay. Character in fiction put to those kinds of uses is a violation of fact. It's just not acceptable. There's only good writing and bad writing and I read John Cheever because I think he's a brilliant writer, not because he writes about rich Protestants or middle-class Protestants. I read Saul Bellow because he's marvellous, not because he's Jewish.

You don't think you read more Jewish novels because you are Jewish?

I read more Jewish history and more Jewish philosophy because I am Jewish, not because I am a writer. I'm also a reader—and I am also Jewish. At the moment Walker Percy gives me a lot of pleasure — a Southerner from New Orleans. And the novelist I most admire of our time is Evelyn Waugh.

You worked with Harry Gulkin [producer of the film version of Jacob Two-Two Meets the Hooded Fang]*, who is about your age, and Jewish, but his background is quite different from yours. He grew up in the Communist Party and left during the great exodus in 1956. Why didn't you belong to the Party?*

Well, because I am younger than they are. And we were all in the Labour Zionist movement. Had I been ten years older, I obviously would have been in the Communist Party. But at the time, it was a different era. We were in an organization called *Habonim*, 1940. I'm fifty-eight years old, and I think Harry is sixty-four or so. We were more concerned about Palestine, and we wanted to go there, and I couldn't go, except later as a journalist. But one of my teenage friends went and settled on a kibbutz. It was a kind of post-Communist group; we all went to the same school. I just wasn't around during the Communist period. Ted Allan was, but Ted is seventy-three.

Did you see the recent article by Ted Solotaroff, 'American-Jewish Writers: On Edge Once More'? Solotaroff says that when Jewish American writers began their trajectory, they were the 'margin': 'to the extent that American Jews are marginal Israelis, we find ourselves connected once again to the Diaspora and to the condition of radical doubt that has produced much of its salient modern fiction.'

Well, Daniel Fuchs is very good. He's kind of a precursor of Saul Bellow. When Daniel Fuchs wrote his novels and they sold maybe 2000 copies, he went to Hollywood. At that time Jewish American experience was considered exotic. Arthur Miller pretended that the family in *Death of a Salesman* [1949] was not Jewish, when it was obviously a Jewish family. I think he felt that at that time Jewish American experience was considered foreign. Then when Saul Bellow wrote *The Adventures of Augie March* [1953], saying 'I am an American, Chicago born,' suddenly Jewish writers came into the mainstream with that novel. Then by the time Philip Roth came along 'Jewish' was considered mainstream experience. Jewish writers in the United States are no longer considered different, or thought of as a group speaking out of a special society.

Solotaroff says that the younger group of Jewish American writers has links with new political movements and feminism, and with Israeli writers and ideas. He thinks there's a new literary movement in the offing.

I don't know what he's talking about. Jewish writers are not homogeneous. There are all kinds of writers who are Jews. And they all deal with things differently. I think Norman Mailer is a Jewish writer, but he's never written particularly about Jewish experience. Harold Pinter is a Jew.

But he's also a Hungarian writing in Britain. I know what you are saying, but the question is out there. Whether you like it or not we all want to know the specificity of a Richler who is a Jew.

What I have to say is in my novels. The rest is gossip.

So, what's so bad about gossip?

Well, novels are gossip. Solotaroff—critics—think they have a key and they construct a machine to fit it.

When questions of ethnicity emerge, it is not uncommon to find that questions about the representation of women are quick to follow. You have not always represented women, or girls, favourably.

Like what? I have nothing against women.

Do you remember the article you wrote titled 'The Temptation Is Great, Sometimes, to Line Up with the Sexual Oppressors'?

No. I'll tell you what. I dislike all kinds of special pleading, and I tend to make fun of it whether it's Jewish, homosexual, or feminist. Special pleaders parody themselves. On the other hand, I am just about to join an organization which is trying to raise money for AIDS.

Do you still want to write about the Holocaust?

There's an anthology just coming out about what the Holocaust meant to our generation in America. I would have contributed but I was in the middle of my novel. It's by the same editor who did an anthology two years ago called *Congregation*, which I did contribute to. What I most remember about the Holocaust is guilt, because we were in the Depression and the time of the war was the first time my parents earned money. It was an ironic situation.

I read about that irony in The Street. *The war meant that the Jews could move from the cold-water flats to apartments in Outremont, or houses in the suburbs. But now, decades later, are you worried about how the Holocaust is going to be remembered?*

I am worried about it being put to cheap purposes—as the background for spurious thrillers and films—and I don't like it being brandished by suburban rabbis for their own grasping reasons. I think it should be treated with great dignity. We weren't there. It was horrendous and that has to be treated very delicately.

Are you concerned that there appears to be an audience for this kind of entertainment, especially as Canadian Nazis become more public?

Well the Nazis have become very glamorous. But a lot of the people who do these thrillers are Jewish producers. When William Styron wrote *Sophie's Choice*—it's not a novel I'm crazy about—he did it very honourably and for very serious reasons. Too often the Holocaust is invoked too glibly. It should be used very sparingly. It's too serious. By bringing it up three times a week, the Jewish community is doing itself a disservice. It should be held very much in reserve and only mentioned at very serious times. I don't care for the policies of the present Israeli government. Neither do a lot of Israelis. But it's possible to object to the policies without being an anti-Semite or without cheapening the memory of the six million dead.

Would you ever live in Israel?

I was invited out twice to be a writer-in-residence, and I couldn't go because I was working on this novel, which I regret. Maybe I'll go there next year. I don't think I'd like to live there. Once Moshe Sharett came to London when I was living there, and we had a dinner. William Frankel, the editor of the London *Jewish Chronicle*, which happens to be a very good Jewish paper, far superior to any of the community papers here, had a dinner, to which he invited ten or twelve Jewish writers. Writers like Pinter, Peter Shaeffer, myself, we were all there. And Sharett said to us, 'Why don't you come to Israel and write?' And we said, 'Because we're not Israelis.' How can you write about Israel except as journalists? He didn't understand, because we come from different societies; it doesn't mean we're not sympathetic, or that we wouldn't go to visit. As Philip Roth put it when [David] Ben-Gurion invited him to Israel, 'I'm an American.'

You wrote that 'every writer has one theme and many variations to play on it.' That was 1970. Do you still believe that?

Yes I do. You can find all of the themes I continue to write about in

The Acrobats [1954], which is a very bad novel, my first novel, but all my preoccupations are there, perfectly and embarrassingly stated.

Did you really go back home [to Montreal from London, England] after that book was published to your father who asked 'What in the hell do you know about the circus?' Followed by: 'Is it about Jews or ordinary people?'

Oh yes. But I adored my father.

Well if every writer has just one theme, would you be able to tell me what your theme is now?

It's always been: how do you live with honour in a time when there is no agreement on values? What is honour? That is really what my novels are about. How do you live well without hurting other people?

I have heard you talk about genre with passion, and I notice you call The Street *a memoir. Do you like that book?*

Well, it's not one of my favourite books. I like maybe three or four of the stories. I don't reread.

I know, but you have memories.

Yes, that's true, but I think some of the stories are fragile.

Because some of the stories verge on sentimental? At the beginning of the book you say the tales are part of a memoir. But writers don't change people's names in a 'real' memoir. It isn't really Fletcher Field High—it's Baron Byng. Do you know what I mean?

Yes, but I took licence. It's up to me what's in the genre.

That's true; you're the boss. So, why did you end up living near the infamous—and sentimental—'street' again after spending so many years in England?

Well, I live mostly in the Eastern townships. It was a big sacrifice for my wife, giving up London. But I felt I had to come back to America, because I am an American, or North American. And I understand things better here. V.S. Naipaul once put it very well. He said, 'I don't know what an Englishman does when he goes home at night.' And you can only write so many novels if you aren't brought up in a country. Novelists have to know so many prosaic things like what the price of haircuts are, or who the baseball stars are, all kinds of dumb things. You don't have to know them if you're a poet, which I consider a higher calling really. But if you're a novelist you have to know all of this kind of crap. And I wasn't brought up in London, so it's difficult. Also in London I lived in a society of writers and actors which was all very pleasant, but it was also very stifling, whereas here I know all kinds of different people. I don't know any writers here. I stay away from all that. I know a lot of writers in New York and London.

In one of your essays you talked about the Jewish writers of the thirties who betrayed you. I am thinking of Henry Roth in particular, who you said left you and your generation's tradition to work a chicken farm.

I think there are more good books than good writers. I think Auden first made that point. Sometimes you are very lucky and write a good book, but you can never do it again. There are more cherished books than writers. You just take the book and forget the writer. Nobody owes us anything. I hate that special pleading by writers. My father had a much more difficult life than I had. I wasn't drafted; I volunteered. This dreadful Canadian business of 'you owe me an audience.' 'You owe me applause.'

You owe me a Canada Council Grant?

Yes. That's dreadful. Nobody asked me to become a writer. You take your own chances. We remember Henry Roth because he wrote one great novel, *Call It Sleep*.

So that even interviewing a writer is . . .

The only thing that should concern you about a writer is what he sends out in a book. Because writers with huge personalities are off on the wrong trip. The best of their lives goes into their work. That's why dentists are a lot more fun.

AUSTIN CLARKE b. 1934

Canadian Experience

He passed in front of the oval-shaped looking glass in the hallway on his way out to go to a job interview, his first in five years. His eyes and their reflection made four. He stood looking at himself, laughing, and seeing only a part of his body in the punishing reflection the glass threw back at him. He was cut off at the neck. He laughed again. This time, at the morbidness of his own thoughts. The knot of his tie was shiny with grease. He did not like himself. He was not dressed the way he had hoped to appear, and his image was incorrect. This made him stop laughing.

So he went back upstairs to his rented room on the second floor at the rear of the rooming house. His room was beside the bathroom used by the two other tenants on that floor, and the actress on the third. He wanted to inspect his hair in the better light in the bathroom. But before he reached it, he heard the spikes of a woman's heels clambering down the rear staircase; and as he listened, they landed on the muffling linoleum in the hallway; and before he could move, the bathroom door was shut. He was not laughing now. It was the actress. She was between parts, without money, and she spent more time in the bathroom when she was waiting for auditions than on her parts after she was called.

He unlocked his door and left it slightly open, to wait his turn. He wanted the actress to know he was next in line, but he didn't want her to feel she was welcome. She liked to talk, and talk bad things about her friends, her father and her step-mother, and laugh about her career, for hours.

He had to change his clothes. He thought of what else he had to wear. Suddenly, he heard the heavy downpour of the shower as the water began to rain. So he closed his door.

The heavy ticking of the cheap clock became very loud now. It was the only one he could afford, and he had bought it in Honest Ed's bargain basement nearby. He had got it mainly for its alarm, not for its accuracy of time, which he had to check against the chimes of a rock-and-roll station. And he listened to this station against his better musical taste whenever he wanted to be punctual, which was not often. For he had been between jobs a long time.

This morning he had to be punctual. He was going to a job interview. It was on Bay Street in the business district of banks, brokerages and corporations. For all the time he had lived in Toronto, this district had frightened him. He tried to pacify his fear of it now by laughing at himself.

The job he was hoping to get was with a bank. He knew nothing about banks. He was always uncomfortable and impatient whenever he had to go into one. The most he had ever withdrawn was twenty dollars. The most money he had ever deposited at one time was fifteen dollars.

For three months now he had been walking the seven blocks from his rooming house on Major Street to the reference library on Asquith Avenue to sit in the reading room, to watch the women and to peruse the classified advertisements in the pages of the three daily newspapers, searching for a job. The *Star* contained about ten pages of advertisements which the paper called 'Employment Opportunities'. He was looking for a job, but he was still able to laugh at his plight. The *Sun* had three pages. Sometimes he would see the same 'employment opportunities' in this newspaper as in the *Star*'s pages, and he would laugh at their stupidity of duplication. He needed a job. And the *Globe and Mail*, which he heard was the best newspaper in the country, carried three pages. He did not like the *Globe and Mail*. There was no laughing matter about its print, which was too small. And it dealt with subjects beyond his understanding and interest, and even if he could smother a laugh about that, he found its small print bad for his deteriorating eyesight; and this made him depressed and bitter. Besides, the 'positions' which the *Globe and Mail* advertised were for executives, executive directors, industrial engineers, administrators and managers of quality assurance. He did not know what they meant. But he knew he wanted a job. Any job. His clothes had been in the cleaners for three months. And his diet, which had never been balanced, was becoming even more topsy-turvy with each succeeding month of joblessness.

It was, however, with an irony he himself could not fathom, but about which he smiled, that in the very pages of the *Globe and Mail*, he had seen the advertisement of the position for which he was promised an interview this Monday morning at ten.

His noisy clock, with a silver-painted bell on it—and white face and black luminous numerals of the Roman kind—said it was nine o'clock. His room was still dark.

The *Globe and Mail's* ad read:

We require an energetic junior executive to take a responsible position in our bank. The successful candidate must have a university degree in business or in finance, or the equivalent in business experience. Salary and benefits to be discussed at interview. Reply to the 14th floor, 198 Bay Street.

He was a man past thirty. But he could not, even at his age, argue about taking this 'junior position', because his desperate circumstances were forcing this stern necessity upon him. Junior or senior, he had to take it. And when he got it, he knew it would not be a laughing matter. Necessity would make him bitter, but thankful.

He had only to remember his old refrigerator, which took up one-eighth of the floor space of his room, and which hissed and stuttered whenever he turned on his electric hot plate. The refrigerator contained a box of baking soda, which the talkative actress had told him would kill the smells of food; and on the top shelf, cold water in a half-gallon bottle that had once been full of grapefruit juice; a half-pint carton of homogenized milk, now going bad; his last wieners from Canada Packers, like three children's joyless penises; six hard slices of white bread in soft, sweating plastic wrapping from Wonder Bread, which was printed below the blonde-haired child who persisted in smiling on the package. And three bottles of Molson's beer. In these circumstances of diving subsistence, he knew he had nothing to lose—and nothing to laugh about—concerning the 'junior position'.

He did not come to this country to attend university. Experience of the world, and his former life at home in Barbados were his only secondary education. He had come here against his father's bitter wishes. But he was not unschooled. He had attended the St Matthias' Elementary School for Boys, Barbados. *For Boys*, he wanted to remember to impress upon his prospective employers, since he was not a believer in the North American practice of having boys going to school with girls. He was a staunch supporter of the British system of public school education. And even though the St Matthias' Elementary School for boys was not, in fact, a public school, it was, nevertheless, a school that was public.

He laughed at his own cleverness of nuance and logic. Besides, no one in Toronto would know the difference. Toronto has Upper Canada College for boys, Trinity College School for boys, Bishop Strachan School for girls and Havergal College for girls. Boys with boys. And girls with girls. His logic was so acerbic and sharp, he was already laughing as he heard himself telling them that St Matthias' Elementary School for Boys was a . . .

But he stopped himself in the tracks of his hilarity: 'I had-better leave out the elementary part and just tell them *St Matthias' School for Boys.*' It was a satisfactory and imaginative rendering of the facts. Bay Street, if not the whole of Canada, he had discovered in his time here, was filled with people of imagination. The actress had been telling him that imagination is something called a euphemism for lies.

But he couldn't take the risk of failure. Failure would breed cynicism. Instead, he had said on his application that he was educated at Harrison College, 'a very prestigious college for men in Barbados, and founded in 1783, which produced the leading brains of the leading leaders in books and banking, of the entire West Indies'. Had he twisted the facts a little too much? Laughter and reassurance about the imaginative men on Bay Street, liars, as the actress called them, and who became quick millionaires, told him he had not stepped off into fraud. Not yet.

In spite of his lack of formal education, he still considered himself well read. Newspapers, magazines, the *Star* newspaper and *Time* magazine did not escape his daily and weekly scrutiny, even long after he had fallen upon the debris of the country's unemployed, in *decreptitude.* 'Decreptitude' was the word he always used to the actress when they talked about their lives, to make her laugh about the apparently irreconcilable differences between her and her own society, and also to impress her that he was not a fool. He had heard the word first on television. And he listened to CBC radio and shortwave broadcasts of the BBC world service, and watched four television news broadcasts each night: two Canadian and two from America. And he never missed *Sixty Minutes* from New York. Except for the three times, consecutive Sundays, when he had lain flat on his back, fed off the public welfare system, on a public ward in the Toronto General Hospital 'under observation' for high blood pressure.

'Pressure in my arse!' he told the actress who visited him every day, as he explained his illness.

In the eight years he had spent in this country, he had lain low for the first five, as a non-landed immigrant, in and out of low-paying jobs given specifically to non-landed immigrants, and all the time waiting for amnesty. One year he worked distributing handbills, most of which, because of boredom, he threw into garbage pails when no one was looking, and laughed, until one cold afternoon in February when his supervisor, who did not trust immigrants, carried out a telephone check behind his back, only to discover that none of the householders on the fifteen streets he had been assigned to had ever heard of or had ever seen the brochures advertising *Pete's Pizza Palace, free delivery*. After that mirthless firing, there were three months during which he laboured as a janitor for the Toronto Board of Education—incidentally, his closest touch with higher learning; two months at Eaton's as a night-shift cleaner; then two months at Simpsons as an assistant shipping clerk until the last job, five years ago, held along with Italians, Greeks and Portuguese, cleaning the offices of First Canadian Place, a building with at least fifty floors, made of glass, near Bay Street, where he was heading this morning.

He laughed at himself as he thought of his former circumstances. For he was ready for bigger things. The murmuring refrigerator could not, within reason, be any emptier.

So with the bathroom next door still occupied, he looked at himself, at the way he was dressed. It was nine-fifteen now. His bladder was full. Whenever he had important things on his mind, his bladder filled itself easily, and more unusually heavy, and it made him tense.

He wished the pink shirt was cleaner. He wished the dark brown suit was a black one. He should not wear a yellow tie, but no other ties he had would match the clothes on his back. And he knew through instinct and not through Canadian experience that a job of this importance, 'junior executive' in a bank, had to be applied for by a man dressed formally in black.

Laughter, his father had told him many times, a smile at the right moment, melts a woman with even the meanest temperament. He tried this philosophy now, and his attitude changed for the better. He put more Vaseline on his hair to make the part on the left side keener, for he had dressed in the dark. And now that the autumn light was coming through the single glass pane, which he could not reach even standing on a chair and from which he could never see the sidewalk, he could see that the shirt he had thought was slightly soiled was dirty.

The morning was getting older, the time of his appointment was getting closer, the hands of the bargain-basement clock were now at nine thirty-five, and he had only twenty-five minutes left to go; and he had to go badly but couldn't, because the actress was still inside the bathroom, singing a popular song. He could hear the water hitting against the bathtub and could imagine her body soaked in the hot beads of the shower, and he could see the red-faced ugly blackheads painted red, at the bottom of her spine. He had asked her once what they were, and she had told him 'cold sores'. He thought they had something to do with winter, that they came out in winter. He laughed each time she told him 'cold sores'. He could see them now, because he had seen them once before. Yesterday, too, for thirty-five minutes counted by his loud, inaccurate, cheap alarm clock, he had heard the torrents of the shower as she washed herself in preparation for an audition.

He had nothing to do now but wait. The shower stopped like a tropical downpour and with a suddenness that jolted him. He opened his door. He listened. Mist floated out of the bathroom door, and he brushed through it as if he were a man seeking passage through thick, white underbrush. And as he got inside and could barely see his way to the toilet bowl, there she was, with one leg on the cover of the bowl, which she had painted black, bending down, wiping the smell of the soap from between her legs and then the red, rough dots of bruises on the bottom of her spine, which she insisted were cold sores. When she named them first, he thought she had said 'cold stores'. He could understand that. 'Cold stores', 'cold storage' — it was enough to make him laugh.

'Oh, it's you.'

He could not move. He did not answer. He could not retreat.

'Close the door and come in.'

The mist came back, thick and sudden as fog swallowing him, debilitating him, blinding him, and he lost his vision. But he could see the lines of four ribs on each side of her body, and her spinal cord that ran clear as a wemm, with the dozen or so cold sores, fresh as the evidence from a recent lash.

'I have an audition in an hour, so I'm washing myself clean. You never know what directors're going to ask you to do.'

He retreated to his room and closed the door. No mist or even warm sores could confuse him now; and he inspected the clothes he was dressed in, unable to change them, and worried about his interview, refusing all the time to think of the naked actress, and ignored her knocking on his door. Whenever he refused to answer her, she would leave a note on his door in her scratchy, left-handed scrawl.

But this time, when he re-opened his door to leave, she was standing there, and he passed her, wrapped in the large *Holiday Inn* towel she had brought from Sherbrooke and which barely covered the red sores at the bottom of her spine. The two small nipples of her dropped breasts were left bare to his undesiring eyes.

'You're too black to wear brown,' she said. He passed her as if she had herpes. 'If you don't mind me saying so,' she shouted at his back, which moved away from her down the stairs.

This time he did not look at himself in the oval-shaped looking glass in the hall. He just walked out of the house. He wished it was for the last time.

The people at the bus stop are standing like sentries, silent and sullen. They look so sleepy he thinks it could be six o'clock. But a clock in the bank beside the bus stop says ten minutes to ten. He hurries the crowded bus on, with the urging of his anxiety.

The only sound that comes from the larger group of people going down into the subway is the hurrying pounding of heels on the clean, granite steps and the rubbing of hands on the squeaking rails, polished like chrome. More people are coming up out of the subway at greater speed as if they are fleeing the smell of something unwholesome. He can smell only the fumes of the trains. And he wonders if it is his imagination. For he knows that the trains run on electricity. It must be the smell of dust, then. Or the people. Or the perfumes.

He watches a woman's hand as it wipes sleep and excreta from the corners of her eyes. He thinks of the actress, who cleans her face this way.

But it is still September, his month of laughter along the crowded sidewalks, amongst the fallen turning leaves. And the furious memory of growing grass, quicker than the pulse was in summer, is still in the air. There are no lamb's wool, no slaughtered seals, no furs, no coats yet to cover the monotony of women's movement, which he sees like the singlemindedness of sheep, one behind the leader, in single file downwards into the subway and in double file upwards.

He boards a crowded subway car and stands among the sardines of silent, serious people. Where he is, with both hands on a pole, he is surrounded by men dressed in grey and black. Some are darker and richer than others. Some of the women too, are dressed in grey; some better made and better built than others. All the men in this car hold briefcases, either on their laps or between their shoes. And the women carry at least two bags, from one of which they occasionally take small balls of Kleenex.

He has just swayed farther from the steadying pole for moving balance as the train turns, and is standing over a woman cleaning her eyes and her nose with a red fingernail. And, immediately, as his eyes and hers meet, she drops her eyes into the pages of a thick paperback book, as if her turned eyes would obliterate her act.

The second bag he sees some women carrying is larger than a handbag, large enough, he thinks, for rolls of toilet paper and paper towels. The men do not read: they watch the women's legs. And they look over their shoulders, between their shoulders and down into their braless bodies, and their eyes touch the pages of the novels the women are reading; and not certain of the enlightenment and pleasure to be got from this rapid-transit fleeting education, the men reluctantly allow their eyes to wander back to the pages of the *Globe and Mail*, which seem to hold no interest for them. Their eyes roam over the puny print of the stock market quotations, the box scores of the Blue Jays baseball team and the results at Woodbine Race Track.

If his own luck had been really luck—and something to laugh about—the actress told him once, he could win thousands of dollars on a two-dollar bet, as easy as one, two, three. When she told him, 'One to win, two to come second and three to come third,' he laughed, thinking she was memorizing lines of a play she was auditioning for.

He had been living with so little luck in his life—three months with no money and no hope of any—that he could afford to dream and to laugh as he dreamed, and fill his empty pockets with imagined wealth.

A man beside him shakes out the pages of the *Globe and Mail* to the racing results: '*and in the fifth race yesterday at Woodbine, the first three horses to come in, 1, 2 and 3, paid $15,595.03. . . .*'

The jerk of the train stopping pushes him against the metal pole and awakens him from his dreaming. When the doors open, he is at his stop.

The air is cool. He can feel his shirt like wet silk against his body. He pulls the lapels of his jacket together to make himself feel warmer.

The sun shines blindingly, but weak, on the tall office buildings that surround him. He is walking in their shadow, as if he is walking in a valley back in Barbados. The buildings look like steel. One facing him, built almost entirely out of glass, shimmers like gold. Its reflection of his body tears him into strides and splatters his suit against four glass panels, and makes him disjointed. It is the building he is going to enter.

The elevator is crowded. The passengers are all looking up at the changing numbers of the floors. He looks up, too. He can hear no breathing. A man shifts his weight from one black alligator shoe to the next. A woman changes her brown leather handbag and her other, larger bag, made of blue parachute material, from her right arm to her left. He reads *Bijoux*, which is printed on it. There is only the humming of the elevator; then the sound of the doors opening; then feet on the polished floor outside; the sound of the doors closing; a deep breath like a sigh of relief or of anticipation for the next floor; then the humming of the next ascent and then silence. The elevator stops on the fourteenth floor. There is no thirteenth. He is at the front, near the door, when it opens. Five men and women are beside and behind him. Facing him is glass and chrome and fresh flowers and Persian rugs and women dressed expensively and stylishly in black, with necklaces of pearls. And chewing gum. It is quiet in the office. Deathly quiet. So he stands his ground.

BANK is written on the glass.

'Getting off?' a man beside him asks.

He stands his ground.

The door closes, and he goes up with the five of them and finds himself, gradually, floor by floor, alone, as they slip out one by one. The elevator takes him to the top. The door does not open. And when it starts its descent, he is feeling braver. He remembers the new vigour he felt at the end of three hours with wax and mops and vacuum cleaners with Italians, Greeks, and Portuguese, going down the elevator. He will ride it to the bottom.

No one enters, even though it stops two times in quick succession. And then it stops once more, and the door opens, and he is facing the same office with BANK written on the glass, cheerless and frightening, and seeing the same chrome, the rugs and the black and pearls of the women. Just as he moves to step out, the closing door, cut into half, and like two large black hands, comes at him. He gets out of the way just as the blue eyes of one of the women approaching the elevator door to see what he wanted are fixed upon him. Those blue eyes are like ice-water; his are brown and laughing.

'. . . this stop, sir?' is all he gets to hear of the woman's flat voice before the two black palms, like a shutter, have taken her eyes from his view and her words from his hearing.

'And you didn't even go into the office?'

'I couldn't do it.'

'Sometimes when I'm auditioning, I get scared and get butterflies.'

'There was so much wealth!'

'Are you a communist? I wish I had money, money and more money. All I think about is money. But here I am in this damn rooming house with a broken shower curtain and a leaky bathtub, trying to be an artist, an actress. Do you think I'll be a dedicated actress because I live in all this shit? When last have I had steak? And a glass of red wine? Or you?'

'I have some wieners.'

'Wieners, for Chrissakes!'

Her flat voice and icy manner killed the kindness in his suggestion.

'The people on the subway looked so educated, like everybody was a university graduate. And not one person, man or woman, asked me if I needed directions.'

'For Chrissakes! How would they know you don't have Canadian experience?'

'They looked on me and at me and through me, right through me. I was a piece of glass.'

'Must have been your brown suit.'

'Everybody else was in grey and black.'

'I hope I get this part. Just to get my hands on some money and rent a decent place. But what can I do? I even get tired taking showers in a bathroom where the water leaks through the curtain. My whole life is like a shower curtain. That leaks. Oh, the landlady was here. Fifteen minutes after you left. She tells me you have to give up your room on Friday. So I tell her not to worry, that you got a job today. And you didn't even go into the office? She wants you to pay two months this month. But you didn't even face the people!'

'With all that glass and steel and chrome?'

'Do you want me to tell her you're not in? You could always slip out without paying the rent, you know. I've done it lots of times. In Sherbrooke and in Rosedale. God, I nearly broke my ass racing down the metal fire escape, carrying my box of French Canadian plays. Everybody skips out on landlords. Try it. She'll never find you in Toronto! The one in Rosedale hasn't found me yet. And here I am, desperate to be an actress and get the money to move back to Rosedale . . .'

'When she's coming back?'

'Seven.'

'She coming in three hours? Are you saying four o'clock, too?'

'You *could* come to my room. I don't have to do the audition. I can skip it. There's a small restaurant on Church Street where a lot of television and radio types eat, and I'm thinking of applying for a waitress job there. It's an artistic restaurant. I'll even slip you a meal if I get the job.'

'She said she's coming back at seven?'

'My room is open to you, as I say. Be free. Feel free. Don't you want to be free? Where could you go, anyhow?'

In his hands is a glass with a pattern on it that advertises peanut butter. It has dried specks like old saliva round the mouth. He passes his fingers round the mouth of the glass, cleaning it; and when it looks clean and is cloudy from his hand-prints, he pours the first of the three Molson's into it. He sits on his bed. There is no chair in the room. Only his television set, which he sits on when he is not watching *Sixty Minutes* or the American news. His dangling feet can barely touch the floor. On the floor is linoleum, with a floral pattern. 'Rose of Sharon,' the actress had told him. 'I was a whiz in Botany at Jarvis Collegiate.'

The sun is brighter now. He can smile in this sun and think of home. He is getting warmer, too. A shaft of dust plays within the arrow of September light that comes through the window. It lands at his feet. The light and the particles of dust on the bright leather of his shoes attract his attention for a moment only. He smiles in that moment. And in that moment, his past life fills his heart and shakes his body like a spasm, like a blast of cold air. His attention then strays to the things around him, his possessions, prized so fondly before, and which now seem to be mere encumbrances: the valise he brought from Barbados and carried through so many changes of address in Toronto; heavier always in winter when he changed rooms, when he carried it late at night on his shoulder, although each time that he moved, he had accumulated no more possessions; the two Christmas cards which the actress mailed to him, even though she had been living in the same house, placed open like two tents and which he keeps on top of a wooden kitchen cupboard, used now as his dressing table. 'To George, at Xmas' is written in ball-point, in red, on each, in capital letters; and an unframed colour photograph taken in Barbados, and fading now, showing him with his father and mother and two younger brothers and three sisters: eight, healthy, well-fed Barbadians, squinting because the sun is in their eyes, standing like proprietors in front of a well-preserved plantation house made of coral stone, covered in vines so thick that their spongy greenness strangles the windows and the doors. The name of this house in Barbados is *Edgehill House.* His present residence has no name. It is on a street named Major. It is a rooming house, similar in size, in build and in dirt to the other houses on the street.

He drains the beer from the peanut-butter glass and refills it. He throws the last bottle into the plastic garbage pail, and the rattle of glass and tin is like a drunken cackle. Inside the garbage pail are the classified pages from the *Globe and Mail,* some shrivelled lettuce leaves, an empty milk carton and the caps of beer bottles. He thinks of the woman in the bank's office, dressed in black, with the blue eyes. He thinks of the flowers and the glass in that office and of flowers more violent in colour, growing in wild profusion, untended, round *Edgehill House,* where he was born in a smiling field of comfortable pasture land.

His father never worked for anyone in his whole life, never had to leave the two hundred and eighty acres of green sugar cane and corn to dirty his hands for anyone's money.

'Work on this blasted plantation, boy. Put your hands in the most stinking dirt and cow-dung on this plantation, and it is a hundred times nobler than working at the most senior position in a country where you wasn't born!'

His father said that almost every day, and more often when his father heard he was leaving for Canada.

'You call yourself a son o' mine? You, a son o' mine? With all this property that I leaving-back for you? You come telling me you going to Canada as a' immigrant? To be a stranger? Where Canada is? What is Canada? They have a Church o' England up there? Canada is no place for you, man. The son of a Barbadian plantation owner? This land was in our family before Canada was even discovered by the blasted Eskimos and the red Indians. Seventeen-something. A.D.! In the year of our Lord, *anno domini*. Who do they worship up there? And you come telling me that you going up there, seeking advancement as a' immigrant? In Canada? Your fortune and your future is *right here*! In this soil. In this mud. In this dirt. 'Pon these two hundred and eighty-something acres o' cane and corn!'

It is six-thirty now. Thirty minutes before the landlady is to arrive. He locks his door. He stands outside in front of it, like a man who has forgotten something inside. There is a red thumb-tack on the door. The actress pins it there whenever she leaves messages that she thinks require urgent replies. Whenever there's a thumb-tack on his door, he thinks of the red cold sores on her back, and it makes him laugh. He does not know why: he just laughs.

He climbs the stairs to go to her room. He can see a red thumb-tack on her door, even before he reaches it. It is similar to the one he has left behind on his own door. She has written his name in red capital letters on a folded piece of lined white paper. He pulls the paper from the tack.

'*I got the waitress job at the restarant.*' He smiles when he sees she has spelled 'restaurant' without a 'u'. She has signed it, '*Pat*'.

He did not throw away the balled-up message, even hours afterwards, in all the walking he did that night, until he was standing on the platform of the subway at the Spadina station where he is now.

He looks to his right and then to his left, and there is no one in sight. Across from him, across the clean cement that is divided by a black river of hard dirty steel, are two large billboards. One advocates 'pigging-out', and the other tells women about 'Light Days, Tampax'. Suddenly, into the frame of these two boards riveted to two steel pillars comes the lone passenger, who stands and waits to take the train going in the other direction.

He does not know why he is in this station and why he has entered on the side for southbound trains.

South is the office building with the glass and the flowers and the women dressed in black and BANK written on the glass. South is Bay Street where no one walks after the Italians and the Greeks and the Portuguese have cleaned the offices and have left to take the subway north to College Street. South is nothing. South is the lake and blackness and cold water that smells of dead fish and screaming children's voices in the short summer, and machines and boats and grease.

The balled-up note from Pat, written on its soiled paper, smelling of the ointment she uses for her cold sores, was in his fist when he first reached this spot where he is standing now. He is standing in the centre of the platform, the same distance from the left end as from the right.

A rumble grows louder. Chains and machinery, iron touching iron, steel rubbing steel, the sound of the approaching train. He can never tell at the first sound of this familiar rumbling, out of a darkened tube, whether it is coming from his left or from his right. He always has to wait longer for the greater roar. Or if it is night-time, watch for the first glare on the tracks.

He thinks the roar is coming from the southbound line. He feels more at ease for a moment, and braver, and he even laughs, although he doesn't know why. The man on the other side stares at him from his seat on the brown leather, between the two advertising boards, and the man remains querulous with his staring until the train moves northwards.

He is alone again. And more at ease. He moves to the end of the platform, nearest the tube through which the train will emerge, to a spot where he could see it clearly. He wants no surprises. He wants to see it the moment it appears out of the blackness. The blackness that is like the South and the lake. And he wants no one else to see him. He wants to be alone, just as he was alone in the descending elevator in the office building.

How comfortable and safe and brave he had felt travelling and laughing and falling so fast and so free, through the bowels of that glassed-in building!

He hears the rumble. He hears the sound of steel or iron — metal anyhow; and the low screech of the train trying to emerge out of the darkened, curved tube.

He thinks of Pat. So he throws the balled-up note onto the tracks. And that act is her being thrown out of his life, along with her red-corpuscled sores. He sees the note fall. But does not hear it reach the surface of the black river of hard dirty steel below him. He does not hear it reach the tracks. He cannot gauge any distance now. Cannot gauge any face. The paper is very light. Almost without weight. Definitely without purpose and love.

But the train is here. Its lights reflect onto the tracks which now are shining and getting wider as the ugly red engine, like her sores, approaches. He knows that the train is as long as the platform, half of which he has already paced off. The train is here. And just as its lights begin to blind him, he makes his own eyes pierce through that weaker brightness and fixes them on the driver dressed in a light-brown uniform. He sees the driver's face, the driver's happy eyes and his relief that this is his last trip; and he himself laughs to an empty platform and station that are not listening, and he steps off the platform, just having seen his own eyes, and the driver's, makes four.

AUSTIN CHESTERFIELD CLARKE was born in 1934 at St James Parish, Barbados, where he received his early education. He came to Toronto in 1955 to study economics and political science at the University of Toronto. Before beginning to write full-time in 1963, he worked as an actor, a journalist, and an industrial photographer. He has been visiting professor of black studies at numerous American colleges (Yale, Duke, Brandeis) and writer-in-residence at several Canadian universities. He has served as cultural attaché at the Barbadian Embassy in Washington, director of Caribbean broadcasting in Barbados, and vice-chairman of the Ontario Board of Censors, and is now a member of the Refugee Board in Ontario. His works include *The Survivors of the Crossing* (Toronto: McClelland and Stewart, 1964); *The Meeting Point* (Toronto: Macmillan, 1967); *When He Was Free and Young and He Used to Wear Silks* (Toronto: Anansi, 1971); *The Bigger Light* (Boston and Toronto: Little, Brown, 1975); *The Prime Minister* (Toronto: General, 1977); *Growing Up Stupid Under the Union Jack: A Memoir* (Toronto: McClelland and Stewart, 1980); *Nine Men Who Laughed* (Toronto: Penguin, 1986); and *Proud Empires* (London: Gollancz, 1986).

MARION RICHMOND was born in Winnipeg of Jewish parents whose families had emigrated from Eastern Europe to escape the persecution there during the late nineteenth century. She is research director of the Canadian Publishing Foundation, London, Ontario. She has previously co-edited *25 Top Canadian Prose Writers: An Anthology* (Hebrew trans., Arie Hashavia; 1982) and *New Essays on 'The Portrait of a Lady'*, a special issue of *The Henry James Review*, 7, 2-3 (1986). She has published articles and book reviews on contemporary Israeli fiction and is currently working on a collection of interviews with Israeli novelists.

In your fiction you chronicle the difficulties, the hopes and aspirations of the black West Indian immigrant to Canada. At the same time, you confront Canadian readers, themselves also immigrants at one time or another, with some of their attitudes toward black people and other more recently arrived immigrants. Generally, what are some of these attitudes?

When I came to this country in 1955 I came as a student from a background in Barbados which I thought had prepared me to enter this society at that particular level—as a student. I had met Canadians in Barbados, white Canadians, and in my mind there was no difference between us; certainly there was no attitude on their part, of course, nor on mine that there was any difference in intellect or in our attitude toward society. In 1955, as foreign students, I think we were looked upon by Canadians as probably special persons who had come from these diverse countries about which not much was known. If we seemed to them a threat, it was a short-lived one, in the sense that in those days, the early fifties, most of us intended to return home for many reasons. I think primary among those reasons was the inhospitableness of the country and its customs, and second to that, we found the food atrocious and tasteless. One reason for our feelings of isolation, I suppose, was that we were strangers to the city, and another reason, of course, could have been that there was so much work to do. So we did not meet the ordinary Canadian except in the long vacation in the summer, and if we were not self-supporting and had to take part-time jobs as I did, then we met the ordinary Canadian—the working man. Now I still am not sure whether I could label the attitudes of the people with whom I worked at the time to be racialistic. Then also, Toronto in 1955 was a very dull, a very provincial, a very introverted society. I think I'm justified in saying that Toronto has always been racist. In those days I remembered Pierre Berton writing articles that shocked us blacks, and I am sure shocked some whites too, about the difficulties that Jewish people had in renting cottages and other things but, even so, we were not prepared for the onslaught of racialistic attitudes when we left the university. I think the most humiliating experiences certainly were in renting property. We all went through, more or less, the indignities of going to rent a flat and finding that it was taken and, then, of course, using a more circuitous route, like an investigative reporter, to find out that it was not taken. However, to most of us, these racist attitudes were not important for many reasons: first of all, we had no intentions of remaining here; secondly, we did not think these attitudes defined us as persons or even curtailed what we could do with our education even in this country, and it certainly could not restrict our potential if we went back home; and also, I think we felt that in time attitudes would change, certainly the attitudes toward us, a special group.

How did you treat Canadian blacks? Did you look down on them?

I must say we did not escape entirely some of the more vicarious aspects of racism; in that kind of situation, when you say that society is anti-black but that those blacks who are educated or behave well will not be treated as badly as the others, and when we looked around on the University of Toronto campus and did not see many black students, we very viciously and stupidly accepted the racialistic rhetoric of those who said that the black Canadian was not as well educated as the West Indian, and therefore we felt, some of us, superior to the Canadian black—which, of course, was absurd. Also, Africans who came to Canada around that time, because of their history, showed a certain superiority toward us, and so, you see, we were caught more or less in a kind of vortex. If you are in a kind of exile, if you are constantly reminded that you are not welcome and, perhaps, that there might be a danger in your presence, should you persist in remaining in the society, you tend to want to question your own worth—and that is where the danger comes. If you have been colonized successfully, and most colonizations have been successful, if only in the short run, then you tend to live as a person who is not only colonized but who desires to be colonized, and from that attitude spring all of the ideas about the superiority of certain races.

Canada and Barbados have a common British colonial heritage; you have lived in both countries. Do you think your colonial background in Barbados has helped you adapt to the colonial mentality in Canada?

Let me say that, when I was growing up in Barbados, I never considered myself to be growing up in a colony, because even though, in law and in fact, Barbados was a colony, my immediate life was not circumscribed by those two factors.

Because you were a majority there?

Yes, we were a majority there, about 98 per cent. The other good thing about growing up there was that all the models of achievement in my time were black, and even though the presence of the white Barbadian was expressed in certain authoritarian institutions, it did not impinge upon us; in other words, the white Barbadian was always in the background. It could no longer be said that we went to him to have justice done in the courts; that we went to him to be educated, because in the late thirties and forties those institutions were almost entirely black.

But the model was British and white.

The model may have been white in the beginning, a British white model, but in my time, it was no longer so, because the people who carried it on were not white. It had been taken over, not by political means—even though the majority of the people in the House of Assembly was black—but through competence, through the competence that was derived from education. When Barbados became independent, I was not in Barbados but I had always felt independent because, as you correctly say, we were in the majority. It was certainly not based on something called 'affirmative action' because we never had 'affirmative action' in Barbados. We had a situation where not only whites and blacks, but all people were able to live as one. When I came to this country I soon realized that I was not, more or less, a brother under the Commonwealth, but I was different because I was black, and different in a way, as they suggested, that was inferior— not only different in an exotic way. But the irony is that we never thought of Canada, to be quite frank, as a society of any great excellence. When we were considering university—Barbados up until recently was considered to be the country with the highest literacy rate in the world—because of our political ties with Britain, we obviously chose Britain. It had to be Oxford or Cambridge, and if that was impossible, then Harvard or Columbia. You see, coming from one colony to another is an easy step, even though Canada had, at the time, a 'whites only' policy on immigrants. I'm making the distinction now between those people who come here by choice, even though they may not be able to return home, and those who come as immigrants and, in recent months, as refugees. What matters to us and what has always mattered to us, of course, is the way we were treated. If we were treated with hostility or with disrespect, we took objection and did something about that. If we read in the papers that Canadians did not like black people, then we said 'To hell with that—so what! We don't want to be white; we will always be black! We can always go back to better kinds of living.' So, you see, integration was not even an academic point for us in those days, and it was not an important point for us many years afterwards; because of our situation here, we had not surrendered our attachment to home, wherever home was.

I wonder whether ethnic and racial integration in this predominantly WASP *country is ever really possible? I am Jewish; my mother was born in Canada; her parents came from Russia in the late nineteenth century; my father emigrated to this country from Romania in the early part of the century. I am a born-and-bred Canadian citizen and have enjoyed, particularly in the last thirty years, many of the advantages and privileges that come with being a Canadian, and yet, to this day, I still feel, at times, or am made to feel, like an outsider. Now this may be, in part, the result of having grown up at a time when there was a policy in this country of 'No Jews Allowed' in certain neighbourhoods, professions, and businesses. It was a time when there were quota systems at universities. Strangely, paradoxically, since the establishment of Israel as a Jewish homeland, I feel more at home in Canada, more of an equal among equals rather than a second-generation immigrant. Have there been any particular incidents that typify for you the immigrant experience in Canada?*

Well, let me give you the positive ones first. I am fascinated and proud that one weekend a year West Indians gather on the streets of Toronto for 'Caribana'—during which time they give Ontario society an injection of health and joy and excitement and lasciviousness and drunkenness, colour and music. I am very proud of that, that is, in spite of the shortcomings of the representation. On the negative side, the incidence of violence and brutality by police toward West Indians is upsetting . . . racialistic.

In your story 'Canadian Experience', the main character seems overwhelmed by 'the system' and alienated not only from the rest of Canadian society but from the West Indian community. We are told that: 'In the eight years he had spent in this country, he had laid low for the first five, as a non-landed immigrant, in and out of low-paying jobs given specifically to non-landed immigrants. . . .' It seems to me the operative word here is specifically. *Isn't it a fact that there are many Canadians who are also in and out of low-paying jobs, because they may lack motivation or formal education? Who or what, then, is responsible for the tragic ending?*

He was responsible, as you see from the flashback, from the discussion between his father and himself. I would say that the immigrant to some extent must bear some responsibility for his plight in this country, but I must also say that the extent to which an immigrant fails or is perceived to be a failure, to my mind, is determined by the decency of the environment in which he finds himself.

In The Journals of Susanna Moodie, *Margaret Atwood writes: 'We are all immigrants to this place even if we were born here.' As an immigrant, what is your reaction to these lines?*

I do not know Margaret Atwood's poetry, but from what you have read I would hazard the opinion that Atwood is talking about the tenuous claim that some persons who have found themselves in this country are making towards superiority or possessiveness or sovereignty, forgetful of their origins. I suppose we could talk about various kinds of ironies — of their materialistic hold on the country, of their political power, of the intellectual direction they have given to the country; but before they exhibited this arrogance, there were in fact people living in the country, and the fact that these people are only recognized and heard about in crises suggests, perhaps, the significance of the statement. It is not ordinary in conversations of this type for a certain kind of Canadian to make any acknowledgement of the fact that they are immigrants. This is the arrogance of possession, the arrogance of imperialism, the arrogance of mercantilism — which is a precursor to nationalism, and if you will pardon the expression, this is the arrogance of the white man. It seems to me that it is easy for Canadians, and I mean not only white Canadians but all Canadians — black, Italian, Jewish, Portuguese, Indian, from the East, that is — it is easy for us, without any guilt or remorse, to live in this country without acknowledging the presence of the founding race, and certainly without acknowledging the historical significance of the native people. So, to some extent, Atwood's lines are very compelling. I consider it to be a weakness in myself, a vacuum in my education, an immorality, that I cannot say today, in 1989, that I know one Indian.

In the same book, Atwood writes: 'in parts unknown . . . [we] move in fear, exiles and invaders. This country is something that must be chosen — it is so easy to leave — and if we do choose it we are still choosing a violent duality.' Living here, do you feel that you have chosen a violent duality?

It took me considerable time to decide to be a Canadian citizen – from 1955 until 1981 – and at that time I was not going through any anxiousness of duality: I just was not Canadian; I was Barbadian. That is not to say that, now that I am a Canadian citizen, I am not Barbadian, because I am Barbadian by nature – the best of me is Barbadian; the best of my memories are Barbadian. But when I look at my presence in this country, the problems of duality arise each time there is a threat to my stability, each time there is a slur on a whole group of persons with whom I could easily identify, each time there is a slur on a larger group of persons with whom I politically have to identify.

What are some of the racial and ethnic stereotypes that you have encountered in Canada?

I think that nowadays one does not have to look very far to see these stereotypes. It happened around the Dubin Inquiry, in which a country or a society was trying to expiate from itself the shame which was inflicted upon it [at the 1988 Olympic Games]. One person [Ben Johnson] has become a symbol of the cause, of the origin of national shame and frustration. He is portrayed as dumb, as shiftless, as bad-tempered, as breaking the law, and, noticeably, he is portrayed as the noble savage – that is to say, that he has an IQ, whatever that means, of a nine-year-old. I do not consider myself capable of being stereotyped, but if I were, in fact, I would only be stereotyped because someone has decided that it is easier in his dealings with me not to be bothered to see the entire situation, that it is not really essential to engage in a reciprocal kind of relationship. I have always insisted that the black cannot be racist in any meaningful sense; he may have attitudes or feelings that may not be entirely endearing to another group, but for him to be racist seems to me to be a contradiction in terms, since he does not have the power in the society in which he is living to take advantage of these feelings of disagreeableness; he could only think or dream that he does not like a person, but he could certainly not do anything to thwart him.

From 1968 to 1974 you were visiting professor of black studies at some American universities. From your experience there, what differences have you observed between Canada and the US in their treatment of racial minorities – blacks, in particular?

As a professor looking at black or non-white students and trying to determine what the attitude was in the institution towards these people, I was amazed to see that at Yale and at Brandeis that the institutions, after having admitted these students, whether on their merits or through affirmative action, were not exactly pleased that they had done this, and they did not make arrangements to protect them from the loneliness and some of the aggression that came out of these students. There was not only a perceived hostility on the part of the administration but, certainly, from the white students, and from some of the agents that one regrettably has on the university campus — the police. At another college where I taught, Williams College in Massachussetts, there was a 'black table'; I think there was a 'black table' at Yale, too. I never did go into the dining hall at Brandeis but, from what I gathered in the classroom, blacks sat together and whites sat together. To say the least, there was a certain hostility on the part of whites who had been going to these colleges for years and who had begun, I suppose, to consider them as their own reservations. I've always been confused about the attitudes of the Americans to minorities — in my case, blacks. If you read magazines which I consider extremely important for black people — *Jet*, *Sepia*, *Ebony*, black magazines — you get the impression, certainly I do, that the possibility for recognition and reward is greater, has always been greater, and comes much more easily in America for blacks than in Canada. I don't think that even white Canadians consider themselves Canadians to the extent that Americans consider themselves Americans, and certainly, it seems to me obvious that the blacks in this country do not consider themselves Canadians to the same extent. They are only Canadian because of the ease with which they can amass money, have a car, a pretty good job, and go back home on vacation. But I would never live in America. America is a thing that boggles the imagination — a place of tremendous power, a place that, for some reason, everybody in the world — except myself — wants to go to live.

RUDY WIEBE b. 1934

Sailing to Danzig

My name is Adam Peter Wiebe. As far as I know, there hasn't been an Adam in the family since the name Wiebe was first recorded in 1616 in Danzig, which is now of course Gdansk, Poland. The first Adam Wiebe was Dutch, and in Danzig he had two sons, Abraham and Jacob. Oddly enough, my own father, who was born in Chortitza Mennonite Colony, the Ukraine, was called Abraham Jacob, which in the Russian Mennonite tradition of naming meant that his father's name before him was Jacob. My oldest brother, who was born in a Mennonite village in the foothills of the Ural Mountains, was named Abram Abraham, my second brother Daniel Abraham, the Daniel coming from my mother's father. How is it then, I asked my parents years ago, that I, the last son, was named Adam Peter?

'Actually you weren't,' my mother tells me without hesitation. 'In the government papers in Saskatchewan, wherever they have them, your name was Heinrich.'

'Heinrich?'

'In the papers, yes, and Abraham your second, like always. You were Heinrich Abraham.'

'I'm not Adam?' At age seventeen I am about to discover my name?

'Of course you're Adam,' she says calmly. 'That was just those government papers. But we were living so far in the Saskatchewan bush when you were born it was seven weeks before your father got to town and he registered your name "Heinrich Abraham".'

My father, across the kitchen table from me, has continued to study his *Mennonitische Rundschau*; his reading glasses, bought at a counter in Eaton's, tilt at the end of his long, almost patrician nose. He sits this way every Sunday afternoon, the only day of the week he does not have to feed cattle on the farm where he will work as a hired man until he is sixty-nine, another seven years, never able to find the one Canadian dream he still has: a job where he can work inside and be warm all winter. He says nothing now, not even at my mother's teasing irony which, we all three know, will prick him eventually into some response.

'He had the day wrong, too,' my mother continues suddenly. 'He remembered it was a Saturday but he got the date wrong a whole week and when we got the registration when he was going to become a citizen Mrs Graham said to me, "My Lloyd was born the same day as your Adam, the midwife came from you to me, how come your day is wrong?" and then I noticed that, too.'

'It was eight weeks after, not seven,' my father mutters finally; as if correcting her fact will balance his.

'But my name, you didn't remember my *name*!'

He seems particularly intent on the *Nachrichten*; he will never understand more than the barest English and it is in the weekly *Rundschau* that he learns what he knows of the news of the world.

'Mr Graham wrote the names in then,' my mother says,' "Adam Peter" and so we corrected both the date and your names.'

'When was this?' I ask.

'Well father, when was it, you became a Canadian citizen?'

'1941. You want my registration number too?'

My mother is knitting and ignores that, easily. She knows he memorized the number immediately in case he was ever forced to cross the border again; when they got to Canada at last on March 5, 1930, he vowed he would never leave of his own free will and he never has.

'But you always called me. . . .'

'Yes, we always have.'

'So how come you called me that, Adam?'

'Oh,' my mother looks up from her knitting, dreamy like the look I now see again on my daughter's young face, 'there was a little boy, a Penner, he was a little Adam and he died just before you were born, he was so beautiful, always singing and only four and so good, laughing in the children's room in church and playing with all the babies to make them laugh too, it was so sad when he drowned in the slough behind their barn. That was a nice name, he was an Adam, so good.'

'Well,' I say bitterly, 'you tried your best, with the name.'

'Adam,' my mother says softly, and touches me. For an instant her voice and fingers seem about to find tears behind my eyes, but my father says gruffly,

'Where did you find out about this Adam Wiebe, in Poland?'

'In a book.'

'Books, books, all your books they'll ruin you.' If I only had the chance. What's ruined him? Being born in 1889 in Russia he always says, a Mennonite hauled into the Czar's forests in lieu of compulsory military service and he had finally finished his four years and come back to his village to marry my mother when World War One erupted and he was dragged back again, another four, or three rather because the glorious October Revolution ended all that, they got so busy killing themselves, all those Communists, and playing games with him forever, what could anyone do but do what he was told? But finally, at forty, he did one thing: he left what little he had, they were poorer than Russian meadow mice, and took his wife and six kids to Moscow to try and get out of there; forever. Astonishing, he did one thing, after a Mennonite father and four older brothers and over seven years of the Czar's army and then ten years of Communists, the Communists, o he had learned to do what he was told.

'What was this Adam?' my mother asks.

Adam/Peter — ground/rock, surely a name significant enough for anyone. Adam/Peter/Abraham — ground/rock/exalted father of a multitude, dear God more than enough, all earth and exaltation, with Wiebe a solid Friesian name to anchor it; a people stubborn and implacable as water. In a class I taught years later at the University of Groningen there was a long blonde Friesian girl named Wiebke den Hoet, her father the dike master on a new polder slowly forming itself out of the North Sea. But I could not know this when I was seventeen, did not know Wiebe was a Friesian given name transformed by deliberate centuries into a patronymic, my mother knitting mittens for poor children on a hot August Sunday in Alberta. That first Adam Wiebe sailed from his Dutch fishing village of Harlingen on the North Sea for Danzig in 1616 because that Hanseatic free city needed a water engineer and he was the best in the world. Harlingen is still a village; its labyrinth of dikes and canals, many of them probably built by Adam, still thrust it out in alternating loops of earth and water against the grey sea. The aerial (KLM) photo I have shows it almost as neat as the 1624 copper engraving of Danzig which in the top left corner features the city's coat of arms and the top right a portrait of Adam Wiebe himself.

'Look,' I say to my mother, and read for my father's benefit, since he won't look up, 'Wybe Adam von Harlingen.'

'That's your father's nose,' my mother says, and so it is. But a higher forehead, heavier eyebrows in a narrower face; an unstoppable genius who served Danzig thirty-two years and before he died had streets and gates and even squares named after him.

'Where's my long nose?' I ask.

My father laughs then. 'It got lost for a turned-up Loewen. Her mother's family.'

'Does your book have pictures of a Loewen?' my mother asks.

If I could answer her now, I would tell her the Loewens were Flemish believers from the other great Hanseatic city Antwerp, probably jewellers who escaped religious persecution and arrived in Danzig even earlier than Adam Wiebe, but perhaps now rather than parade all my dubious facts of history I would ask her to sing, that beautiful soprano now lost forever except in the folds of my memory. Any of the songs she sang when the leaves came out green as frogs in the Saskatchewan poplar May and she began to cook on the stove outside to keep the house cool for sleeping. It would be a song from the *Dreiband*, their pocket-size hymnal without notes but of course a person who sang in a church choir then knew at least five hundred songs from memory, and my father across the yard somewhere within earshot would answer her in tenor harmony, their voices floating like lovers hand in hand high in the bright air. By some genetic shift more drastic than my nose the two musical rocks of Flemish Loewen and Friesian Wiebe have faulted into my tunelessness: though I can recognize any melody, I cannot reproduce or mirror one either close or at a distance. Not even the overwhelming choir of thirty-six Peter Wiebe descendants in Gladbach, West Germany last year helped me to one tuneful sound, the over two dozen children from two families finding hours of melodies in that tiny apartment, their heads filled endlessly with identical words and notes.

'Peter Wiebe,' my father would have slowly raised himself erect. 'That was my brother, the rich one with us in Moscow in 1929, he always . . .'

'Leave that old story,' my mother would have said quickly. 'We have to forget such things.'

'Forget!' my father's thick worker hands are crumpling the paper. 'You forget when your own brother who's as rich as the dead Czar keeps saying to you, "How do you think you'll get out to Germany, you and your Marie and six kids, when you don't have three kopecks to rub together?" How do you forget that?'

'Abraham,' my mother murmurs, 'God needs money for nothing.'

'And the Communists don't either, thank God,' my father laughs sardonically at his own wit. 'Having money in '29 was the end of any going, no beginning.'

'So forget that old story, it . . .'

But I would have to interrupt her. 'This isn't your brother Peter, Pa, it's his son, he was in Moscow with you too, young, he . . .'

'Peter Wiebe is in Germany now? Did he buy his way out, now?'

'It's your nephew, not your . . .'

'That young Peter was nineteen in '29,' my mother says dreamily. 'Short, very thin, and very bright eyes. Such an open Wiebe face.'

And he still has it the first time I see Peter Wiebe. In 1982. He was coming towards me through several thousand Mennonites at their annual reunion in Germany to celebrate their seventies escape at last from the Soviet Union; exclaiming, 'That's a Wiebe face, a Wiebe face!' and for that moment he appeared to be my father reincarnated in a slight, short body, his thin blond hair which would never turn grey and that patrician nose and square jaw, limping towards me through the crowd that turns to stare and then laugh aloud at our happiness, at our embrace, and enfolding double kiss. I might have been holding my father, alive again after seven years; though he had never in a lifetime held me like that.

'I never wanted a Peter in my family,' my father says. 'An Adam I didn't care, but a Peter, another Peter . . .'

My mother is singing. She will be singing not to avoid my father: they did not live sixty-one years with each other that way; rather, that wordless sound suspended by her voice, a broadening colour which does not hesitate at sadness or laughter, or break because of anger, unforgiveness: it is a sound which slowly, slowly threads brightness over the glowering, stifling Sunday afternoon. It is like the story young Peter Wiebe, now seventy-two, will tell me of his second arrest and his second transport to the Gulag in the last fierce days of the dying Stalin. He will say:

'We had religious freedom, of course, it was official, guaranteed by the Soviet Constitution of course, but no more than three people could talk politics together and the police must suspect everything so when our village met every Wednesday evening for Bible reading, faith became politics. I had the only Bible and the room was full, always tight full and I read in German, no one ever said a single word not used by Luther — where would you get a Russian Bible? This German Bible from my father was the only one in the village, and even if we had spoken Russian, who knew what person had been pressured by what police, and why? Your own sister or cousin or even husband would never dare tell you if they *had* to inform to prevent something worse. That was the way they controlled us, fear, and if *you* had to inform at least you knew how to protect yourself because you knew at least something they knew because you'd told them—well, why would Soviet police and party members believe us when we told them again and again we never spoke anything at all but the words of Jesus, and sometimes his words, well the way you say them can sound like something a little slanted and people will smile as if they know something, just for a second they know and can think, something. So that time they came in as I was reading John 15: "I am the vine, you are the branches. They that abide in me . . ." they were pounding loud on the house door, and of course it takes a while to get the door open and there's always so many big men and women around the door that they can't actually get in for a while and when the knock came I had to leave the room, like I'd done two times before but this time they are smarter: two of them greet me by the kitchen door as I come out. "We just want to ask you a few questions, nothing more, don't worry, Katerina Petrovna, he'll be back for night." Of course, but which night? Four years later, when Stalin is dead three years and Khruschev reviews all the ten or eleven, maybe it's thirteen, million political prisoners' records, I am released just as quick, I can go not even into free exile as they call living anywhere in the Soviet Union except within five hundred kilometres of your home village, I can go, go home. I am alive only because I am small, and because I can keep books. Even sitting on a stool in a heated room all day you get barely enough food to keep a body as small as mine breathing year after year, but if you have to labour in the mines or the forests in the terrible cold, especially if your body is big like yours, you do not last a month; the smaller people last longer, sometimes almost half a year, but me they would have stuffed with black bread gladly forever, sometimes even a fish-head in the soup because every camp administrator has to have a bookkeeper who will keep him ahead of his boss—you cannot imagine the unbelievable records that have to be kept, every turnip peel weighed and written down to whom it went and to have a prisoner in camp who can add and is honest, well, honesty is so unbelievable that every camp boss I ever had kissed me and cried when he had to let me go. By God's grace there I am, four years of a twenty-five year sentence, the food ration is the same whether you have to meet an impossible quota set in the Kremlin of trees cut in waist-deep snow or add numbers all day, columns like forests down page after page growing themselves green in your head until you are an adding machine, your eye sliding down their wrinkled bark and clicking so exactly even the unexpected Kremlin inspector with machines can't do anything faster, leave alone find a mistake in books stacked to the ceiling, thank the dearest God who gives you this year after year mind of numbers and denial, nothing more, "No, I did not . . . No, I never said . . . No, I know of no one . . ." the unending questions that come to you at any time of any night and only the numbers are constant, solid as rock and the frozen spruce piling up like corpses around the camp you have no idea where it is buried in the taiga but you know exactly how many bodies there are, trees or people. You become numbers; soon an axeblow no matter how feeble in the farthest swamp is already written on the paper of your mind, eleven to seventeen chops per tree up to thirty centimetres in width for a fresh prisoner, seventy-six to ninety-three for the same tree for some-one who will be dead in her bunk rags tomorrow, the skin stretched stiff across her torn teeth and you have another statistic: longevity calculated in relation to declining rations, in relation to quotas not filled, how long can rations be cut for the prisoner coming in weighing thirty to forty kilos, forty to fifty kilos, do women last longer than men even though their initial production is never as high and they have the same quotas, same food ration? The largest men always die first. But I am small, I work inside where it's warm, I last four years; until Stalin is dead. It is Wednesday evening again when I get off the train and walk to my village along the empty farm roads and I open the door of our house, the same door where they took my father in 1936, and the woman inside who is reading stops and she gives me back my father's German Bible and I open it and read as if I had never left, aloud in that room crowded with the same white, silent faces the words of Jesus, ". . . they that abide in me and I in them, the same bring forth much fruit, for without me you can do nothing." That was my second return, the first time was in the war when I was falsely accused and our collective farm worked two years to get me out. But my father never came back the first time. They came for him in 1936, and Stalin still lived then for almost twenty years.'

This story, and all the other stories I will hear from Peter Wiebe are already there in my mother's song as she sings until my father joins her, their voices singing this story which has already taken place but which they will never hear nor speak about sitting at the worn kitchen table in Alberta, Canada, my memory of them like their memories of Moscow, like Peter's memories of his father, my uncle Peter Jacob, the rock and the deceiver, my father's brother having to live on in the Mennonite village in the Ural foothills to which he and his family are returned from Moscow in 1929 while my father and his family travel to Germany and finally Canada. My uncle has to wait seven more years until that knocking on the door he has always known will come finally comes, and he disappears into the winter darkness leaving only memory and his German Bible, a tall, strong man like my father who has no mind for numbers either but can chop down a thirty-centimetre tree in nine strokes of an axe, easily, and so fill his quota. At least for the first three or four days. With the square Wiebe face we all have, but a nose unlike mine; a patrician nose like Adam Wiebe in 1616, the year Shakespeare died and Adam sails to Danzig to lay the city's first wooden watermains and set artesian wells in its squares and drain the marshlands along the Radaune River by building dikes and canals and wind and horse-drawn mills that lift the turgid water up into the slate-gray sea.

'What is this,' my mother says, pointing with her knitting needles, 'these strings here?'

She is studying the grey picture of the copper engraving of Danzig, the coat of arms in its top left corner, the narrow, energetic face of Adam in its top right. Below the coat of arms is a line drawing of a high hill labelled Bischoffs Berg, the centre is low sagging land along the river and marshes with the church spires and gates of the city beyond; but below Adam's picture on the right there is an elevation almost as high as the hill: it is labelled Wieben Bastion. Adam built that fortification to protect the city from the army of King Gustavus Adolphus of Sweden, and he constructed the city walls and the bastion above the swamps of the river by using earth from the Bischoffs Berg. The strings between the two my mother is puzzling over is the double cable Adam Wiebe strung on poles so that, by means of an endless stream of moving buckets attached to this cable, the earth could be carried over the river and the swamps from hill to bastion. So exactly were these buckets designed, so precisely were distance and weight calculated that no power was needed to make them move: the weight of the filled buckets at the top of the hill carried them down across the valley to the bastion while returning the empty buckets back up to the top. And though the gigantic Gustavus Adolphus and his mercenaries destroyed much of Europe for hire and the unending glory of the Protestant Church, they never got inside the walls of Danzig, leave alone near its central bastion, because in 1622 my ancestor invented the cable car to defend a defenceless city.

'When did this Wybe Adam von Harlingen die?' my father asks abruptly.

'1652. Pa, he built all that for them, and Danzig never even made him a citizen.'

It is then my father looks up. 'Yeah, yeah,' he says, heavily, 'that's the way. It always is. When those Communists hammered on our door in Moscow and told me to get on that train to Germany, they gave me a yellow card. "Stateless refugee," that's all it said. A hundred and fifty years of Russia and they send us out, a piece of yellow paper and fill in your own name. "Stateless refugee." '

I had not known that either. I suppose it doesn't really matter. After all, over how many lakes and rivers and parts of oceans, across how many fairgrounds, up how many mountains on how many continents have I sailed through air suspended somehow from a cable and not known about my ancestor Adam Wiebe? My ignorance has, of course, never made any of those cables less real, any sailing less beautiful. Or potentially dangerous.

And in my memory my parents sit at our kitchen table in Alberta suspending the thin thread of their songs across the marshes and bitter rivers of their memories building what bastions? Against what fearfully anticipated or remembered war, against what knock at what door, 'We just want to ask you a few questions, come, you'll be home for night'? Slight, bent Peter, the rich Wiebe's son having to live a sort of a life in the Soviet Union, I the poor Wiebe's son living a different sort in Canada: which would one actually prefer? Peter Jacob who vanished in 1936, Peter Peter bringing that Bible to Germany when he is too old even to keep other books and still so immovably honest and absolutely immovably stubborn and he is told to go at last, go, who wants you, you old bastard, you troublemaker—these are facts, were already becoming facts one August Sunday afternoon long ago when I was a teenager and discovering that my mother and father could tell me so little about the names I had, could tell me only small facts that explained nothing; facts like intermittent poles sticking up out of sinking ground, holding up cables no one could explain what genius, what vision had once made them possible so that all that solid earth could be moved so beautifully over swamp from the Bischoffs Berg to build the Wieben Bastion.

Wybe Adam von Harlingen, where are you now? Your cables are gone. Only the memories of songs remain.

◆ ◆ ◆

RUDY WIEBE was born in 1934 on a farm in a Mennonite community near Fairholme, Saskatchewan, and grew up in Coaldale, Alberta. His parents had immigrated to Canada from the Soviet Union in 1930. He received his Th.B. from the Mennonite Brethren Bible College in Winnipeg, his B.A. and M.A. (in creative writing) from the University of Alberta. After studying in Tübingen, Germany, he returned to teach at his first alma mater, before moving to the United States to teach at Goshen College, Indiana. Since 1967 he has taught English and creative writing at the University of Alberta in Edmonton. His fiction (all published by McClelland and Stewart, Toronto) includes *Peace Shall Destroy Many*, 1962; *The First and Vital Candle*, 1966; *The Blue Mountains of China*, 1970; *The Temptations of Big Bear*, 1973; *Where Is the Voice Coming From? Stories*, 1974; *The Scorched-Wood People*, 1977; *The Mad Trapper*, 1980; *The Angel of the Tar Sands and Other Stories*, 1982; *My Lovely Enemy*, 1983.

LINDA HUTCHEON is the daughter and granddaughter of Italian immigrants from Bagni di Lucca, Tuscany (1925, to Toronto) and Maiano, Friuli (1910, to Viscount, Saskatchewan). She teaches English and comparative literature at the University of Toronto. She is the author of *Narcissistic Narrative* (1980); *Formalism and the Freudian Aesthetic* (1984); *A Theory of Parody* (1985); *A Poetics of Postmodernism: History, Theory, Fiction* (1988); *The Canadian Postmodern* (1988); and *The Politics of Postmodernism* (1989).

As a Mennonite, do you consider yourself part of an 'ethnic' group? Do you even think of yourself in this light at all?

Very rarely. I'm a Canadian because I was born here; I'm as Canadian as anyone can be, though my parents had only lived here four years when I was born. The fact is, a Mennonite has no country; that makes one different from being a Ukrainian, Greek or, as in your case, Italian. Since I come from no country, I also cannot 'return' to one; so in effect wherever I am, that's my country.

I asked because you once said that Mennonites were not an ethnic group, but rather a religious one. What is the distinction for you?

There is a major difference. Mennonites are nothing quite so simple as an ethnic group, that is, racially something specific. Even historically they come from at least three or four different ethnic groups. Anabaptism begins in Switzerland at the time of the Reformation about 1520 — though the forces are in motion there earlier than that. Anabaptism is a way of seeing the Church, of being a Christian, and its ideas move up the Rhine valley to the Germans. It springs up almost by itself in Holland at roughly the same time, about 1530. So the beginnings of all we now call 'Mennonite' are racially very diverse. They're all central European, but that doesn't make them the same.

Where does language fit into your distinction here?

When people speak of Mennonites and language they often mean Low German, but that's only one language that one kind of Mennonite speaks. They speak very many different languages as a matter of fact, and the Germanic-Friesian dialect that I speak is a dialect peculiar to Russian Mennonites, that is Mennonites of Dutch-North German origin. But there are Swiss-origin Mennonites — the kind you find in Kitchener-Waterloo — who speak a completely different kind of dialect. It's Germanic, true, but quite different — as you can say Dutch is Germanic and Friesian is Germanic. The identity of a Mennonite, then, is complicated by the fact that various racial groups form one religious movement, which then comes to have some of the characteristics of an ethnic group because they are persecuted by the larger society. They turn in upon themselves, intermarry, have a distinctive history, but in different areas where they develop different customs and languages. The food of Russian and Swiss Mennonites, for example, is totally different. So, I'm not right when I say it is a religious group either; it's much more complicated. Over the 400 years of its history, it has become almost a number of ethnic groups. How long does it take to become an ethnic group? I suppose if you share certain customs and speak certain languages, that is what you've become. On the other hand, the Mennonites, as proselytizing churches, have spread all over the world and now there are more Indian Mennonites in India, and African Mennonites, and certainly Indonesian Mennonites than there are, say, Low German-speaking Canadian Mennonites.

In a panel on ethnicity in Edmonton about ten years ago, you said that language was not particularly important to Mennonites, and you cited their ability to adapt to whatever country they were in by adopting its language. Now, other writers and critics have

*claimed, to the contrary, that language is central to Mennonite
identity, both as a defining mark of difference and as the willed
inscription of community—and deliberate isolation from other
groups. I know I'm not the only reader to think that your own work
seems very self-conscious about language, and here I'm thinking
about the long explanations of the use of Low and High German
vs. English in the community discussions of* Peace Shall Destroy
Many, *or in your play with Low German rhythms in the English of
Frieda Friesen in* The Blue Mountains of China. *Do you still believe
that language is not important to Mennonites or their writers?*

Again, it's a complicated matter. Which language are you talking
about? My kind of Mennonites in Russia spoke a Friesian-Prussian
Low German, but the Kitchener-Waterloo people don't—they speak
a Schwäbisch south German dialect. Really nothing can be understood between them, though the structures are Germanic—as are
those of English! In fact, if you analyse my Low German, it is structur-
ally closer to English than it is to High German. So which language
are we talking about? One of the reasons I made that statement is
that Mennonites have never been very 'literate'—highly oral, yes, but
not very literate, so that the language that I spoke as a kid is only
now being written as a kind of continuing literary experiment. In
fact, professors and linguists at the University of Winnipeg are only
now debating a consistent spelling for it. That's what I mean by
'which language are we talking about?' I'm particularly careful in
Peace Shall Destroy Many because of the particular group of people
I was writing about. No one speaks a 'general' language—they speak
something very precise. And every informed person in this country
must know that all Mennonites do not speak the same ethnic language. And as for writing, they all now write in English—or as English
as they can make it!

*You have also said, not without irony, that you only learned English
in school, and that some critics claimed that you had never learned
it properly! This might suggest that you still feel somewhat like an
outsider in some way. Do you? Is there such a thing as a Canadian
'mosaic' where each part is valued equally?*

I'm not an outsider in that I now do use English. But if I had been
writing as, for instance, the Mennonite Arnold Dyck did in Manitoba
just a generation before me in the thirties and forties, it would have
been different. He did write in Low German, as a matter of literary

principle. If I wrote in his language I would certainly be an outsider still.

I remember when your books first came out and the response within your community to finding that world represented in fiction. Are there special dangers in writing 'realistically' or 'honestly'—as opposed to 'idealistically' or 'nostalgically'—about your own community?

Well, many Mennonite readers accept my fictions very gladly, but there was a larger community that was quite disturbed by them—at least with *Peace Shall Destroy Many* and *My Lovely Enemy*. But I don't think they are being any more reactive than small groups usually are when something is written about their specific community. The classic case is, of course, Salman Rushdie: you are an insider writing out of the particular pains and struggles of a community and you know absolutely what bothers them most and what will make them most furious. You know instinctively where the rubs are because you've grown up in it. Rushdie writes about a Muslim community the way no non-Muslim ever could. The same thing happened with Philip Roth or Mordecai Richler within the Jewish community. Even a highly literate community like that reacts this way.

In fact, that very response is why there are two Jewish writers in this volume: Richler is not considered the 'voice' of that group by many within it.

Well, that may throw off the balance of the volume, but that community *has* produced many extraordinary writers in Canada.

In Peace Shall Destroy Many, *the use of the Low German language separates the Mennonite people from all the others—including the half-breeds who live and work among them. Now, in that novel, the protagonist discovers, much to his shock and embarrassment, that this separation has contributed to his ignoring and his ignorance of the entire history and culture of the native and Métis people, whose original land he farms. Was it your Mennonite background that led you too to your fictional recovering of that particular history and culture in* The Temptations of Big Bear *and* The Scorched-Wood People?

One of the things I like so much about Canada is the particular richness that we have. When I grew up in western Canada, I had not only the particular hereditary culture given me by my immigrant parents, but I also had another world around me, the aboriginal people of the prairies. This is quite different from the experience of someone whose ancestors have lived on the downs of England for the last six hundred years, for example. This gives me in a sense at least two worlds to operate in — to say nothing of the white Canadian world — and it's that kind of richness that I find particularly attractive. That has probably attracted me to history. Certainly my own people's displacement allowed me to see, with somewhat more perception perhaps, the displacement of Canada's aboriginal people around me. In a sense, the kind of thing that the Mennonites did to the Ukrainians and the Cossacks in the eighteenth century when they settled on the steppes of the Ukraine, they did again, quite unwittingly, when they came to western Canada. They came to southern Manitoba just after the first Riel Rebellion and to the plains of Saskatchewan in the 1890s right after the Second. They became the unwitting beneficiaries of violence that had been applied to suppress and dominate the aboriginal peoples.

The protagonist of My Lovely Enemy *is a Mennonite historian; Rudy Wiebe is a Mennonite historical novelist. Is there a relation here between your Mennonite background and your desire to write* history — *in the first place — and, then, history in the particular fictional way you have chosen?*

I suppose history has taught me this: every person has an individual story. The stories have similar patterns, but each is unique and particular. When I think of myself as a little kid growing up in northern Saskatchewan, I remember my particular story, but around me there are people who had their own stories too. I suppose it is simply that a writer develops an awareness of these things. I always found, in the past, that there are so many good and living stories all around me that that is a fine base for my imaginative development to begin. So I often start from a nodule of historical truth, even in the most obviously fictional of my books, and carry on from there. In the same way, you can reverse it and go the other way and do something as relatively drastic as *Big Bear* where I try to describe only verifiable historical events or at least historical probabilities, using only historical persons, because so little of that story is at all known.

Some writers today are very nervous about speaking for the 'Other' — be it the native people, as you do in Big Bear, *or someone of a different gender or race. Did that bother you at all, or did you feel that someone had to tell this story?*

One of the beautiful things about telling stories is that you never tell them completely: if I had known or could have imagined everything I know now about Big Bear when I wrote it, my story would have been quite different. When I talk now to some of the really militant native people who are learning more and more about Big Bear, I know they will tell his story very differently than I did. This doesn't mean that I couldn't tell it, or that there was no point in my telling it at a certain moment. You don't steal anything from anyone when you tell their story; you make them live. And you can never tell any individual story so that you *exhaust* it. It would be the death of story-telling, the death of the imagination, if you could not try to imagine the 'Other', as you put it. Whom am I allowed to imagine? Only myself? I'm right now working on a piece about a nineteenth-century Indian woman—an Indian tribe wiped out about 150 years ago. Who will imagine this? Who will remember this? An 'Other' must. Who else?

So the question of gender doesn't bother you there?

Why should it bother me any more than the fact of racial—or perceptual or spiritual—difference? A writer who cannot imagine 'Other' is no writer at all.

As a Mennonite male, how do you react to something like Di Brandt's Questions i asked my mother *or some of the stories in Sandra Birdsell's* Ladies of the House *in which the particularly patriarchal side of Mennonite thought and practice is what gets brought to the fore?*

As a kid I was perfectly aware of the structures within our Mennonite household. Now, my particular family was not a patriarchal family: my father was not a patriarch in the sense that he dominated the family. My mother was the family power, the centre around which the family turned. My father went away working for months at a time and my mother stayed home and made all the practical decisions. Certainly in the church and in the community, however, it was clear who the leaders were; they were male.

In your fictional representations of both, it is also very clear.

Sure. I am aware of that; I don't believe I was then aware of the marvellous intricacies and sensitivities that, say, Di Brandt reveals in her poetry, or Sandra Birdsell or Audrey Poetcker. These kinds of perceptions are achieved through hard experience. And in many ways I wasn't a particularly sensitive young male, at least as a beginning writer; I hope I am now. Life has taught me a few things. But it's clear when you read *Peace Shall Destroy Many* that I make certain fundamental assumptions about patriarchal values. It would, I think, be ludicrous to rewrite the book now to try and change the world view that clearly dominates it. One would hope that this is the kind of thing in which one might see some progression as a writer gets older, but you can't rewrite what you once wrote!

Some people think today that this 'postmodern' age in which we are living has made the 'Other' into a new norm: in other words, it's better to be different today. Is that just wishful thinking?

Speaking ethnically, I think the strongest strand in Canadian writing is still the English tradition: Findley, Atwood, Munro, Davies, Birney, David Adams Richards. That's clearly the dominant ethnic writing strand; there is no question about that. It may well remain so. At the same time, all Canadians, *we* others are also writing. If you think of the diverse ethnic origins of writers, the list of writers in this volume is not an inconsiderable one. These are writers, many of them young, who, given a little more time, may well become the Atwoods and Findleys of the next generation. I think this is part of our richness as Canadians — that we bring into the stream of literature other traditions, but when we bring them in we all end up being Canadians in a remarkable way. What would I be if I weren't Canadian? Canada's my country. It's the country my parents deliberately chose and I am very happy they did. It wasn't an accident that they came here. Maybe in that sense I am more of a Canadian than people who are just born here because their parents happened to be here. I certainly have had plenty of chances to leave; I was once pressured to become a citizen of the United States but I never really seriously considered that; it just wasn't my place on the earth.

JOY KOGAWA b. 1935

Obasan

She is sitting at the kitchen table when I come in. She is so deaf now that my knocking does not rouse her and when she sees me she is startled.

'O,' she says, and the sound is short and dry as if there is no energy left to put any inflection into her voice. She begins to rise but falters and her hands outstretched in greeting, fall to the table. She says my name as a question.

I put my shoulder bag down, remove the mud-caked boots and stand before her.

'Obasan,' I say loudly and take her hands. My aunt is not one for hugs and kisses.

She peers into my face. 'O,' she says again.

I nod in reply. We stand for a long time in silence. I open my mouth to ask, 'Did he suffer very much?' but the question feels pornographic.

'Everyone dies some day,' she says eventually. She tilts her head to the side as if it's all too heavy inside.

I hang my jacket on a coat peg and sit beside her.

The house is familiar but has shrunk over the years and is even more cluttered than I remember. The wooden table is covered with a plastic table cloth over a blue and white cloth. Along one edge are African violets in profuse bloom, salt and pepper shakers, a soya sauce bottle, an old radio, a non-automatic toaster, a small bottle full of toothpicks. She goes to the stove and turns on the gas flame under the kettle.

'Everyone dies some day,' she says again and looks in my direction, her eyes unclear and sticky with a gum-like mucus. She pours the tea. Tiny twigs and bits of popcorn circle in the cup.

When I last saw her nine years ago, she told me her tear ducts were clogged. I have never seen her cry. Her mouth is filled with a gummy saliva as well. She drinks warm water often because her tongue sticks to the roof of her false plate.

'Thank you,' I say, taking the cup in both hands.

Uncle was disoriented for weeks, my cousin's letter told me. Towards the end he got dizzier and dizzier and couldn't move without clutching things. By the time they got him to the hospital, his eyes were rolling.

'I think he was beginning to see everything upside down again,' she wrote, 'the way we see when we are born.' Perhaps for Uncle, everything had started reversing and he was growing top to bottom, his mind rooted in an upstairs attic of humus and memory, groping backwards through cracks and walls to a moist cellar. Down to water. Down to the underground sea.

Back to the fishing boat, the ocean, the skiff moored off Vancouver Island where he was born. Like Moses, he was an infant of the waves, rocked to sleep by the lap lap and '*Nen, nen, korori*', his mother's voice singing the ancient Japanese lullaby. His father, Japanese craftsman, was also a son of the sea which had tossed and coddled his boatbuilding ancestors for centuries. And though he had crossed the ocean from one island as a stranger coming to an island of strangers, it was the sea who was his constant landlord. His fellow tenants, the Songhee Indians of Esquimalt, and the fishermen, came from up and down the BC coast to his workshop in Victoria, to watch, to barter, and to buy.

In the framed family photograph hanging above the sideboard, Grandfather sits on a chair with his short legs not quite square on the floor. A long black cape hangs from his shoulders. His left hand clutches a pair of gloves and the top of a cane. On a pedestal beside him is a top hat, open end up. Uncle stands slightly to his right, and behind, with his hand like Napoleon's in his vest. Sitting to their left is Grandmother in a lace and velvet suit with my mother in her arms. They all look in different directions, carved and rigid with their expressionless Japanese faces and their bodies pasted over with Rule Britannia. There's not a ripple out of place.

And then there is the picture, not framed, not on display, showing Uncle as a young man smiling and proud in front of an exquisitely detailed craft. Not a fishing boat, not an ordinary yacht — a creation of many years and many winter evenings — a work of art. Uncle stands, happy enough for the attention of the camera, eager to pass on the message that all is well. That forever and ever all is well.

But many things happen. There is the voice of the RCMP officer saying, 'I'll keep that one,' and laughing as he cuts through the water. 'Don't worry, I'll make good use of her.' The other boats are towed away and left to rot. Hundreds of Grandfather's boats belonging to hundreds of fishermen.

The memories are drowned in a whirlpool of protective silence. 'For the sake of the children,' it is whispered over and over. '*Kodomo no tame*.'

And several years later, sitting in a shack on the edge of a sugar beet field in southern Alberta, Obasan is watching her two young daughters with their school books doing homework in the light of a coal oil lamp. Her words are the same. '*Kodomo no tame*.' For their sakes, they will survive the dust and the wind, the gumbo, the summer oven sun. For their sakes, they will work in the fields, hoeing, thinning acres of sugar beets, irrigating, topping, harvesting.

'We must go back,' Uncle would say on winter evenings, the ice thick on the windows. But later, he became more silent.

'*Nen nen*.' Rest, my dear uncle. The sea is severed from your veins. You have been cut loose.

They were feeding him intravenously for two days, the tubes sticking into him like grafting on a tree. But Death won against the medical artistry.

'Obasan, will you be all right?' I ask.

She clears her throat and wipes dry skin off her lips but does not speak. She rolls a bit of dried up jam off the table cloth. She isn't going to answer.

The language of grief is silence. She knows it well, its idioms, its nuances. She's had some of the best tutors available. Grief inside her body is fat and powerful. An almighty tapeworm.

Over the years, Grief has roamed like a highwayman down the channels of her body with its dynamite and its weapons blowing up every moment of relief that tried to make its way down the road. It grew rich off the unburied corpses inside her body.

Grief acted in mysterious ways, its melancholy wonders to perform. When it had claimed her kingdom fully, it admitted no enemies and no vengeance. Enemies belonged in a corridor of experience with sense and meaning, with justice and reason. Her Grief knew nothing of these and whipped her body to resignation until the kingdom was secure. But inside the fortress, Obasan's silence was that of a child bewildered.

'What will you do now?' I ask.

What choices does she have? Her daughters, unable to rescue her or bear the silent rebuke of her suffering have long since fled to the ends of the earth. Each has lived a life in perpetual flight from the density of her inner retreat — from the rays of her inverted sun sucking in their lives with the voracious appetite of a dwarf star. Approaching her, they become balls of liquid metal — mercurial — unpredictable in their moods and sudden departures. Especially for the younger daughter, departure is as necessary as breath. What metallic spider is it in her night that hammers a constant transformation, lacing open doors and windows with iron bars.

'What will you do?' I repeat.

She folds her hands together. I pour her some more tea and she bows her thanks. I take her hands in mine, feeling the silky wax texture.

'Will you come and stay with us?' Are there any other words to say? Her hands move under mine and I release them. Her face is motionless. 'We could leave in a few days and come back next month.'

'The plants. . . .'

'Neighbours can water them.'

'There is trouble with the house,' she says. 'This is an old house. If I leave. . . .'

'Obasan,' I say nodding, 'it is your house.'

She is an old woman. Every homemade piece of furniture, each pot holder and child's paper doily, is a link in her lifeline. She has preserved in shelves and in cupboards, under layers of clothing in closets — a daughter's rubber ball, colouring books, old hats, children's dresses. The items are endless. Every short stub pencil, every cornflake box stuffed with paper bags and old letters is of her ordering. They rest in the corners of the house like parts of her body, hair cells, skin tissue, food particles, tiny specks of memory. This house is now her blood and bones.

She is all old women in every hamlet in the world. You see her on a street corner in a village in southern France, in her black dress and her black stockings. She is squatting on stone steps in a Mexican mountain village. Everywhere she stands as the true and rightful owner of the earth, the bearer of love's keys to unknown doorways, to a network of astonishing tunnels, the possessor of life's infinite personal details.

'I am old,' she says.

These are the words my grandmother spoke that night in the

house in Victoria. Grandmother was too old then to understand political expediency, race riots, the yellow peril. I was too young.

She stands up slowly, 'Something in the attic for you,' she says. We climb the narrow stairs one step at a time carrying a flashlight with us. Its dull beam reveals mounds of cardboard boxes, newspapers, magazines, a trunk. A dead sparrow lies in the nearest corner by the eaves.

She attempts to lift the lid of the trunk. Black fly corpses fall to the floor. Between the wooden planks, more flies fill the cracks. Old spider webs hang like blood clots, thick and black from the rough angled ceiling.

Our past is as clotted as old webs hung in dark attics, still sticky and hovering, waiting for us to adhere and submit or depart. Or like a spider with its skinny hairy legs, the past skitters out of the dark, spinning and netting the air, ready to snap us up and ensnare our thoughts in old and complex perceptions. And when its feasting is complete, it leaves its victims locked up forever, dangling like hollowed out insect skins, a fearful calligraphy, dry reminders that once there was life flitting about in the weather.

But occasionally a memory that refuses to be hollowed out, to be categorized, to be identified, to be explained away, comes thudding into the web like a giant moth. And in the daylight, what's left hanging there, ragged and shredded is a demolished fly trap, and beside it a bewildered eight-legged spinning animal.

My dead refuse to bury themselves. Each story from the past is changed and distorted, altered as much by the present as the present is shaped by the past. But potent and pervasive as a prairie dust storm, memory and dream seep and mingle through cracks, settling on furniture, into upholstery. The attic and the living room encroach onto each other, deep into their invisible places.

I sneeze and dust specks pummel across the flashlight beam. Will we all be dust in the end—a jumble of faces and lives compressed and powdered into a few lines of statistics—fading photographs in family albums, the faces no longer familiar, the clothing quaint, the anecdotes lost?

I use the flashlight to break off a web and lift the lid of the trunk. A strong whiff of mothballs assaults us. The odour of preservation. Inside, there are bits of lace and fur, a 1920s nightgown, a shoe box, red and white striped socks. She sifts through the contents, one by one.

'That's strange,' she says several times.

'What are you looking for?' I ask.

'Not here. It isn't here.'

She turns to face me in the darkness. 'That's strange,' she says and leaves her questions enclosed in silence.

I pry open the folds of a cardboard box. The thick dust slides off like chocolate icing sugar—antique pollen. Grandfather's boat building tools are wrapped in heavy cloth. These are all he brought when he came to this country wearing a western suit, western shoes, a round black hat. Here is the plane with a wooden handle which he worked by pulling it towards him. A fundamental difference in workmanship—to pull rather than push. Chisels, hammer, a mallet, a thin pointed saw, the handle extending from the blade like that of a kitchen knife.

'What will you do with these?' I ask.

'The junk in the attic', my cousin's letter said, 'should be burned. When I come there this summer, I'll have a big bonfire. It's a fire trap. I've taken the only things that are worth keeping.'

Beneath the box of tools is a pile of *Life* magazines dated in the 1950s. A subscription maintained while the two daughters were home. Beside the pile is another box containing shoe boxes, a metal box with a disintegrating elastic band, several chocolate boxes. Inside the metal box are pictures, duplicates of some I have seen in our family albums. Obasan's wedding photo—her mid-calf dress hanging straight down from her shoulders, her smile glued on. In the next picture, Uncle is a child wearing a sailor suit.

The shoe box is full of documents.

Royal Canadian Mounted Police, Vancouver, BC, March 4, 1942. A folded mimeographed paper authorizes Uncle as the holder of a numbered Registration Card to leave a Registered Area by truck for Vernon where he is required to report to the local Registrar of Enemy Aliens, not later than the following day. It is signed by the RCMP superintendent.

Uncle's face, young and unsmiling looks up at me from the bottom right hand corner of a wallet size ID card. 'The bearer whose photograph and specimen of signature appear hereon, has been duly registered in compliance with the provisions of Order-in-Council PC 117.' A purple stamp underneath states 'Canadian Born'. His thumb print appears on the back with marks of identification specified—scar on back of right hand.

There is a letter from the Department of the Secretary of State. Office of the Custodian. Japanese Evacuation Section. 506 Royal Bank Bldg. Hastings and Granville. Vancouver, BC.

Dear Sir.

Dear Uncle. With whom were you corresponding and for what did you hope? That the enmity would cease? That you could return to your boats? I have grown tired, Uncle, of seeking the face of the enemy hiding in the thick forests of the past. You were not the enemy. The police who came to your door were not the enemy. The men who rioted against you were not the enemy. The Vancouver alderman who said 'Keep BC White' was not the enemy. The men who drafted the Order-in-Council were not the enemy. He does not wear a uniform or sit at a long meeting table. The man who read your timid letter, read your polite request, skimmed over your impossible plea, was not your enemy. He had an urgent report to complete. His wife was ill. The phone rang all the time. The senior staff was meeting in two hours. The secretary was spending too much time over coffee breaks. There were a billion problems to attend to. Injustice was the only constant in a world of flux. There were moments when expedience demanded decisions which would later be judged unjust. Uncle, he did not always know what he was doing. You too did not have an all compassionate imagination. He was just doing his job. I am just doing my work. Uncle. We are all just doing our jobs.

My dear dead Uncle. Am I come to unearth our bitterness that our buried love too may revive?

'Obasan, what shall we do with these?'

She has been waiting at the top of the stairs, holding the railing with both hands. I close the shoe box and replace the four interlocking flaps of the cardboard box. With one hand I shine the flashlight and with the other, guide her as I precede her slowly down the stairs. Near the bottom she stumbles and I hold her small body upright.

'Thank you, thank you,' she says. This is the first time my arms have held her. We walk slowly through the living room and back to the kitchen. Her lips are trembling as she sits on the wooden stool.

Outside, the sky of the prairie spring is painfully blue. The trees are shooting out their leaves in the fierce wind, the new branches elastic as whips. The sharp-edged clarity is insistent as trumpets.

But inside, the rooms are muted. Our inner trees, our veins, are involuted, cocooned, webbed. The blood cells in the trunks of our bodies, like tiny specks of light, move in a sluggish river. It is more a potential than an actual river—an electric liquid—the current flowing in and between us, between our generations. Not circular, as in a whirlpool, or climactic and tidal as in fountains or spray—but brooding. Bubbling. You expect to hear barely audible pip-pip electronic tones, a pre-concert tuning up behind the curtains in the darkness. Towards the ends of our branches and fingertips, tiny human-shaped flames or leaves break off and leap towards the shadows. My arms are suffused with a suppressed urge to hold.

At the edges of our flesh is a hint of a spiritual osmosis, an eagerness within matter, waiting to brighten our dormant neurons, to entrust our stagnant cells with movement and dance.

Obasan drinks her tea and makes a shallow scratching sound in her throat. She shuffles to the door and squats beside the boot tray. With a putty knife, she begins to scrape off the thick clay like mud that sticks to my boots.

JOY KOGAWA was born in Vancouver in 1935. She is part of the second generation of Japanese Canadians—the *nissei*. Her father, Gordon Nakayama, is an Anglican clergyman and her mother's Japanese background is also Christian. In 1942, during the Second World War, the family was evacuated to Slocan, BC where they lived until 1945, when they were moved to Coaldale, Alberta. After taking teacher training at the University of Alberta for one year, Joy Kogawa returned to Coaldale to teach in an elementary school for a year. In 1955 she moved to Toronto to study music, and the next year to Vancouver, where she married David Kogawa in 1957. With their two children, the couple moved frequently—from Vancouver to Grand Forks, BC to Moose Jaw, to Saskatoon, and finally to Ottawa—before divorcing in 1968. Since 1979 Joy Kogawa has lived in Toronto. Her works include *The Splintered Moon* (Fredericton: University of New Brunswick Press, 1968); *A Choice of Dreams* (Toronto: McClelland and Stewart, 1974); *Jericho Road* (Toronto: McClelland and Stewart, 1978); *Obasan* (Toronto: Lester and Orpen Dennys, 1981) (translated as *Ushinawareta Sokoku* by Sari Nagaoka [Tokyo: Futami Shobo, 1983]; *Woman in the Woods* (Oakville, Ont.: Mosaic Press, 1985); *Naomi's Road* (Toronto: Oxford University Press, 1986).

MAGDALENE REDEKOP grew up on a farm in the Mennonite community of southern Manitoba. She did her undergraduate degree at the University of Manitoba and her graduate degrees at the University of Toronto. She has published articles on Canadian, American, and Scottish literature and a book on Alice Munro is forthcoming. She has also been involved in writing family memoirs and stories in dialogue with her sisters. In 1982-83 she lived in Japan, where she taught at Kwansei Gakuin University. She now teaches in the English department at Victoria College in the University of Toronto.

Since the publication of Obasan, *you have been heavily involved in political activity within and for the Japanese-Canadian community. I'm curious whether you have any reservations about this role. Has it become a kind of tyranny, or do you happily choose it?*

Well, life is a matter of being chosen and choosing at the same time. The primary thing for me is a sense of being aligned to something that makes me feel at peace. There's a sense of — for want of a better word — obedience. When I'm doing what I'm supposed to be doing, then I can sleep at night. I've often felt that my primary calling is to write and that somehow I was erring in doing a lot of the political work. But I proceed with a kind of blindness, a kind of trust, fundamentally, that if it's the wrong direction I'll be prodded back. I'm therefore full of prod marks all over, and the book that I've just written [a sequel to *Obasan*] has been written in that fashion, with a lot of prod marks, in stops and goes.

Since you've become a voice for the Japanese-Canadian community, your poetry has gone into the background. Is poetry somehow less 'ethnic' than fiction?

I've always been curious about this very human thing we do which is to seek definitions. Ethnicity is a definition. We can view something when we can put it within that boundary. It's inevitable that we have these definitions put upon us like different articles of clothing. Ethnicity is something that got put onto me by the country. In those early days when I was writing poetry, I was not conscious of why I was wearing that particular kind of clothing. It's only people who would then point it out to me who made me aware of that. But I am now increasingly conscious of it.

The idea of a national literature is another boundary. What makes a story Canadian?

In the new novel, Aunt Emily tells Naomi that a Canadian is a hyphen and that we're diplomats by birth. Aunt Emily works for an organization called 'Bridge'. She experiences 'bridge' as a verb: a bridge is what takes you from one side to otherness.

I was living in Japan during the year after your novel Obasan *came out and read it there first. I gave a public lecture in Kyoto — entitled 'Joy Kogawa and the Moving Mosaic of Canadian Literature'. I was being rather presumptuously proprietorial. You had done us proud and I tried to claim you by arguing that the hyphen — the bridging — was quintessentially Canadian. Have you travelled to Japan, and did that experience influence the writing of* Obasan?

I went in '69 first and *A Choice of Dreams* came out of that. I travelled on my own and I was there for three months. The second time that I went was in 1984. I went with my Dad then and that was totally different. It was a lot of pizzazz, a lot of media stuff, and I didn't get any real sense of anything much except living in hotels and in front of cameras. I guess the thing was I felt a lot of discomfort in my own skin being in Japan. I was aware always of being rude and terribly uncomfortable with the fact that I was so rude.

I was thinking about Nagasaki and wondering whether your grandparents — their experience of being Christian in Japan — would have prepared them to prepare you for an experience of difference. There's so much that is frightening in Obasan *and yet it is a deeply hopeful book. Is it Christian faith that is the secret of your strength?*

I think that Christianity is possibly the deepest aspect of me. But I think the strength comes from a number of things. The *issei* generation were very powerful people and I think that the kind of parenting that was there is very strengthening to the child. You'll see in the new novel there's the negative side of Christianity which came out of Coaldale and that kind of fundamentalism.

That's interesting for me because Coaldale is a Mennonite town and I'm of Mennonite background. I find myself — largely as a result of my emerging feminism — more and more in deep conflict with aspects of fundamentalist Christianity. There is a long history of struggles about whether or not you are Mennonite if you eat borscht or if you believe in the literal word of God. In your case, is there a different way that ethnicity and religion are in conflict with each other? The language of the Bible is an important aspect of Obasan, but are there ways in which being Japanese by cultural background is at odds with being Christian?

I know that there are some Japanese-Americans who feel that basically the Japanese-ness within them requires them to be Buddhists or Shintoists. I don't know that I experienced any conflict with it, perhaps because my parents were Christians and they were also Japanese, and so whatever they offered me, on that mixed plate which had rice *and* potatoes on it, wasn't strange to me. That was what came with the mix of who I am. So I don't know what is Japanese about me.

I was trying to relate you as a writer to, say, Endo — who explores the way the values of Japanese society sometimes are uneasily superimposed on Christian values. You haven't experienced those kinds of tensions?

I have not experienced the kinds of tensions that he has. I have very little consciousness of the Japanese reader. I'm connected to something from the past but I'm not sure that I feel connected to Japan today.

Do you find that you are ambivalent about your ethnicity? Sometimes when people call me Mennonite I like it; other times I don't. On the one hand, I like to think of myself as different. On the other hand, I resent being defined as different. Do you experience this?

Oh, yes. Almost all of my life I would have done anything to be white, I just wanted it so desperately.

I wondered if you have any reservations about the Canadian government's policy on multiculturalism. An argument can be made that the policy of multiculturalism perpetuates separateness and thus makes it more difficult for minorities to take their rightful place in Canadian society.

Well, I think that there is a need for people to feel a sense of strength in belongingness. Some people can get that by belonging to a community of writers. Some people get that by belonging to an ethnic community. Whatever it is, people get strength from belonging. So I think that whatever promotes places of belonging — choices of areas of belonging — is OK. And true, it could mean that some people would stay ghettoized — which is a negative way of saying that — rather than getting out into the mainstream. On the other hand, we might also say that because they have a voice there, then that can be put into the mainstream, whereas it might not otherwise have had a chance at all. I think it's like the existence of the family, a natural human grouping that exists whether there is government funding for it or not. Funding can have, certainly, very negative aspects. It can be used as a single pie that is meted out, and therefore it can be controlled and people can become bitterly separated and can become rivals.

Speaking of government money, how about the issue of redress? In your book there is a strong sense of forgiveness. How can healing and forgiveness be achieved in the real, political realm?

What is healing for a community is more than just a solution of a political kind. What heals is a process of empowerment, the process that heals is one where there is a striving for and an attainment of mutuality.

Why is the Japanese-Canadian community so deeply divided?

Depending on your point of view, one could say Japanese-Canadians are amazingly united. We have just one national association. In the circumstances, this is almost miraculous. Japanese-Canadians, as opposed to other groups, were dispersed across the country. The identity that we had given to us as we were growing up was that we couldn't associate with one another. In other words, we had to be 'the only Jap in town'. We had to be proud of not knowing each other. We were ordered to become betrayers; we were ordered to betray our own. It would have been the most natural thing for us to have been splattered and squished.

In terms of this division within the community, I was wondering how the Japanese-Canadian community here compares with groups elsewhere. We tend to be a little smug in Canada about our mosaic. Do you know any Japanese-American writers, and do you think that maybe they're less ghettoized than Japanese-Canadian writers, less obligated to write from inside that painful hyphen? If you could just be an American writer, would that give you an extra freedom?

Isn't it interesting about Bharati Mukherjee feeling that she, that she . . .

. . . she feels more free there? How do you respond?

To her statement and to her experience? And to the Canadian reality? I don't know how to answer this. I'm thinking that during these last few years when it has been *so* hard to be a Japanese-Canadian I have wanted to leave Canada. Over and over again, I've just been thinking I can't bear it. . . . I have to get out. But I haven't really known where to go. I mean, I thought of going to Hawaii. There are so many Japanese-Americans there.

In a way, that speaks of the limitations of our so-called mosaic as a paradigm. If it causes such pain to live in the hyphen, is it worth it?

It's the redress movement. I think if everybody was involved in the hyphen, then we would all be together. Even if we are all in different hyphens, we could put a line through the hyphens and be connected as hyphenated people.

My impression is that your commitment is not just to the Japanese-Canadian people as a people but to certain values for which we think we stand in Canada. It's just such a burden to articulate them if you are a member of a visible minority. One of the things that I've done to respond to similar tensions is that I like to have it both ways. I wouldn't like to live inside a Mennonite community, but I like to have access.

I feel exactly the same way, and I think it's a situation of great privilege to be able to do this. But I think there are some people who don't have that choice, who are locked in, who cannot move out because they are too uncomfortable elsewhere. Sometimes I can sense a rage towards me because I'm able to leave.

I want to ask you a question about racism. My experience living in Japan made me aware of what it's like to be part of a visible minority. Of course it's very different if you're all of a sudden visible only for one year and you haven't been born that way, but it did sensitize me to the converse, to the reality of being an oriental woman in Canada. It happens that, since then, we've adopted two children and my daughter is oriental. How can I prepare my daughter for racism?

I can't defend against the hurt. The hurt comes. It's there. In fact, it feels like a disease within me that I'm on the look-out for. It's a kind of paranoia. If you touch the fire you're going to get burned. You walk around and sometimes you can look and the scar's not there. It's clean because nobody's hurt you for a long time. And then suddenly it's gushing because somebody stabs you. Well, I think that to be constantly aware that you're going to be hurt is to be scratching at the scab all the time. I think it's better not to even think about it. You've taken upon yourself a burden and you have accepted it. I think that's all you can do, accept the fact that you are going to be hurt when your child is hurt and simply love the child. My daughter is in Hawaii because she experiences the comfort of being part of a racial majority there.

Where does the Japanese-Canadian community go from here? What about the fourth generation? What will they be called?

Yonsei.

Will the policy of multiculturalism keep the yonsei *aware of themselves as a separate and distinct group? Should it?*

It's likely that there aren't going to be any Japanese Canadians. They'll just be all mixed up. I've seen grandchildren of *nisseis* . . . you can't see any Japanese-ness in their physical features at all. I imagine that's the way it's going to be in the future. There'll be the story of a people; something happened once, and it'll be part of their background. But I think that will be part of a new gathering of people with a growing identity. I think the Canadian identity is evolving.

So what will happen to those values, the values that you now are fighting to affirm?

The values that I personally want to see go on are really universal values: the struggle for justice, all these things, they are universal values and my hope, whether they're expressed through the Christian mythology or whatever. It seems to me it doesn't matter what the vessel is. The substance of what one takes in for nourishment has the same name whatever the vessel is that is carrying it.

There's an interesting dilemma raised by that. I think it was Achebe who said recently something to the effect that African literature wasn't going to go anywhere until we eliminate the word 'universal' and realize that what people had thought were 'universals' were really dominant white values. The word 'universal' often is used as a way of concealing what is in fact culturally biased, racially biased, gender biased. That's why I would be hesitant to end on the word 'universal'.

OK. All these abstractions. . . . What's another word?

Ultimately it is an act that you are affirming, is it not? An act of compassion that reaches beyond the cultural boundaries, beyond the abstractions and words.

Yes, I'd agree with that. In my new novel Aunt Emily feels called to where the struggle for justice takes place and because it's happening in her backyard, that's where she goes. Action is specific. Let's end with 'act'.

KATHERINE VLASSIE b. 1935

A *Proper Goodbye*

Eleni was on her knees in the garden when the phone started ringing. She was kneading the earth around the freshly-planted eggplant seeds and trying to decide whether to cook chicken for the dinner on Sunday or a nice leg of lamb. The grandchildren always asked for chicken, but Costa liked lamb on a festive occasion. Her sons would want to cook outdoors on that contraption they'd bought her the summer before. They'd thought she was being difficult when she'd refused to go near the thing. Would they have understood if she'd told them that in Greece they'd have no choice but to cook in an outdoor oven that had to be watched every minute because in the summer it heated so quickly the food burned, while in winter it needed to be fed a continual supply of twigs so the heat wouldn't give out, and that having her own lovely indoor stove which could be regulated by the switch of a knob meant a sort of freedom to her?

Costa understood. As well as the stove, he'd bought her a huge refrigerator that made its own ice and needed to be defrosted only once a week, and a washing machine that rumbled quietly in the corner as it filled and emptied itself and even wrung the clothes out so all she had to do was hang them up to dry. He was a good man, her Costa. She'd make the lamb. After all, the family dinner was for his birthday. They'd already had his annual Name Day party for family and friends, but the children liked the Canadian custom of celebrating birthdays.

Her Stephano would've been thirty-four now. And the baby, the one she barely remembered — there hadn't even been time to photograph her before God took her away — would've been thirty-five. It was hard to mourn an infant she'd known for only a few months so long ago, but with Stephano it was different. She'd asked Costa over and over to find out where their son was so they could visit, take flowers, but all he'd say was it was better left alone.

The feeling that she'd let her children down wouldn't leave Eleni, not with two of them gone and Angela over thirty and still unmarried.

It was something she could never put into words. All she could do was pray to the Virgin, asking forgiveness for she knew not what. Yet even with all her prayers, the deaths of two children continued to hang like a cloud over the happiness her others gave her, and the goodness of her husband.

The phone was still ringing. Didn't Angela realize it might be her Papa? He liked to go to the store every day—to keep an eye on things, he'd say—but he'd often tire quickly and call Angela to pick him up.

Eleni sighed, rocked back on her knees. She'd better go in and see what was going on. Anyway, there was nothing more to be done in the garden for now. The eggplant was being stubborn as usual. Unlike the zucchini that blossomed beautifully year after year, nothing seemed to work with the eggplant. She'd tried different mixes of soils, different patches of garden for a little more sunlight or a little less, but the result was always the same: leathery lumps the size of walnuts. The worst thing was they seemed to lie there, contentedly nestling among the dark green leaves, mocking her.

The phone finally stopped ringing as she got up off her knees. She rubbed the loose dirt from her hands, went to the side of the house, turned on the hose and washed her hands. When she came around the corner, shaking her dripping hands, Angela was standing on the porch steps.

'Who was on the phone?'

Angela reached out to her mother.

'Did you answer?'

Angela took her mother's hands.

'You'll get all wet.' Eleni was getting impatient.

Angela put her arms around her mother, drew her close.

Eleni stiffened, then quickly pulled away, saw her daughter's eyes brimming with tears. 'Your Papa?' she whispered.

Angela nodded. 'I'll take you, Mama.'

Eleni rushed into the house, grabbed a light coat to cover her old housedress and ran out the front door. Angela was waiting for her in the car.

They drove in silence. Eleni pulled her coat tight around her. She shouldn't have let Costa go this morning. Some days, when he seemed more tired than others, she would get after him to stay home. Not that he would. But she'd try. This morning though, he had seemed almost his old self, joking with her as she'd helped him pick out a tie. He'd probably done too much at the store, tried to help out when he should've just sat quietly and let his sons do the work.

'Why didn't you answer the phone right away?'

'I was taking the *koulourákia* out of the oven — I was afraid they'd burn if I left them to answer the phone.'

'Burnt cookies are more important than your Papa!'

'I'm sorry, Mama.'

'I didn't . . . oh, never mind.' She couldn't sit still, couldn't move, it was taking forever. Costa had never been sick, apart from the recent tiredness, and that had only started after the trip to Greece.

Visiting their homeland after so many years had been difficult for both of them. Their parents had been dead for years, and the relatives and friends they'd met after so long had been unrecognizable. The stern middle-aged women who'd said they were her sisters had nothing in common with the laughing children she'd left behind. For Costa it had been worse; he'd found one of his brothers dying, another a sickly old man, and three of his aging sisters swathed in widow's black.

After a few days, Eleni had grown accustomed to her adult sisters and to being back in Greece, but Costa had been on edge no matter what they did or who they saw. When he'd suggested she take her sisters on a holiday to Rhodes, she hadn't wanted to leave him, but he'd insisted, saying it would give him a chance to visit some of the people and places from his youth that would have no meaning for her. Whatever past he'd relived while she was gone had done nothing but bring him sorrow, and she'd always regretted leaving him alone that time.

'Can't you go faster?' Eleni said. Angela was always so careful.

'We'll be there in a minute, Mama.'

Eleni smoothed down her hair. She had to look nice for Costa. 'Why are you going this way?'

'He's not at the store, Mama.'   When Eleni saw they were turning into the entrance of the Miseracordia, her breath caught in her throat. She'd only been to the hospital to visit others, never for anyone in her family, except the grandchildren, but childbirth was different. Her sons were walking quickly toward the car. Why weren't they with their papa?

Paul held the car door open and Tim helped her out. They huddled around her on the sidewalk in front of the entrance, but neither one spoke. Then she looked at their faces. She clutched at the lapels of her coat, pulling it even tighter around her throat. She knew what they couldn't tell her. 'I want to see him.'

'Mama, he's . . .'

'I know. I want to see him.'

They led her to a room and she saw her husband lying on a cot, his head turned to one side, his mouth slightly open as if he was asleep. His tie had been pulled away, and his shirt collar unbuttoned. In their bedroom that morning, he'd held out two ties to Eleni, and she'd picked the grey striped one, teasing him about how distinguished he looked in his new light-grey summer suit. They never talked about how tired he seemed so much of the time, how haggard. He didn't look haggard any longer, lying as though asleep, the care finally gone from his face.

Eleni had never seen death before. She'd known it, but she'd never seen it. Her Stephano had died far away in a strange place. As for the baby, one day she was there, sick and crying, and the next she was gone. She used to think sometimes that if only she'd known some English she might have been able to find out where they'd taken her dead baby and where her son had been buried. But Costa had always said it wasn't necessary for her to know more than a few words of English to do the shopping. He looked after everything else, didn't he? He did. He had. He'd looked after her from the time she'd come to him as a bride of sixteen.

She reached a hand to him. Her sons tried to hold her back, but she pushed them away. His cheek was warm, soft; he'd shaved in the morning before Angela had driven him downtown. She'd had his usual cornflakes with sliced peaches ready for him in the kitchen when he'd come downstairs and a second cup of coffee for Eleni. He hadn't seemed tired at all. They'd talked about the dinner on Sunday and how he was looking forward to seeing the grandchildren. Eleni stroked his face, rearranged his tie so that it was resting nicely on his shirt, leaned over and kissed his brow. Then she sat down beside him. She began to whisper. Soon strong hands lifted her and led her away.

After, at home, a glass of brandy in her hand, at her lips, the worried looks and hushed voices of family, friends, Priest, drew in closer and closer until she gasped out in suffocation. Even Matina, who'd been her first friend when she'd come to Canada, and was still the person she felt closest to, could say nothing to appease her.

She ran out of the room, upstairs, threw off her clothes. Her old chenille bathrobe felt good. She started for the bathroom. Angela was waiting in the hall. 'Let me help, Mama, please.'

'I'm going to have a bath.'

'Don't lock the door, Mama.' Angela was clenching her hands, a habit she'd acquired lately.

'I'm going to have a bath!'

'In case you need anything.' Angela never raised her voice from that whining tone. It was enough to drive a person crazy.

'Fine. I'll leave the door wide open so you can all come and watch!'

She slammed the door shut, locked it, and turned the faucets on full force. She poured a handful of bath salts into the water and tossed in some bubble bath capsules—gifts from tiny grandchildren at Christmas—lowered herself into the water, let the tub fill, turned off the faucets, lay back and closed her eyes.

People came and went, walking up to the casket, crossing themselves, whispering words to Eleni sitting stiffly between her two sons in the dark-panelled room.

Costa was laid out in ivory satin inside a dark mahogany box, baskets of white lilies on either side. His hair was neatly combed. He had on his good black suit and black tie. She'd wanted to dress him herself, but her sons had said it wasn't allowed. And so strangers had tended to his final needs, the way they had for her son. She closed her eyes to the image of Stephano and tried to focus on Costa as she'd seen him earlier on that last day, helping him on with his tie, or at breakfast. She shouldn't have let him go out, he was tired, but she'd been thinking about her gardening, and so had paid him little attention. She liked her garden, liked the feel of the house when the men were gone, only she and Angela quietly going about their work, sometimes not talking for hours.

'We should go now, Mama.' Paul, sombre, like his father, squeezed her hand. Tim, on the other side, had his arm linked through hers. Their wives sat across from them.

'Where's your sister?'

'Right here, Mama.' Angela leaned across Tim.

'Go now, all of you. I want to talk to your Papa.'

Ignoring the whispers, nudges, looks of concern, Eleni insisted on her time alone with her husband. Matina paused on her way out. 'I'll be fine,' Eleni assured her.

The Priest grasped her hands. 'Think of your children now, *Kyría Eléni*,' he said. '*Zoí se más*, life to the living.'

The living, always the living. But the dead lingered on. She would have liked to have explained to the Priest that she'd never properly said her goodbyes to the dead—her parents in Greece, her infant child buried in an unknown cemetery right here in this city, her son somewhere in Europe—but he'd only murmur men's words of faith that meant nothing to her. It was to the Virgin she prayed nightly, the Virgin who offered her comfort.

'I'd like to stay here with Costa a little longer, *Páter*.'

He left her finally to join the others. They would all wait for her so they could go to the house together. Once there, Paul and Tim would preside over bottles of liquor and their wives would be in the kitchen with Angela preparing coffee and filling plates with *paximádia*, the crisp biscuits always served at times like these. Eleni knew she was holding everyone up, but she couldn't leave, not yet. She needed to say a proper goodbye to Costa and this was their last chance to be alone.

She tried looking down at him, at the stiff, white figure in the casket, surrounded by floral tributes from family and friends, the prayers of the Priest still fresh in the air, but all Eleni could see was her son, her Stephano, dead, alone in a foreign land with no one to mourn him, no one to take flowers to his grave, no one to brush away the leaves in autumn, the snow in winter. 'Not even a headstone,' she whispered, 'nothing to mark the place.'

She started to cry. 'It's not right. Those people who sent him to war should've been able to find him for us.' She wiped her eyes with the back of her hand. 'It's not right, Costa, not right.' She fumbled in her pocket for a handkerchief, blew her nose. 'Remember how tall he was, Costa, how handsome? He had your eyes, always smiling. Remember his letters, the way he described the places he visited? Such beautiful words, Costa. Like poems.'

The room was getting very warm. Eleni took off her coat, pushed the veiled hat off her head. She searched in her purse for a clean handkerchief. 'Forgive me, Costa. I shouldn't be telling you these things, upsetting you.' She wiped her eyes, paused to collect her thoughts. 'You were a good husband, Costa. That what I started to say. My prayers go with you.' She crossed herself. 'Keep his soul safe, *Panagía*. Amen.'

Eleni sat quietly, letting the silent tears flow, not knowing any more whether she was crying for a lost son or a dead husband. For a moment, she wished someone was with her, someone who would help her understand. But who? Even Matina could do nothing now. For all her kindness, she hadn't been able to help when Stephano had been taken from her, or the first tiny baby. Like everyone else, she'd hover, shush her when she'd try to speak, murmur condolences, talk about God's will. It was better this way, at least for a little while.

She sat for a long time; then, when she couldn't bear either the silence or her own thoughts any longer and was getting ready to face the others, a voice intruded. 'Oh, Eleni, Eleni.' Both the voice and the ample body that almost covered hers in an embrace were instantly recognizable.

Tasia was one of the oldest of what the children called the old-timers. Since her own husband had been dead for years and she'd had no children of her own, everyone else's life was Tasia's concern. Out of respect, no one excluded her from any occasion, be it wedding, christening, name-day celebration, even funeral.

'*Paidí mou*, my child,' old Tasia cried. 'My dear, my child,' she crooned. 'Such a loss. Such a fine man.'

As wearisome as Tasia was even at the best of times, Eleni was relieved to see her now, for the old woman's lament would force Eleni to concentrate on mourning Costa instead of indulging her own confused thoughts.

'Ah,' Tasia wailed. 'Such a loss, such a terrible loss . . . a fine man . . . a good man.' Eleni let herself drift away from the words, searching her cluttered mind for memories, happy memories, while Tasia droned on — 'good man . . . well-loved . . . pillar of the community' — but all her memories were shrouded in pain. She tried to think about Costa and the way he'd been before he'd taken her to Greece and had begun looking ill, but that always took her to Stephano and the awful day the first telegram arrived.

She didn't want to think about Stephano any more today. It wasn't fair to Costa. She needed to grieve for Costa, pray for his soul. 'So brave . . . at his age . . . honour his son.' Tasia's words were slowly coming into focus. 'Poor boy . . . taken so young . . . honour his son . . . brave man . . . travel so far . . . honour his son.'

Eleni grabbed the old woman, stared her full in the face.

'My dear, you mustn't blame yourself,' Tasia said. 'It was right of him to go. Take comfort, my child, take comfort. Costa did the right thing.'

'Right?' Eleni echoed.

'At his age, and ill, to travel so far to honour his son.' Tasia was patting her hand, smiling through tears. 'Stephano will rest now.' Eleni jerked away. 'Leave me. Go now. Please. Go.'

She heard the soft intake of breath, the abrupt closing of a door, and she was alone with the cruel words the old woman had thrown in her face. Unbelievable words. They horrified her. Costa had known where Stephano was; worse, he'd gone there without her. No. He wouldn't have done that. It was a mistake, Tasia was wrong, she'd misunderstood, was repeating malicious gossip.

Eleni shivered. She huddled back into her coat. Costa had never been a cruel man. He would not have denied her a final goodbye to her son. But the seed the old woman had planted wouldn't be rooted out, and Eleni's thoughts flew to the early years when their first baby had died and Costa had taken her away in the night. Perhaps Costa had been right to try and protect her then; she had been a very young bride and the baby a mere infant. But Stephano? She'd raised him to manhood. Surely Costa would've seen the difference!

Suddenly her children were surrounding her. 'Tell me the truth,' she cried. Pavlo bowed his head. 'You can't look me in the face,' she accused.

'Papa didn't want you to know,' he mumbled.

Eleni grasped her son's lapels. 'It's true? You mean it's true? Everyone knew? Even that old crone?' She clutched at him, gasping in anger. 'Your Papa went to the grave? Did you go too? Did you? And me? What about me?'

'Mama, don't.' Tim was holding her arms. 'It's not Paul's fault. Papa made us promise.'

She pushed them both away. 'Why?' she screamed at them. 'Why?' She turned on her husband. 'Why?' She tore her hands through her hair. 'Why?'

'He didn't want to upset you,' Paul said.

'Like you are now,' Tim added.

'He wanted to spare you, Mama, to protect you,' Paul added.

'Protect? Upset? How could you, Costa! How could you!' She screamed and cried and Matina came, tried to hold her, shush her, but she wouldn't be stopped. Propriety meant nothing to her now. Neither the words nor the feelings of others mattered any longer. Nothing mattered except this betrayal. She clutched Matina's arm. 'Did you know?' she demanded.

Matina shook her head.

'I want to talk to your Papa,' she cried to her sons.

'But, Mama . . .'

'Now.'

'Mama, please . . .'

'Alone.'

'Eleni . . .'

'I have to.'

Whispers, nudges, looks of concern; all of them smugly thinking they knew what was best for her. Like Costa. But she'd have it out with him when the others were gone. She took the glass of water someone handed her, but refused the tiny pills probably meant to calm her down. She wouldn't be calm. She waved everyone away, shaking her head, refusing to speak or to listen to any of them, children, friends, relatives, even the Priest.

When they finally left, she crossed herself, begged forgiveness of the Virgin for what she was about to say, and turned on her husband.

'What I said before, about you being a good husband, I always thought you were, even when I didn't agree with everything you said but now I'm not so sure.' Eleni's voice was low. 'You gave me many things, Costa, a nice house, there were no other women—at least I don't think so—and you never gambled or came home drunk, so I should be grateful. But you did other things I didn't like and I never spoke out. Well, I'm going to speak now.'

She paused, swallowed, took off her coat and laid it on the bench. Her hat was there too; when did it come off? She would have liked to have got rid of the black dress as well. She yearned to be back home, in her floral housedress, a scarf around her head, digging in the earth in her backyard, tending to her flowers, struggling with the eggplant. But she wasn't. She was here, and there were things that had to be said. She crossed herself once more. 'Forgive me, *Panagía*,' she said again.

She stood up, leaned her hands on the arms of the bench next to her. 'You kept me in darkness, Costa. Yes, in darkness. I came to you a young girl and it was your duty to teach me about this new country. When I'd tell you I wanted to learn English, you'd say we were Greek, what did I need to know English for? So I could speak properly to people at stores when I went shopping, or to the neighbours, or read about what was happening in the world, that was why, Costa!'

'I don't know what's going on so much of the time, Costa, because you kept me in darkness. When the children were young, I didn't notice so much because we all spoke Greek, but once the boys grew up and went into business with you, it was different. After supper you'd send me into the kitchen with Angela so you could talk with your sons, and it was always English, English, English! Why, Costa? So I wouldn't know what you were talking about? And you wanted Angela like me. I was so proud, Costa, when you praised me to our daughter and told her you wanted her to grow up to be as wonderful a woman as her mother. Proud! That's how stupid I was. And what did Angela learn? All the things I knew, things any fool can do, cook, and clean and sew. And now our daughter's growing old, with no husband, heaven knows why, and no life outside the house because you wouldn't allow it. When she started growing up you said she mustn't go out with Canadian boys because they weren't like us and wouldn't respect her. Maybe you were right, I don't know; I would've felt strange with a *xéno* son-in-law, it's true. But, Costa, there weren't many Greek boys to choose from, and she's getting old now, what's to become of her?'

'Something else, Costa. Do you know how I feel when my little grandchildren come up to me, hold out an English book and say "*giagía* read" and I have to pretend I can't find my glasses, or they're broken, or my head hurts.'

'Even the little babies can read the language of this country, but not their ignorant *giagía*. Remember when those papers and medals and letters came about Stephano? You said they were expressions of condolence. They were more though, Costa. They told you where our son was, but you wouldn't tell me. Paul and Tim say this was to protect me. Was I so delicate, Costa? I gave birth to five children and never mind how many I lost that you never knew about. Did you know how hard that was, Costa, one baby after another, and no machines then for the piles of washing day after day? How could I have done all that if I was so weak? And what about crossing the ocean all by myself to come to you when I was only sixteen?'

'Did you never wonder how a delicate flower could carry loads of washing up and down stairs and go for days without sleep because of sick children? I was strong, Costa, couldn't you see how strong? But I was stupid, wasn't I? Yet you said you respected me. How could you respect a stupid woman who can't read and write like everyone else? And how can I respect you now, Costa, and keep your memory pure, when you've left me with this bitterness?'

Eleni turned and stood silently until she was composed again. 'All those years I told myself I was lucky to have such a good husband,' she said quietly, her back still to him. She took a deep breath. 'I can forgive you for keeping me stupid and in darkness, Costa. I can even forgive you for taking my baby away from me, but may the Virgin excuse me, I will, never, ever forgive you for keeping the truth from me about my son.'

She turned to him, her fists clenched by her sides. 'You paid your final respects to him, Costa, but you would not allow me to do that. You did not have that right, Costa, do you hear? Do you hear me? *You did not have that right!*'

She slumped onto the bench, closed her eyes for a moment. 'Forgive me, *Panagía*,' she whispered, crossing herself, 'but I had to tell him.'

She picked up her coat, hat, gloves and purse, got up, and without looking toward the coffin, walked steadily out of the room.

Later that evening, after the others had done with their whispering and staring and hovering and had gone home, Eleni called Angela to sit on the couch with her.

'Did you know about Stephano?'

'No, Mama. Truly. No one said anything.'

'Your Papa wanted to protect you as well, it seems,' Eleni said, her mouth dry.

'It's all right, Mama. I understand.'

'I raised you well, didn't I, daughter?'

Eleni pushed off her black shoes, loosened her belt. She removed the rings from her fingers, the diamond Costa had given her on their twenty-fifth wedding anniversary — it was wartime; Stephano had just left for overseas and Paul was in training school — and the cocktail ring for her fiftieth birthday two years ago, but she left the plain gold wedding band in its place. She lay her head on the back of the couch, soft blue brocade to pick up the blue in the Persian carpet Tim's wife had suggested when she'd asked for help in picking out fabric.

She had much to be thankful for. She ought, like a good woman, to dwell on that. For it seemed, from all she'd heard from her sons in the past few hours, anything their papa had done, or not done, had always been with her best interests at heart. And so he'd flown to visit Stephano's grave that week he'd sent her to Rhodes with her sisters. They'd all known, of course. And for a long time before that there had been a stone to mark her son's grave, and a foreign woman paid to keep it clean and covered in flowers. Her sons seemed to think she'd take comfort in the knowledge that another woman had been looking after her child's grave these many years. What strange creatures these men she'd been living with, how distorted their ideas. Eleni looked over at her daughter. Something had to be done, at least for her. It wasn't clear to Eleni how, or what, but she knew she had to try. But first she needed one final gesture from her daughter.

'Would you go with me to visit your brother's grave?'

'Go to France?' Angela seemed surprised. 'On our own?'

'Yes,' Eleni said. 'On our own.'

◆ ◆ ◆

KATHERINE VLASSIE was born in 1935 in Winnipeg, a second-generation Greek Canadian. She has lived in Winnipeg, Athens, Montreal, and Toronto. Her first career was traditional for her generation: she was a homemaker. In 1980, after her children were grown, she began to write, secretly at first, and then enrolled in a creative writing course. 'A world opened up inside me,' she said. Now a full-time writer, Vlassie lives in Toronto, just off the Danforth, the major Greek district in the city. *Children of Byzantium* (Dunvegan, Ont.: Cormorant Books, 1987) is her first published book.

KAREN MULHALLEN is an editor, poet, broadcaster, and teacher. She is editor of *Descant* magazine and the former Arts Features Editor of *The Canadian Forum*. She has edited *Views from the North: An Anthology of Travel Writing* and co-edited *Tasks of Passion: Dennis Lee at Mid-Career*. She is the author of *Sheba and Solomon*, a long poem, and *Modern Love, Poems 1970-1989*. She is a professor of English at Ryerson Polytechnical Institute and can be heard on CJRT:FM 91.1, on 'The Tale and the Teller', interviewing authors and talking about current English Canadian fiction.

You told me that Children of Byzantium *came out of a move and that, somehow, the move precipitated the book. How?*

I was unpacking boxes and I found some letters that my father had sent to my mother, when they were engaged. They were letters that had been lying around and, for some reason, I just wanted to look through them. I spent the afternoon reading them instead of unpacking.

And were the letters written in Greek to her in Greece?

Yes, my father was in Canada. It was an arranged marriage. They had never met each other, but my father nonetheless wrote these lovely romantic letters about 'how I long for the day when you come' and 'I dream of you'. They were nice sorts of sentiments and, when I saw the letters, I started thinking about how my mother would have felt reading these. What were her expectations, being a young girl, a teenager, in a small Greek town, being sent off to Canada? My parents never really talked about all this and I knew if I asked my mother she wouldn't really say.

When were the letters written?

1915.

1915? During the First World War?

Yes — an odd time for this all to be happening. She came over in the middle of the war. Well, Greece wasn't in the war at that time.

But she crossed the north Atlantic.

She did, yes, by herself, much the way Eleni [the protagonist of *Children of Byzantium*] does. But I started thinking, as I said, about my mother, and since I couldn't put myself into her head, and I knew I couldn't get any information out of her, I started thinking about what it would be like for a young girl. And out of that afternoon of just reading and thinking, Eleni emerged.

So she's not your mother?

No. Many of the facts in the stories really are my mother's, in that she crossed the ocean, took the train, and ended up in Winnipeg.

You have told me that you began this book in June of 1985, and it took you about two years. Were you writing about things from your childhood or your background before this?

No.

So this was a change for you, to address your Greek roots?

I didn't want to have to deal with it. As far as I was concerned, I was Canadian. I had dealt with that and I didn't want to spend my time writing about my Greek background. I thought it was all very silly. I wanted to write about women, because that was my interest.

Well, that shows in this book, too. It is very clearly a book about women and women's roles and plight—and also, women bonding together, teaching each other.

I did see that in my mother's friends. They really only had each other. But actually this started out being a novel. I had written the first draft of a novel where I decided to use my Greek background too. They say: write from what you know. So, I thought: well, OK, I'll make the character of Greek descent. But that wasn't the focus; it was just the background. Somehow the Greek background kept coming up. It wouldn't leave me alone. All these characters kept coming up. And I thought: I might as well deal with them and then, when I read the letters and Eleni sort of came to the fore, I thought: well, I guess I have to get this all out and deal with it.

Do you feel that in order to understand the book your Greek background is essential? Or do you feel that's, in a way, a red herring?

I suppose I would like the book to stand on its own—as the story of a woman, because that's really what I was writing about. I was writing about a woman who lives in silence, and what it does to her. I guess in my mind I play down the ethnic connection, and play up the role of the church, the patriarchal world, being a stranger in a strange land, both the male world and a different country—not necessarily that this is a Greek story. Of course, I wrote out of my background.

What else would you write out of? It seemed to me to be the story of a woman who yearns to break out of the silence too.

But she isn't strong enough to. People have said to me that, for some reason, they see me as being brave, because I have broken away. I don't feel particularly brave. And yet other people, who live a more traditional life than I, have commented on that, and then I think it's so sad. I guess it's the sadness of the lives of women I see that really bothers me.

Yes, there is something even with Eleni at the end of 'A Proper Goodbye'. I think the ending is very moving and powerful, but she's impotent in a way, isn't she? I mean: Costa's dead and she's talking to a dead body. It's too late; he can't hear her.

Yes, exactly. She still can't stand on her own: she still turns to her daughter. Eleni does break away a bit. She has broken out in the book that I have written now. There she plays a very minor role, but she does break away. But she doesn't become a flag-waving feminist or anything like that. She doesn't walk away from her family, and she doesn't do anything that's outwardly different. She changes a little bit inside—as much as she is capable. It's not possible for her, given her background, her attitudes, and her age at the time, to break away totally. She would be lost.

You start the first story, 'The Garden with Flowers', with the image of flowers, and that image is woven all through the eight tales, becoming an important metaphor. The books starts and ends in the garden.

Yes, except, at the beginning she thinks of lovely flowers and at the end, she's tending her eggplants.

Yes, it's her eggplants—which won't grow. Is there some importance to the fact that now it's a vegetable garden that won't grow? Is that an image of the way her life has been stopped up?

Yes, but it hasn't been totally stopped. Her life is not a tragic one. She's only fifty-two but, as far as she is concerned, she's old. After all, she has three grown children, and she's been raising kids since she was a teenager. I think, back in the fifties, she would have been considered old in our society, whereas now, those of us in that age group are considered still in middle age. Not old.

That's right. What about the patriarchal society as it's set up in the book? Is that something you are familiar with?

Oh, absolutely, yes.

That was the way your father and mother related to each other?

Yes, it's what I saw in my own home.

Your mother really didn't read English?

That's right. My father was a very kind and protective man. I saw this in other Greek families around me, because my whole life was centred on the Greek community. My parents were very strict and they wanted to maintain Greek traditions.

It's amazing, isn't it, how women of that first generation, who didn't learn English, nonetheless were able to create lives for themselves. In your book, Matina is one example: she taught herself English.

Yes, well, some did. You see, I didn't want it to come across that all of them were like Eleni. Eleni wouldn't dare go against her husband; she was afraid to. She would have called it 'respect'—not fear. So I think you had both kinds.

And how do people take the next step—out of that community? Is that something that just happens naturally?

I don't think the first generation really does take a step out. In the second generation, some break out and some stay within it. My feeling now is that the second generation tries to step out a bit; some find it a little uncomfortable.

Why? Are they seen as different?

They have been told they are different. I mean, I was told, for the first eighteen years of my life, that I was Greek, even though I was born in Canada, educated in English. I was told I was Greek and I believed it. I felt apart from the girls I went to school with. I used to think that they set me apart, but I found out years later that they didn't—that I set myself apart. I remember meeting someone, a number of years later, whom I had gone to school with, and she commented on the fact that I was rather stand-offish and that I didn't want to mix. I was appalled at this, because I didn't see myself that way. I had been brainwashed so much at home into thinking I was different, I was Greek—they wouldn't want to mix with me. So I kept myself apart. But in my case, I finally did break away. I've seen others who haven't.

Is there a large Greek community in this country?

Oh, yes. Just walk down the Danforth here in Toronto, or down Park Avenue in Montreal.

But what about in the west?

Well, there aren't hundreds of thousands, but there are quite a few.

In your book, I remember, there was no church because there seemed to be not enough people. There was only a priest.

Well, this was the early group. After the 1950s, there was a huge influx of Greeks and the community in Winnipeg, for instance, changed completely. They didn't build a church: they bought it! At the time of these stories, there was no church, because the community was very small. This is how it was when I was growing up.

Was there any reason for you not to deal with your Greek background: it's a very rich one and it's as much a part of our society as any other, isn't it?

Well, yes, but it's just that there's a part of me that has a bit of a problem with our multiculturalism in Canada. I wrote a book which, as far as I was concerned, was about a woman, Eleni, and her life. She happened to be Greek. And what has happened as a result of it . . .

Now they want to put you in a multicultural volume?

Yes, and anyone who has questioned me about the book stresses the fact that Eleni is Greek and asks about my particular background.

Why should you have to do this? You're a writer, not a Greek.

And I'm a woman, and I guess that I would like Eleni to be not representative of a *Greek* woman but representative of women. And I am pleased that I have had some feedback from people who say to me that 'this reminded me of my Romanian grandmother' or 'I heard stories like this from my Ukrainian grandmother'.

This reminds me of my grandmother, actually, who came from Beirut in the 1860s and never learned to read English. She spoke English. She was educated in a French convent, so she spoke Arabic and French, but could never read the newspapers here. There were no French papers in Ontario where she lived, and there were no Arabic papers. She was, in effect, illiterate: she wasn't, but she was functionally so in the life that she had to lead. So it is a story of a certain kind of woman who comes from another world, and who marries—and marries a man who does the public business. And her life, her job is to rear the children. It's a universal story. I don't think it's Greek. In the book, you do have moments—the dancing, the food, and so on—but that's the texture of life. There's no reason not to give the food its Greek name.

I don't mind writing about it. In fact, I had given up and felt I might as well write about it.

Do you feel imprisoned or constrained by your background? Do you still fell that people are making you continue to be some kind of 'ethnic'?

Well, yes, but it's not a major problem. I don't want to be thought of as a Greek writer—you know, the way Mordecai Richler is considered the Jewish writer from Montreal. Even though he writes about the Jewish community, he is a *Canadian* writer. We have a tendency to want to put people in little pockets here.

That's the multicultural thing you were worrying about.

I know, and I would like to see us be closer to each other too. I have very mixed feelings about this. I live just off the Danforth, which is ironic. I chose that particular area, which just happens to be Greek. I walk down the street and I see signs in Greek. There's a whole Greek community here. These people have come over from Greece, much the way my parents came. They walk right into a community, though: they have their own church, their grocery store where the meat man will talk to them in Greek.

And you think there's a problem with this? I live in a Portuguese neighbourhood, by the way, and it's exactly the same. I think there's a richness that comes from cultures that have come into the country that makes Canada a pluralist society.

Yes, but you can retain these without living in a ghetto.

How could you retain your Greekness? There's two models: the melting pot and the salad bowl.

Well, I don't want us to melt! I don't want us to be just little blobs in there somewhere. I don't know. It's not what I want really, because I only observe what is, and I live my life the way it's comfortable for me. I could not stay within the confines of the Greek community, because it was too restrictive. Yet, I see that other people need to.

So that, in the end, it comes down to the individual temperament? After the first generation?

Yes, some people feel safer. And it isn't just Greeks—it's other nationalities too. They just feel more secure with their own kind, as they say. Well, I feel more comfortable with my own kind. My own kind, though, happen to be people who see the world the way I see it—which is not necessarily a good thing.

Not necessarily an ethnic thing, but a vision of the way life is.

Yes, that's right.

W.D. VALGARDSON b. 1939

The Man from Snaefellsness

'*Tala thu izlensku?*' she asked.
'What?' I said, staring at the phone. I didn't remember picking it up.
'Do you speak Icelandic?'
'Who wants to know? Good God, it's four in the morning.'
'Is this Axel Borgfjord? I'm calling on behalf of the committee for relationships with Canada.'
'Who are you?'
'Axel, who is it?' Helen mumbled. Her face was still in her pillow and her voice was muffled, softened with sleep.
The telephone crackled with static and the faint woman's voice added, 'We would like you to visit Iceland as our guest. Have you been to Iceland?'
'Is it the babysitter?' When Helen stayed overnight, I paid for a sitter. Three of the four last times, her daughter had managed to get sick.
'No. It's a prank.'
'I'm sorry, I didn't hear you,' the voice said.
'What do you want me to do? Write an article?' I asked, playing along. I have some peculiar friends. As kids they used to phone up corner stores and ask if the store had Prince Albert in a tin and when the owner said, yes, they'd shriek with delight and say, 'Then let him out.' Now their gags are more sophisticated, more complex but their sense of humour just as juvenile.
'You do nothing. We know all about your writing. Your stories and plays. Now we want you to learn about us.'
'If everything is paid for. Sure I'll come.'
'Yes. You pay nothing. We will take you to the farm from which your great-grandfather came.'
'What do you know about my great-grandfather?' I snapped but simultaneously, she said 'I'll send you the ticket. *Godan dagun*,' and the phone went dead and I shouted, 'Wait. I can't come. Don't . . .'

and then I stopped and sat staring at the phone. Sitting in the darkness, it was as though I could hear the distant surf of Iceland breaking on the skerries, shattering on the shingle beach my great-grandfather had described to me. The ice grinding itself to pieces at the foot of the home field.

I fell asleep to dream of hills. At first I thought I was alone, then, in the distance, against the horizon, a Viking with a spear, then closer, on another hill, another Viking, then another. I would have fled but suddenly, appearing out of deep fissures in the lava behind me, looking like my father and grandfather, my brother and uncles, came other men, their weapons drawn, facing those who now thronged from the hills. One of those who confronted me raised his axe and I shouted and struck out with my sword and battle was joined. My kinsmen and I fought unceasingly but no matter how many we killed, there were always more. And then it was morning and the apple tree outside my window was drenched in bloom and I reached out and plucked a sprig of blossoms and gave them to Helen. I wondered if I had only dreamt the phone call like I had dreamt the battle.

'No, you were quite rude to her. By the end you were shouting,' Helen said over coffee.

The battle faded away and I'd nearly forgotten about the phone call until two weeks later when an airplane ticket arrived by registered mail.

'I thought you were going to tell them you couldn't come?' Helen said. She was helping me plant the garden.

'I forgot about it.'

'It's for August first. A charter out of Winnipeg.'

'I can't go. Anyway, why should I? Good God my great-grandfather arrived in Sandy Bar in 1878. No one has ever gone back. It's history.'

'Talk Icelandic to me,' Helen said.

'Forget it.'

'Come on,' she answered, holding up some marigolds. 'How does an Icelander say "Let's hop in the sack." '

'I haven't the faintest idea.'

'Everybody can swear in their mother tongue.'

'English is my mother tongue. I was born here.'

'How do you say grandma?'

'Let's drop it, OK?'

'Boy, are you touchy.' she said, her feelings hurt. She was vaguely

WASP but not in any connected way, no accent, no relatives in the British Isles, no Christmas customs except frantic shopping and paying too much for a tree imported from the US. She missed what I had, she said, belonging to a specific place. She loved going to the Multicultural Festival and drifting from booth to booth, eating langosh, satee, peroghis and washing it all down with cappucino and German beer. The folkdance costume she wore to parties was made up of pieces from India, Yugoslavia, Germany, Finland. People who didn't know better thought it was authentic.

'*Amma*,' I offered. Her white blouse showed the tanned curve of her neck and a loop of dark hair had fallen over one eye. I reached up and brushed her hair back over her ear. Although she was thirty, there was something innocent about her. When she played about the yard with her daughter, it was like both of them were four. 'That's how you say grandma.'

We had planned a romantic afternoon together. The wine was in the fridge and the avacado and shrimp prepared for lunch but the glow was off the day. I threw the ticket into a dresser and slammed the drawer shut.

What was Iceland to me? I was fifth generation Canadian. That should have been the end of the matter but every time I went out to cut the grass or weed the garden or trim the ivy, my great-grandfather's face appeared. At times, I could smell his pipe tobacco. More than once I was certain he was standing behind me, watching, and I turned suddenly as if to catch him but there was never anyone there. At last, I gave up. Come on, I said, out loud, let's get this over with and suddenly, it was like I was six again, dressed in my sailor's uniform, standing in my great-grandfather's back yard. He was wearing his black pants, suspenders, and his long underwear but no shirt. He was splitting wood and as he chopped, he and my father were talking.

'Are you going to come to *Islindingadagurinn* this year?' my father asked.

'Those who enjoy these things can go.'

'All your friends will be there.'

'If Einar from Vithir is still alive, or Hannes from Arborg, they know where to find my house.' All the time they talked, he split kindling from a round of birch.

'The Ladies Aide is serving coffee and rosettes. Fresh whipped cream.'

'*Hreppsomagur* don't go to celebrations.' When he was fourteen, he had been given a one-way ticket to Canada. Five dollars in his pocket. He knew no English. During the trip eleven people had died. He had stolen a language text from one of the dead women. After that, when he had needed something, he pointed to a word in Icelandic and people would read the word beside it in English. Then they would point at a word in English and he'd read the Icelandic. 'Let them choke on their rosettes and whipped cream.'

'That was sixty-seven years ago.'

'Do you know what they wrote in the paper after they kicked people like me out? They wrote that when times got tough, we were cowards and ran away. I think maybe they got it backwards. Pontius Pilate didn't die. He just moved to Iceland and had lots of children.'

Stiff-necked, unforgiving, proud, Icelandic to the core. That was Ketil, my great-grandfather. At one time, his father had been *bondi*, a farmer, and his mother had been *husmothir*. They operated an independent farm which they rented from the church. A volcanic eruption covered most of the hayfields with ash and toxic gases poisoned the cattle so that their legs became disjointed and tumours grew on their bones. Rather than see them die in agony, Ketil and his father had slaughtered both cattle and sheep with an axe. To try to feed themselves and the five others still on the farm they turned to the sea. They had an open boat suitable for four men. Each day, the two of them with their two hired men risked the surf, then rowed three miles to fish for cod. They might have survived but the weather turned unseasonably cold, filling the bay with ice. They were reduced to scavenging along the beach for fish that were washed up in the ice. The women gathered lichens to make porridge.

When there was nothing but starvation, Ketil's father, along with his family, was forced, by law, to return to the Snaefellsness Peninsula, to the *hreppar*, or district where he was born. That made them *hreppsomagur*, beggermen, welfare cases. Ketil's father pleaded with the district council to let the family remain together. He was prepared to fix up an abandoned house but the local farmers needed hired help. They insisted that the family be broken up, each going to work for a different farmer. The local council went further and got an order to seize everything except the clothes that the three of them were wearing. When Ketil's father protested, he was told that poor men who could not look after their families did not need more than one set of clothes. They were worked from dawn to dusk but the farmer responsible for Ketil, rather than face years of feeding him, paid his passage to Canada. Ketil had tried to resist but two burly farmers had forcibly put him on a Danish fishing boat. Two weeks later he was in Scotland. Three weeks later he was in Montreal. Once there was no hope of turning back Ketil could think of only one destination. *Nya Island*. New Iceland.

It took him six months but, finally, he reached Winnipeg and with wages he had earned as a labourer, purchased a ticket on a freight boat that was going to Icelandic River.

He stood on the narrow deck as the boat entered Lake Winnipeg. By this time he had a travelling companion, Gudmunder Einarsson. Einarsson had come by Halifax, and for three years had gradually made his way across Canada and so could understand English. However, he was quite shy because of his accent and pretended he could not speak anything but Icelandic. As Gudmunder and Ketil watched the thickly wooded shore pass by, an Englishwoman and her husband came out of their cabin and the Englishwoman said, 'Do you think these are Icelanders?' Gudmunder translated for Ketil. The resulting exchange became a family story.

'I don't think so,' the husband replied, shaking his head. 'Icelanders are short and dark like Eskimos.'

'No. No. There are a lot of Icelandic women working as domestics in Winnipeg. They wear those long black dresses and have blonde hair.'

'Swedes, I would think or Germans.'

'Ask them.'

'Are you Icelanders?' he said, raising his voice.

'*Hvat?*' my great-grandfather asked.

The Englishman shouted, spacing out his words, 'Are you Germans? Deutsche?' and pulled himself to attention and moved about as if he were marching.

'*Ert han vitless?*' Ketil asked Gudmunder.

'*Yow.*'

'I told you! That's their way of saying yes,' the Englishwoman exclaimed. 'I wrote to you about them. They had that terrible smallpox epidemic two years ago and they died like flies. The whole community was quarantined. No one allowed past Boundary Creek. When they let them back into Winnipeg, they didn't have a penny. You could hire them for nothing. Emma says they're excellent workers and clean. Another thing, they make their coffee in an old sock.'

Coffee made in an old sock. I'd forgotten about that. It wasn't an old sock actually. It was a linen bag sewed around a handle made of copper wire. The bag sat in the coffee all day. You just kept adding more grounds. And Ketil taking lump sugar between his teeth and sucking his coffee through it.

'But what did they call this old sock?' Helen asked when I told her about Ketil's story. 'They must have had a name for it.' She was always hunting for ethnic experience. Odd words, bits of information. Her previous boyfriend had been Russian and had given her a samovar and a marushka. She still made tea with the samovar. The boyfriend before that had been an Arab and gave her two Persian carpets she hung on her wall. She considered people with roots to be the most fortunate of creatures.

'I don't know. I probably never heard it. My mother was Irish. I was a half-breed.'

Remembering was like digging up the dead, not whole people but bits and pieces, a finger-bone here, a vertebra there. Fragments of memory. Things forgotten or half-remembered. Eddyville, when I was a child, was still mostly swamp. People had built on the high ground and the houses were separated by property that was never dry until the middle of summer. By then the grass would be head high and the willows thick and tangled, the perfect place to play away from the prying eyes of adults. One day a dozen of us had been running the trails, playing cowboys and Indians when we decided to build a fort we would call Valhalla. There was lumber we could steal from various yards and old blankets for a floor. Here, we were to be Vikings. We would bring food and soft drinks and comic books and organize raids upon neighbourhood gardens and fruit trees.

We dispersed then returned with our loot. When we had all gathered, Clarence had pushed me back and said, 'You can't come to Valhalla.'

I had pinched a pocket full of my father's nails and an old tablecloth.

'Why not?'

'You're not Icelandic.'

'I am so.'

'My mother says you're not. She says your mother is an *utlander*.'

'She is not!' I'd shouted, enraged and Clarence and his brothers and sisters all began to shout, '*Utlander. Utlander.*'

'She is not. She is not,' I'd yelled back but it did no good. The others took it up. *Utlander*. Foreigner, outsider, other than us. None of the English words do it justice. Not wanted, perhaps. I remember that with absolute clarity. The bone-coloured grass, the clumps of willow, the yelling, my feeling of helpless rage. I remember the next day even more clearly because that was the day Ketil, still proud, still strong, his moustaches yellow from snuff, died on his living room floor. He had hoped, I'd heard him say to my father, to die in his boat or in a woman's bed but, somehow, it was better that he'd died in his beloved house. It still stands today, nothing special now that houses are two thousand, four thousand square feet, even in Eddyville. It is small, wood frame, sits on a basement. Although I've not been in it in thirty years, I know it exactly. Back door entrance at ground level, stairs up and stairs to basement. When I think of the basement, I shiver because he kept his coffin there on two saw horses. To keep the dust off, he covered it with a white sheet. Once when my father and I came, Ketil was polishing the brass handles.

Upstairs, the kitchen, with a table in one corner. Two chairs. A washstand with a basin and a pitcher of water. Cupboards but the colours escape me. Then the living room but this is vague, the furniture uncertain, a couch, a trilight lamp, a front door and two bedroom doors but these are dark holes behind cloth curtains. This house was his palace. It was his solace for failed dreams. His plan was to bring his mother and father to join him. To pay their fare, to build a place for them. He worked like a madman. Taking anything that came his way—cutting wood, carrying mail, fishing, working on the railway but by the time he had saved their fare, his mother was dead from starvation and overwork and his father too ill to make the journey. His mother had been buried without a coffin. He sent his father money so that he could escape from the farmer's council. Then he began to save for his property, for his house. He built it himself, sometimes buying the lumber a board at a time. He married, had three children and those children had grandchildren and those, too, had children. I was one of those.

A month after Ketil's death, his son, my grandfather died. With that, two generations were buried in Canadian soil. Each of them was an Icelander. The man from Snaefellsness, the son of the man from Snaefellsness. My father, the next in line, was only twenty-eight. He was the grandson of the man from Snaefellsness. Then there was me. I was not the great-grandson of the man from Snaefellsness. I was *utlander*, not Icelandic but not Canadian either. No one was Canadian in those days.

At school, we aped the English. We sang 'God Save The King' at the end of every school day. We learned to proudly recite Kipling and Wordsworth and Shelley. And we were taught to forget. 'What was that I heard you speaking? Was that English? It wasn't, was it?' the grade one teacher demanded and standing at the front of the class, she punctuated each word with the leather strap which always hung at the side of her desk. What, strap, was, strap, that, strap, until Clarence was screaming and crying and trying to pull away as she beat his hands red. Afterwards, twisted in his desk, his voice a high-pitched whine of pain, he rocked back and forth.

We were taught no sagas. No Eddas. No mention of Skarphedin or Njal, Iceland's greatest hero, nor Thingveddlir, the site of the oldest parliament in the world, nor Yggdrasil, the tree upon which the world is held, nor Ragnorak, the day of doom. Instead, we memorized the names and dates of English kings and queens. It did no good of course. When the summer time came and the Winnipeg campers opened up their cottages, they protectively shut their children behind fences, on verandas. Even if we stood on the Eddyville dock wrapped in the Union Jack and recited sentimental poems about wattles and daffodils and wanting to be in England there was no disguising our foreignness.

In Iceland, the passion for reading and writing had survived natural disaster and human cruelty. Even the *breppsomagur* brought books to Canada. There was nothing greater than to be *skald*, writer. In Ketil's living room there were eight books in Icelandic. They were set on a small shelf above the couch, precisely where emigrants from other groups might have put an icon or a plaster saint. Unfortunately, in these books there were no instructions which would help him deal with Canada. The sagas and Eddas dealt with family feuds, with honour and lineage. Nor did we have any practical experience. In Iceland he had never seen a forest, had only heard rumours of caribou and polar bear brought to land on drift ice. He had never eaten vegetables except potatoes and until the day he died refused all offers of vegetables with the words, 'I don't eat grass.'

Fishing is what the Icelanders knew and fishing is why they came to Manitoba. They tried other places but they were fishermen and Lake Winnipeg was an inland ocean. Except it froze over in winter.

They didn't know what to do about that but they figured it out. They chopped a hole and put down nets with poles and then they invented a jigger that pulled nets under the ice. And they left home and went north for fall fishing and winter fishing and went still further north for whitefishing. And the women, if they didn't go north to cook for a gang of men, moved in together to save money on fuel and groceries and kept each other company until the season was over. When Ketil arrived, the settlers were fishing for food but a market soon developed in Winnipeg and from Winnipeg to Chicago.

Having arrived with nothing, they had nothing with which to buy equipment but the fish companies, financed by Americans, were eager to lend them whatever they needed. Before the season began, each fisherman would go to Winnipeg cap in hand. I need a new set of nets, he'd say and the company owner would say and corks and leads and bridles? and the fisherman would add, I'll need credit for fuel and the owner would say and groceries for yourself and your family and how many men? and northwesters and woollen mittens and socks, the fisherman would say and the owner would say just remember you sell your fish to us and nobody else. Ketil borrowed from us but sold his fish to someone else. There's no credit for him. Not here. Not anywhere. You tell him that. You tell him he'll have to find some other work than fishing. And he did. He became a dairyman. He considered himself to be well out of it because when a fisherman came back after two months of shipping his fish to Winnipeg, the company informed him of the price they'd pay him. A cent a pound, two cents a pound, whatever they felt like. If he protested, there was no credit next year. Many years, a fisherman worked all season and owed more at the end than when he began. No wonder when the men came back the first place they headed was the beer parlour. And their wives, our mothers, the brave ones that was, would go to the hotel door and demand that the waiters send their husbands out so they could get part of the cheque to buy groceries and school clothes and a new dress and something decent for the house and often what they got was a black eye.

Three days of Icelandic Celebration didn't leave much. And then it'd be grovelling to the company for more credit and the women helping each other out and making do. It was the women who persevered, who held everything together, who pushed their children through school and away to the city, to university if humanly possible. My mother was one of those.

'I've arranged for you to go to Winnipeg to stay with your grandmother,' my mother said the August after I'd finished high school. 'I don't want to go to Winnipeg,' I replied. 'I'm getting a boat and going fishing.'

'I've taken my knitting money and given it to your grandmother. It will pay for your tuition to United College.'

'You can't do this,' I protested. Her knitting money had been saved for years to buy a dining room suite.

'Your grandmother will keep you for no charge. I've got work for one day a week at the fish packers. I get five dollars a day. I'll give you that. You'll have to find the rest yourself. Your Uncle says he can get you a job as a bus boy on the weekends at Eaton's.'

'I'm going fishing with Dad. The company is going to give me credit.'

'If you do well, there are some scholarships for Icelandic Canadians. They're all in *Logberg*.'

'Icelanders are fishermen.'

'Not in the West End of Winnipeg. If you go to First Lutheran, you'll meet Icelanders who work in an office and get their fish from the store.'

'I'm not clearing dishes in Eaton's.'

'Signy Eaton is Icelandic. It'll get you a job, it won't keep it for you. Remember that.'

And that was that. Off to Winnipeg a week later and sitting at the back of the class, arms crossed, listening to truth and beauty when I wanted to be ripping the guts out of fish, chopping off their heads and getting drunk in the Eddyville parlour and dancing polkas to Johnny and His Musical Mates and getting laid in the back seat of the car outside the Eddyville Community Hall but by the time I managed to get back to fishing in the spring it was too late. I didn't belong anymore. At the beer parlour, when I sat down, everyone got quiet. It was like the minister had arrived. They were talking outboard motors and dirty nets and lousy fish inspectors and when they asked me what I was learning and I tried to tell them about Rousseau or Hobbes or Shakespeare, it was like I was showing off. I tried a couple more times but it was no good and after that I didn't go back.

'Axel!' Helen said.

'What?'

'We came out for a walk. You've been standing there for five minutes staring across the marsh. Ever since you got that call from Iceland, you've been lost in a daze.'

'No!' I said, brushing off a mosquito.

'Yesterday, at the ballet you sat like you were mesmerized. I don't think you saw a thing.'

'What?'

'Oh, God,' she said, 'I give up.'

Icelandic horses invaded my dreams. Shaggy Icelandic ponies, a long line of them climbing up a mountain of lava, black, convoluted, the horses outlined against the sky, short sturdy horses, with their shaggy manes, topping the crest and descending to a lava desert which goes on as far as the horizon. *Hestur*. The word jumped unbidden into my mind. And with it the teacher screaming.

'What's that? What did you call them?'

And I whispered, '*Hestur*.' It was what my great-grandfather had always called his horse with the white blaze on its forehead.

'What did I tell you? What kind of a word is that? Show me what a *hestur* is. Here, this picture. What is this? Well, speak up. I can't hear you.'

'*Hestur*.' The word was as thin and faint as monofilament.

'It is not,' she screamed. 'It is a horse. Horse, you idiot. Class, here is a horse and standing in front of the picture of a horse is an idiot. Hold out your hand!' She grabbed my wrist and dragged me to the desk, raised the strap above her shoulders.

'What is this?' she yelled and when I wouldn't open my hand brought the strap down on my clenched fingers.

'A horse,' I screamed. ' A horse.'

'Again.'

'Horse.'

'Again.'

'Horse. Horse. Horse. Horse. Horse.'

I woke up in a terrible panic. Although it was thirty-four years earlier that I had been beaten, my hands were so stiff and swollen that I could barely move them. It was as if I had stored not only the memory but the actual physical experience. I sat in bed, holding my hands in front of me. The pain was so intense that I did not dare touch the light switch.

'Let's have *panacooker*,' Helen said a few days later. She'd been rummaging around my kitchen cupboards and had found a cook-book. She held it up so I could see the cover. 'The Lutheran Ladies Aide. Eddyville. Are you going to take me there sometime?'

'Sure,' I said.

'*Vinarterta* sounds interesting. And *asta bolur*.' She flipped through the pages. 'And rosettes with fresh whipped cream. And *hangikjot*.' She couldn't make any sense out of the k and j together. 'And *hardfisk*.'

They used to make hardfish in Eddyville. They split saugers and small pickerel and hung them on wires above the fly line. They cured in the sun, curling as the skin shrank. I got a tapeworm that way. Stealing hardfish before it was ready, my cousin stealing butter from his mother's kitchen. Then we put the fish skin side on the sidewalk, pounded it with a hammer until the flesh softened and we could tear off strips and drag them through the butter.

'It stinks,' I said.

'What does?'

'Hardfish. It smells like an outhouse on a hot day.'

'*Skyr*,' she said. 'A milk product. That doesn't tell you much, does it? *Rullapilsa*. That sounds vile.' She read the description. 'A sheep's flank rolled tightly, boiled, pickled, then sliced thin and served on brown bread. Did you eat this stuff?'

'With half a loaf and a tilted cup, I got myself a friend,' I replied, without thinking.

'What is that all about?' She was onto it in a flash.

'Nothing.'

'Oh, come on. Don't be so chintzy with your life.'

'It was a saying of my great-grandfather's. He got it from a book called *Havamal*.'

I'd probably have picked a fight with her for being so nosy but just then the phone rang and Disa somebody-or-other's-daughter said, 'Did your airplane ticket arrive?'

'Yes, but . . .'

'That is good. Someone will meet you at the airport. We have a very nice apartment for you at the university. I look forward to seeing you.'

And then she hung up. Icelanders are like that. Abrupt. Not much subtlety. No small talk. In the sagas they're always saying 'Now I'm going to kill you,' or something similar and then they proceed to do it.

'Wait,' I yelled. 'You can't do this to me. Wait. I can't, I can't.'

'What?' Helen said.

'Iceland.'

'You were yelling at Iceland?'

'It's hard to explain.'

'You might as well go. You haven't been yourself for the last six weeks. I'll drop by and take care of your cat every day. I promise. I'll even water your plants. Just bring me back one of those Icelandic sweaters.'

'They can't do this. They didn't want us and now they're going to shanghai me.'

'The people who didn't want your family are all dead.'

'No, they're not. If they were I wouldn't dream about them every night.'

'You've earned your way back.'

'With a couple of books of stories? You would think it would cost more than that.'

'*Skald.*'

'That's a bad burn.'

'That's a writer. It is a title of honour. That's what they called you in their letter.'

'You've been learning a lot.'

'The flight from Winnipeg is a charter. It only takes five hours.'

'You're one of them.'

'You can't let her win.'

'Exactly. She can't just phone up here . . .'

'Not her. The old bitch with the strap. You can't you know. It's not over yet. Your great-grandfather couldn't go back. Your grandfather couldn't go back. You can go back for them.'

'He wouldn't walk down the block. He wouldn't watch the Fjalkona lay the wreath at the monument. He split wood on Icelandic Celebration. All day.'

'It must have been hard. Staying away.'

The phone started to ring again. I let it ring, five, six times, then I said, 'That's her calling back. What am I going to say? Shit! I can't do this. It's too hard.' And then I grabbed the phone in a rage. '*Yow.*' I shouted. '*Godan dagun. Thetta er Axel Borgfjord. Yow. Yow.* Goddam you, goddam you, yes I'm coming.'

◆ ◆ ◆

WILLIAM DEMPSEY VALGARDSON was born in Winnipeg, in 1939, and grew up in Gimli—the centre of *Nya Island*, the area of Manitoba where his Icelandic ancestors settled. Valgardson's great-great-grandfather and great-grandfather came from the Snaefellsness Peninsula of Iceland, in 1878, to Sandy Bar, just north of Gimli. His great-great-grandfather died in 1881 but his great-grandfather lived until Valgardson was six years old, and his great-grandmother, who remembered the smallpox epidemic of 1876, lived until he was in high school, so he has a strong sense of connection back into the original settlement. Although he was born in Canada, and his mother's people are Irish, Valgardson has always identified strongly with his Icelandic predecessors. His works include *Bloodflowers* (Ottawa: Oberon, 1973); *God Is Not a Fish Inspector* (Ottawa: Oberon, 1975); *In the Gutting Shed* (Winnipeg: Turnstone, 1976); *Red Dust* (Ottawa: Oberon, 1978); *Gentle Sinners* (Ottawa: Oberon, 1980); *The Carpenter of Dreams* (Victoria: Skaldhus, 1986).

JUDITH MILLER was born in Montreal, where she grew up in the middle of a French Canadian Catholic community, in a Scots Presbyterian household, with many Jewish friends at school. She then moved to Kitchener-Waterloo, Ontario, a community with heavy German influences. As Valgardson would say, that is the Canadian experience. She is currently associate professor of English at Renison College, University of Waterloo and is the author of *The Art of Alice Munro* (1984) and *Timbrel in Her Hand* (1988), a music-drama for which she wrote the poetry and Carol Ann Weaver wrote the music.

What brought your ancestors from Iceland to Gimli?

Poverty. There had been tremendous weather changes. At one time the weather was so moderate in the area around Iceland that the settlements in Greenland were able to export grain. With the weather changing and turning colder, gradually the Greenland Viking settlements disappeared. In Iceland there was starvation. The population at one point was as low as 30,000 people. Also the Danes had taken over Iceland and exploited it tremendously because it was far away. It was like any colony, no different than Angola and Portugal. But the precipitating factor came finally in the 1870s. There were volcanic eruptions, and they spread poisonous gas, lava and ash over the hayfields. So the grazing animals, the sheep and the cattle, either starved to death or died from the poisonous effects of the eruptions. With this amount of starvation, people had to find someplace to go. It was a bit like the potato famine in Ireland. Some of the people voluntarily came to North America but quite a lot of them didn't come voluntarily. They were forced to leave. Iceland had a kind of welfare system, but there was no compassion in it. If somebody found that he could not support himself or his family, these people were forced to return to the birth area of the man. Then the local farmers bid, and the farmer who made the lowest bid for the keep of a person, got him or her.

Got that person as a worker?

Well, essentially as a slave. People were worked to death, starved to death. There was no compassion in the system. The Allen Shipping Line and the Canadian government—various factors—came together, to subsidize immigration to Canada because Canada wanted immigrants. For about $30 these people could be shipped out of the country, so if you had people who couldn't take care of themselves because of circumstance, mental illness, or disease, or whatever reason, for $30 you could be rid of them. It was a cheap way of getting rid of misfits, getting rid of a problem. Castro didn't invent it, and this has always been a big secret in the Icelandic community. I only discovered it in recent years. There was always a myth that was propagated that everybody danced and sang and voluntarily came to Canada. There has always been a dark undercurrent that never gets talked about much. It is only as I have been doing research that I have come across these people who are called *Hreppsomagur*. Gradually I began to get some understanding about this dark undercurrent of bitterness.

Would they have any choice about their destination or were they again being herded to Scotland or to England and then moved from there to Canada?

Some of them obviously had a say. I don't know in the case of where people were having choices made for them. Once New Iceland was established it was a big group. People had gone ahead and tried to find a place. Some of them deliberately chose to go to Nova Scotia, for example, but the Nova Scotia colony didn't work; it has always had a problem with poverty, and by the time the Icelanders got there, the land that they had planned on taking up had already been taken. There was no way of earning a living, so only a few stayed and some moved on. A group then came to Ontario. Some of them simply disappeared, and their descendants have only recently been rediscovered, in the Muskoka district [by Don Giesleson]. A lot of them went to Kinmount, Ontario, and they had a dreadful year there: I believe every child under the age of four died. In the meantime, of course, they were sending people out, trying to find someplace else to settle. Somebody found Lake Winnipeg — in a dry year — and the land looked very lush with all the marshes full of hay. Of course they didn't realize that what they were seeing was an extraordinary dry year. They didn't realize that this was all swamp. Of course they didn't know what swamp was. They might as well have been coming from Mars. In Iceland, by the time the settlers were leaving, all the trees had been cut down for hundreds of years so there were no forests. They weren't woodsmen. There was no agriculture. People didn't grow grain. They grew hay because that is what would grow in a short growing season. They also fished, and they had sheep, but the only vegetables that they grew were potatoes and maybe turnips, but they weren't gardeners. There was just nothing in Iceland to prepare them for life in the forested lands of Canada. The Ukrainians — whom I have written a tremendous amount about; I went to Russia last year and spent two weeks in the Ukraine — came to land that was like the land they left. When I was travelling through the Ukraine I felt at home because it was like Manitoba with the poplar trees, the land and the crops. Those people brought all the right tools, and they brought seed. They got here and within no time at all they had built log cabins and tilled the land. They were moving from A to A. The Icelanders were moving from A to Z. It was terrible.

Did the Icelanders feel any affinity to that countryside around Gimli? Would that be the reason why they would choose to settle there, or was it just a mistake that they ended up there? They seem to have survived well there in the community.

They were fishermen, and so they felt that they could fish in Lake Winnipeg. What they did not understand was that Lake Winnipeg for a large part of the year was going to be frozen over with three to four feet of ice. The water in Iceland is salt water. The other thing was that, because in a normal year there was high water, all the wonderful hay fields flooded. And of course they were settling an area that was all covered with forest, and here were people who really did not understand how to build with wood. So the colony settled, but at heavy cost. They settled in 1875 and suffered a number of deaths from scurvy and various other things. In 1876 they lost about 10 per cent of the population to smallpox. The colony was riven with conflict over all this, and a large number of them left for the Dakotas and other areas, so that the colony nearly disappeared. It became so weakened that they lost their colony status that had given them the right to their own laws—no one else was allowed to settle there except Icelanders. They lost that right, and the colony then began to build again over a period of time, but in the meantime they had lost the political and legal control they had over their own lives. It no longer was *Nya Island*. It became part of Manitoba.

How did you see that community as a child when you were growing up? Was it a close-knit community to grow up within or was it still very disparate? Did you think of yourself as an Icelander growing up?

No, my mother was Irish, and I was very conscious of the fact that I was a half-breed. Whenever you have a very strong ethnic community, if you are not 100 per cent genetically pure you are very aware: that is the Canadian experience. The whole thing about the integration into becoming Canadian, of course, is very difficult and is most difficult in those who are the first to cross the boundary. Gimli was in many ways a good place to grow up in. It was idyllic in some ways for a small child growing up because the lake was there, and summertimes were beautiful. The winters were long, but you were indoors, and there was very little movement back and forth since nobody had cars—or very few, like the doctor. There was no television, and there was radio, but you very much lived in your own community. I was privileged because we had a real house instead of a shanty, and I had my Irish grandparents in Winnipeg. I was regularly put on the bus and shipped off there, so I grew up in two worlds. Everyone knows me as being Icelandic, but the truth is that 50 per cent of my life was spent being brought up Protestant, Orange, Irish. My grandfather was an Orangeman, a Mason, who marched in the Orange parade every year, and I learned to walk along with King Billy on his white horse. That was a big part of my life, although it hasn't surfaced in my writing.

Did you see that as a conflict at all? Were those two things compatible, being Icelandic and Irish?

No, they weren't compatible at all: it was like being schizophrenic.

The one life had nothing to do with the other. One was Winnipeg and urban, art galleries, museums, and going to Eaton's for lunch and all those things. That separated me out very much from the people I went to school with and lived with in Gimli. In grade eight when I went to the city with a group of kids that won a Red Cross poster contest, it turned out that eight of us went, and six had never been to Winnipeg before.

Did you ever integrate those two strands or do they remain separate?

What has happened is that with the death of my grandparents, my mother's parents, the Irish connection has just been lost. I am obviously very much a Celt in many ways. I mean, I look like a Celt. I do not look like an Icelander, and there are just all kinds of things about me that say I am a Celt.

That is why I am interested in what you did. It seems that you made a choice that you were going to be Icelander rather than Irish. Do you remember that as any kind of conscious choice?

I think it was a kind of negative thing, in the sense that when my grandfather and my great uncle said to me that they wanted me to join the Orange Order when I was eighteen, I knew that was going to hurt them terribly, but I had to go away, and I had to think for days. When I came back I said I did not want to join the Orange Order.

So those were actual choices, not something you just fell into?

Those were real choices. There was a strong sense of pride in being Icelandic, a love of the language and a love of literature: the whole thing of the tradition and the sagas and the Eddas. One of the greatest advantages of growing up in Gimli was that writing was admired. There was very little social distance in Iceland. The wealthy farmer and the poverty-stricken welfare case weren't all that far apart. He who had, had very little, and he who had not, had nothing—it was a very narrow gap. Many of the people who came, or were forced to come, to Canada, brought books with them. People in the Icelandic community have always been very proud that they brought books with them. When I was in Iceland, someone said to me, 'Well, they brought books with them but they never read them. It would never have occurred to them to read them.' He said the books were icons. And that's right: they were icons. They were set up in little shacks — on shelves — and they weren't opened and read and understood in many cases, but it did not matter, because they created an attitude and *that* was what mattered, so that when people like me came along — David Arnason and all those other people who write in the community — those icons made that writing possible. They were the permission and the approval. It was like saying, 'Here are the gods. At the moment we are so busy struggling to survive that all we can do is put the gods up there. But now that we have survived, you, the next generation, can worship there.'

You said it was very difficult — or is very difficult — to integrate into Canadian society. I wondered what you meant by that exactly? Have you become a Canadian?

I have given up all the terrible despair that I felt over not being totally Icelandic and not being totally Irish. It would have been much easier if both parents had been Irish or both parents had been Icelandic. Belonging to two communities forces a kind of growth, and it forces a kind of struggle with something other people do not have to struggle with. That growth is painful, but that is part of the Canadian experience. Then you add on the fact that surrounding all these Icelanders were a group of people whom I loved very much — because there is something in them that just appeals to me — that is, the Ukrainians. Slavs are very different from Icelanders. They are very emotional and outgoing and non-Protestant. They have all their excesses and all their faults just like anybody else, but there is something about them that I love, and that has been part of my Canadian experience. In the same way, when I went to Winnipeg, I became very aware of the Jewish community in Winnipeg and discovered in it many things to admire. It is because of that community that Winnipeg is the cultural centre that it is: the symphony, art gallery, and everything. The Jewish community had poured itself into culture in Winnipeg and into creating opportunities. That is all part of me as a Canadian. Somehow, if my writing is going to be true and is going to be honest, it has to reflect the fact that all those people have contributed to who I am at the age of forty-nine.

Where did the story 'The Man from Snaefellsness' come from?

It came from the head of the Icelandic club in Vancouver saying to me at a banquet for the President of Iceland: 'Some day, write about the fact that people were shipped to Canada and all their lives felt that they weren't wanted.'

Is there something in particular that you would want readers to see in this story?

I would hope that they would see a need for a letting go of the past and the need for forgiveness, especially the healing power of forgiveness. The brunt of the problem with Protestants is that we do not have confession. And so we carry all this baggage around with us. I think that probably the story might be best understood by young people who are close to the immigration experience. It is not a foreign story that happened to someone else. I have students in my workshops now who are one generation out of the immigration experience, and there are things that I say that they automatically understand that other students who have been here for many generations do not understand. And the trick, of course, is that the author is always trying to write a story so well that, although there is not a shared commonality of experience, the reader is still able to emotionally and intellectually understand. At least to some degree. And there is the whole thing about ethnicity with the girlfriend in Canada who loves ethnics. It is like a fetish. Every boyfriend she has she collects. This one was Latvian, this one was Russian, this was German, and she was all for it. In her character I am criticizing that whole concept of ethnicity which I have seen so clearly in the Icelandic and Ukrainian communities where they really are not the slightest bit interested in the Ukraine or in Iceland. They are only interested in the folk memories of the time of immigration. One year, for the Icelandic celebration, they advertised that a musical group from Iceland was coming and all these people came. They were all set to hear songs from the 1880s, but it was an Icelandic rock group. If you wanted to see culture shock!

HIMANI BANNERJI b. 1942

The Other Family

When the little girl came home it was already getting dark. The winter twilight had transformed the sheer blue sky of the day into the colour of steel, on which were etched a few stars, the bare winter trees and the dark wedges of the house tops. A few lit windows cast a faint glow on the snow outside. The mother stood at her window and watched the little hooded figure walking toward the house. The child looked like a shadow, her blue coat blended into the shadows of the evening. This child, her own, how small and insubstantial she seemed, and how alone, walking home through a pavement covered with ice and snow! It felt unreal. So different was this childhood from her own, so far away from the sun, the trees and the peopled streets of her own country! What did I do, she thought, I took her away from her own people and her own language, and now here she comes walking alone, through an alien street in a country named Canada.

As she contemplated the solitary, moving figure, her own solitude rushed over her like a tide. She had drifted away from a world that she had lived in and understood, and now she stood here at the same distance from her home as from the homes which she glimpsed while walking past the sparkling clean windows of the sandblasted houses. And now the door bell rang, and here was her daughter scraping the snow off her boots on the door mat.

Dinner time was a good time. A time of warmth, of putting hot, steaming food onto the table. A time to chat about the important things of the day, a time to show each other what they had acquired. Sometimes, however, her mother would be absent-minded, worried perhaps about work, unsettled perhaps by letters that had arrived from home, scraping her feelings into a state of rawness. This was such an evening. She had served herself and her child, started a conversation about their two cats and fallen into a silence after a few minutes.

'You aren't listening to me, Mother.'

The complaining voice got through to her, and she looked at the indignant face demanding attention from the other side of the table. She gathered herself together.

'So what did he do, when you gave him dried food?'

'Oh, I don't quite remember, I think he scratched the ground near his bowl and left.'

The child laughed.

'That was smart of him! So why don't we buy tinned food for them?'

'Maybe we should,' she said, and tried to change the topic.

'So what did you do in your school today?'

'Oh, we drew pictures like we do every day. We never study anything—not like you said you did in your school. We drew a family—our family. Want to see it?'

'Sure, and let's go to the living room, OK? This is messy.' Scraping of chairs and the lighting of the lamps in the other room. They both made a rush for the most comfortable chair, both reached it at the same time and made a compromise.

'How about you sit in my lap? No? OK, sit next to me then and we will squeeze in somehow.'

There was a remarkable resemblance between the two faces, except that the face of the child had a greater intensity, given by the wide open eyes. She was fine boned, and had black hair framing her face. Right now she was struggling with the contents of her satchel, apparently trying to feel her way to the paintings.

'Here it is,' she said, producing a piece of paper. 'Here's the family!'

The mother looked at the picture for a long time. She was very still. Her face had set into an expression of anger and sadness. She was trying very hard not to cry. She didn't want to frighten the child, and yet what she saw made her feel distant from her daughter, as though she was looking at her through the reverse end of a telescope. She couldn't speak at all. The little girl too sat very still, a little recoiled from the body of her mother, as though expecting a blow. Her hands were clenched into fists, but finally it was she who broke the silence.

'What happened?' she said. 'Don't you like it?'

'Listen,' said the mother, 'this is not your family. I, you and your father are dark-skinned, dark-haired. I don't have a blond wig hidden in my closet, my eyes are black, not blue, and your father's beard is black, not red, and you, do you have a white skin, a button nose with freckles, blue eyes and blond hair tied into a pony tail? You said you drew our family. This is not it, is it?'

The child was now feeling distinctly cornered. At first she was startled and frightened by her mother's response, but now she was prepared to be defiant. She had the greatest authority behind her, and she now summoned it to her help.

'I drew it from a book,' she said, 'all our books have this same picture of the family. You can go and see it for yourself. And everyone else drew it too. You can ask our teacher tomorrow. She liked it, so there!'

The little girl was clutching at her last straw.

'But you? Where are you in this picture?' demanded her mother, by now thoroughly aroused. 'Where are we? Is this the family you would like to have? Don't you want us anymore? You want to be a *mem-sahib*, a white girl?'

But even as she lashed out these questions the mother regretted them. She could see that she made no sense to the child. She could feel the unfairness of it all. She was sorry that she was putting such a heavy burden on such young shoulders.

'First I bring her here,' she thought, 'and then I try to make her feel guilty for wanting to be the same as the others.' But something had taken hold of her this evening. Panic at the thought of losing her child, despair and guilt galvanized her into speech she regretted, and she looked with anger at her only child, who it seemed wanted to be white, who had rejected her dark mother. Someday this child would be ashamed of her, she thought, someday would move out into the world of those others. Someday they would be enemies. Confusing thoughts ran through her head like images on an uncontrollable television screen, in the chaos of which she heard her ultimate justification flung at her by her daughter—they wanted me to draw the family, didn't they? 'They' wanted 'her' to draw 'the family'. The way her daughter pronounced the words 'they' or 'the family' indicated that she knew what she was talking about. The simple pronoun 'they' definitely stood for authority, for that uncontrollable yet organized world immediately outside, of which the school was the ultimate expression. It surrounded their own private space. 'They' had power, 'they' could crush little people like her anytime 'they' wanted to, and in 'their' world that was the picture of the family. Whether her mother liked it or not, whether she looked like the little girl in it or not, made not one jot of difference. That was, yes, that was the right picture. As these thoughts passed through her mind, her anger ebbed away. Abandoning her fury and distance, the mother bowed her head at the image of this family and burst into sobs.

'What will happen to you?' she said. 'What did I do to you?'

She cried a great deal and said many incoherent things. The little girl was patient, quietly absorbing her mother's change of mood. She had a thoughtful look on her face, and bit her nails from time to time. She did not protest any more, but nor did she cry. After a while her mother took her to bed and tucked her in, and sat in the kitchen with the fearful vision of her daughter always outside of the window of the blond family, never the centre of her own life, always rejecting herself, and her life transformed into a gigantic peep show. She wept very bitterly because she had caused this destruction, and because she had hated her child in her own fear of rejection, and because she had sowed guilt into her mind.

When her mother went to bed and closed the door, the child, who had been waiting for long, left the bed. She crossed the corridor on her tiptoes, past the row of shoes, the silent gathering of the overcoats and the mirror with the wavy surface, and went into the washroom. Behind the door was another mirror, of full length, and clear. Deliberately and slowly the child took off the top of her pyjamas and surveyed herself with grave scrutiny. She saw the brownness of her skin, the wide, staring, dark eyes, the black hair now tousled from the pillows, the scar on her nose and the brownish pink of her mouth. She stood a while lost in this act of contemplation, until the sound of soft padded feet neared the door, and a whiskered face peeped in. She stooped and picked up the cat and walked back to her own room.

It was snowing again, and little elves with bright coloured coats and snow in their boots had reappeared in the classroom. When finally the coats were hung under pegs with names and boots neatly stowed away, the little girl approached her teacher. She had her painting from the day before in her hand.

'I have brought it back,' she said.

'Why?' asked her teacher, 'don't you like it any more?'

The little girl was looking around very intently.

'It's not finished yet,' she said. 'The books I looked at didn't have something. Can I finish it now?'

'Go ahead,' said the teacher, moving on to get the colours from the cupboard.

The little girl was looking at the classroom. It was full of children of all colours, of all kinds of shapes of noses and of different colours of hair. She sat on the floor, placed the incomplete picture on a big piece of newspaper and started to paint. She worked long at it — and with great concentration. Finally it was finished. She went back to her teacher.

'It's finished now,' she said, 'I drew the rest.'

The teacher reached out for the picture and spread it neatly on a desk. There they were, the blond family arranged in a semicircle with a dip in the middle, but next to them, arranged alike, stood another group — a man, a woman, and a child, but they were dark-skinned, dark-haired, the woman wore clothes from her own country, and the little girl in the middle had a scar on her nose.

'Do you like it?'

'Who are they?' asked the teacher, though she should have known. But the little girl didn't mind answering this question one bit.

'It's the other family,' she said.

HIMANI BANNERJI was born in 1942 in Bangladesh, which was part of pre-partition India at the time. She was educated in Visva Bharati University, Shantiniketan, the renowned experimental university set up by Rabindranath Tagore. After receiving her Master's degree in English, with top honours, from Jadavpur University in West Bengal, India, in 1965, she joined the English department of that university and taught there until 1969, the year she came to Canada to do graduate work at the University of Toronto. She teaches sociology at York University, and is the mother of a daughter, Kaushalya. Her work — short stories, poetry, critical articles — has been published in *Toronto South Asian Review*, *Fuse Magazine*, *Fireweed: A Feminist Journal*, *Asianadian*, and *Tiger Lily*. She has published two books of poetry: *A Separate Sky* (Toronto: Domestic Bliss, 1982), and *Doing Time* (Toronto: Sister Vision, 1986). Her children's novel *Coloured Pictures* is forthcoming from Sister Vision.

ARUN PRABHA MUKHERJEE was born in 1946 in Lahore, India. After the partition, her parents fled to India and she was raised and educated in Tikamgarh, Madhya Pradesh. She did her graduate work in English at the University of Saugar, India and came to Canada as a Commonwealth Scholar in 1971 to do graduate work at the University of Toronto. She has taught at several universities in Canada. The mother of a twelve-year-old son, Gautam, she is presently a Canada Research Fellow at York University. She is the author of *The Gospel of Wealth in the American Novel: The Rhetoric of Dreiser and His Contemporaries* (1987), and *Towards an Aesthetic of Opposition: Essays on Literature, Criticism and Cultural Imperialism* (1988).

As both of us belong to this group called the 'visible minorities', we have had to think very hard about what it means to be ethnic and what ethnicity has to do with being a 'visible minority'.

It means that we are not considered to be Canadians. We are 'immigrant women'. This is a prominent category. They don't even talk about us as Canadians.

You are saying that the dominant culture obliterates and marginalizes our experience, whereas the official discourse says that multiculturalism means this mosaic which cherishes difference and plurality. Could that become a reality?

No. I see it as a way to contain and marginalize us. The very fact that this interview is a designated activity, one day picked out of the everyday life of people like us who are daily perceived with so much disrespect, suggests to me that it is a way of 'managing' and subsuming us. Suddenly one day or ten days a year, our life becomes relevant and valid, but only within an agenda which is put in place by the state. They decide where and how we may become ethnic. It is a way of containing that part of our subjectivity that is not assimilated. People's memories of the places they have come from persist with them. So this spill of memory has to be contained, and the dominant group contains this spill through various means so it does not take over politics and become anti-racist but remains at the level of song and dance. Multiculturalism to me is a way of managing seepage of persistent subjectivity of people that come from other parts of the world, people that are seen as undesirable because they have once been colonized, now neo-colonized. So we are not talking about Germans or Finns and Swedes or the French, for that matter. We are talking about the undesirables. It is southern Europeans, sometimes, and Third World people who have to be ethnic. Now the fact that our children may not even feel like becoming ethnic is another problem for them. They may not want multiculturalism, one day set aside to eat yams and get dressed up.

Are you saying that our children will want to be completely assimilated, at the cost of forgetting their heritage?

Now, if you ask, can we reproduce Indian culture here, I don't think it is possible, I don't think you can transplant. I don't think the issue is culture; the issue is politics. Neither Tinni nor Guatam can be raised in Toronto as though we were in Delhi or Calcutta, and if we wanted to do that we would go crazy and the children would go crazy. We both know many such cases. But there is something possible. There is a political truth that is possible, affirmation that is possible. We can point out to the children the meaning of our life in Canada—that it is not that India is better, but that it is different and no worse than Canada. The child has to feel, and we have to feel, that politically there is an imperialistic relationship, whether it is India or China or the Caribbean, and that this is what is in question. The question is the degradation of a large part of the world on which brutality was done, and that if we are here, we came here as a result of our colonization and that all of us altogether are going through a hard time. So, I think, in some ways we can give our children a separate culture to make them present in the here and now in Canada. They don't have to shut themselves off from everything around here, saying it isn't us. It *is* us: we are here. We are different from what we were. And how I think we can make sense of this whole situation and leave something for our children, a legacy, is not simply through a museum piece of cultural life—the parading around in costume, the song and dance stuff—but through communicating to them the meaning of being Indian in Canada—beyond ethnicity and cultural talk. It is in some way like the meaning of being Jamaican, the meaning of being Vietnamese, the meaning of being Chinese.

Are you suggesting that we build a culture of resistance vis-à-vis the dominant culture?

Yes, but not so self-conscious either. It is an expressive act that I am talking about. See, you and I have changed after being here twenty years. When we have a festival at home, it is a mixture. But it is not a hybrid, it is something substantive. So we have a peculiar formation that we have evolved which is a synthetic formation. It is not an imitation. We have changed because our consciousness cannot remain fossilized from the India of 1969. For example, the food we cook. It is Indian but there is also the birthday cake and pasta.

I am thinking of your poem 'A Letter from Home', where the poetic persona talks about bringing her umbilical cord in a jar and burying it in the ground in Canada. Now, that to me is 'synthetic', a joining of the disparate elements of our existence. But there is this conflicting demand that we be one or the other. Multiculturalism demands that we bring out our costumes for Caravan, and, at other times, the demand is that we behave like the dominant culture and eat steak and potatoes. It is assumed that we all lead identical lives. It is never articulated but there is this demand that we be assimilated.

As to assimilation versus synthesis, I think that our options are not fossilization and a reification of cultural forms that we brought twenty years ago. We must not carry on as though India is not changing. Things are going on, and people are not sitting there worrying about the need to preserve culture because the culture is living. It is a dynamic form. The reason why we do this here is because we feel such an impact negatively that we tend to solidify and ossify. I see ossification as a form of neo-conservatism.

Would you say that the multicultural notion of culture is 'ossificatory'?

Yes. On the one hand, you have the multicultural ossificatory impera-tive. On the other, you have the state and the dominant media with their assimilative imperative. Eat steak and potatoes. Be like us. If you are not like us then you are a nobody. And even if you are like us, you are really not us, so you are an imitation of us. I see the options of ossification versus assimilation as two poles. Neither of them, I think answers our needs. I think we really have to get out of the bounds of that frame and begin to talk in terms of expression. We have the right to express ourselves, substantively, and within this environment called Canada. I think it is very important that we don't allow this 'other-ization' of ourselves. The frame itself is wrong because it still makes you stay within that dominant definition of the negation of the point that somebody is trying to make about you. I am not interested in negating, I am interested in being substantive. I am not even going to conceive of what I am not; I'm going to think in terms of what I am.

How do we make sure that this gets articulated? That we don't feel oppressed by the dominant culture?

We will always feel oppressed because it is their intention to oppress us. I think that the thing to do is to develop our own, what I have called, 'substantive', 'synthetic', culture. You know how in the women's movement they stopped talking about men altogether. At least there is a whole genre of literature in the women's movement that no longer talks about men. It talks simply about women's culture, women's needs, and so on. Yes, patriarchy is a point of reference for them. Racism is a point of reference for us. I am not denying the fact that our lives are encrusted and surrounded by racism. But I still think that it is possible for us to stop talking about white people entirely. The dominant narrative is my life or your life or your child's life, and I will talk about white people only as they enter this dominant narrative. If I write a novel, I am not going to write it to prove to white people that I am not what they think I am. I don't want to prove anything to them. I want to write about how you and I live here and only insofar as white people impinge on our lives, will they become part of my narrative. There are areas of our lives, areas where we shop and read and live and love poetry or clothes, where we live like every human being lives, in the world, in some sensuality—and not just sexuality—and the white people will not enter that part of my narrative.

In your story, 'The Other Family', you show the terrible cost of assimilation, of wiping out one's racial identity when the non-white child draws a picture of her parents as blond-haired and blue-eyed for her teacher.

That's why I don't want white people to dominate my narrative. To me, writing is not simply your own expression but also an affirmation of yourself and people like you. To write without a community is something I could never do. I really don't think people from our situation could even ontologically and psychologically understand the universalist position: when someone says art is transcendent, universal, etc., they presuppose that some people—that is, the bourgeois white people—don't have to leave their life history and world behind to enjoy that art; it is rooted socially in their world. We, however, can only enjoy it if we transcend the actual conditions of living that separate us from the bourgeois world. So in order to 'enjoy' art, the universal bit, you have to have an education in dominant ideology.

Now, the dominant ideology of literary criticism would consider your poetry to be 'political propaganda'. How do you respond?

If you are writing for your community, and by that I don't mean India, but people who are not white, people who, for instance, have suffered from racism and fascism, you would say things and present experiences that would not be universally acceptable in this society. It is people who don't have much pressure bearing on them every day, people who are professionals and who belong to the dominant section of the population one way or another, it is they who can afford to make a distinction between the personal and the political. You have to come from above to have the luxury, the privilege of making a separation and being able to shut the door where your personal life is unpenetrated by all that happens on the street. But the street doesn't end for us at the door. It comes right through the door into your brain and your bedroom and goes back out again. So it is not we who can make the distinction. It is not that when I write I say to myself, well I will write political poetry. Something happens to me and then something responds in me. What happens to us every day is living within power. We experience it every day, everywhere. And so we don't ever know the split.

You have said elsewhere that we live in 'a culture of deafness'. You can talk and talk and those in power refuse to hear you. Now, you have published and written extensively. Do you think that your work has been acknowledged in terms of getting reviews and being taught on literature or women's studies courses and so on?

No, I don't think so. I don't think that there has been any recognition except in token slot-filling, by three poems here and two poems there. And what happens is that they want something 'black'. I, Dionne Brand, Lillian Allen, we all write very different poetry, though our concerns overlap because our lives overlap. But we are looked at as a sample.

An ethnic sample?

Yes. So, if one of Lillian's poems is there, that will do. It is enough to have a 'black' sample, and I fall, as you do, somewhere between the cracks because we are not quite black, though politically the metaphor applies because whatever is not white is black. On the other hand, there is no category called 'brown poetry'. I don't think they really see our poetry as poetry.

I think they are applying some hidden criteria which writers like you don't meet. For example, I was reading the manuscript of your children's novel, Coloured Pictures. *Now, I also read the letter of rejection from a mainstream publisher where they tell you that you are using too much discussion and that it will bore the children. But how did they decide that the children will be bored? When I read the novel, it came across as a very forceful work because it addressed for me, for the first time, the reality of racism in my child's life. Now, my child discusses racism all the time, because he must learn to face it as a fact of life. And so I don't think my child would have been bored by your novel. In fact, he would have been deeply absorbed by it because all the other stuff that he reads is about white children and their summer camps and their private schools and their mystery adventures. This book had children with names like his, who ate similar foods, and called their parents 'Amma' and 'Baba' and faced similar problems on the street. And yet, this very powerful novel has been sitting around in manuscript for the last ten years because they don't like 'discussion'! Now I call that being silenced.*

Yes, and I was demoralized by the realization that there was not a place for us to put things forward. I did not feel encouraged at all, coming up against the same old complaint that it was not literature but propaganda. I asked Tinni and other children to read the manuscript, and they were quite able to handle the conflicts in the novel. I think children are quite different from what this publisher thinks they are.

I think, Himani, our children's lives are painful in some ways.

Yes. Things happen in backyards; comments, racist jokes are made against them. It is not as though children live in some kind of paradise. Schoolyards and classrooms are really savage places. There is this notion about childhood being an age of innocence, that children should not be told about the realities of life, but our children are already living them. When you are a black kid and you are three years old and you go out for a walk with your father and you see your father becoming edgy and frightened in front of a policeman, do they think that the child does not know?

You have said that books give a version of reality. Does that mean that you don't believe in 'art for art's sake'?

I don't understand 'art' you know. I mean art for its own sake. The only thing I am concerned with is seeing how the form and content are expressive or mutually elaborative or mediative of each other, and that, to me, is true of the smallest as of the greatest writer. If they feel that I am using a bourgeois form to express a socialist content, I think that the critics should point it out and help me develop. But the problem I have is that literary criticism, as we know it, does not do that.

That kind of aesthetic approach, I think, would go beyond just talking about your imagery and formal complexity and so on, and also look at your constant subverting of the dominant ideology. It seems to me that you wrote the story 'The Other Family' to generate a discussion of what is happening at school. How are the teachers teaching our children? How our children are unobtrusively being assimilated into this so-called Canadian culture. Would you say that this story in particular and your work in general have generated such a debate?

No. It does not happen because there is this papering over. But it does not really make much difference, because frankly the last thing that I want to say is that I don't write for white middle-class readers. I write for you and me.

MATT COHEN b. 1942

Racial Memories

The beard of my grandfather was trimmed in the shape of a spade. Black at first, later laced liberally with white, it was also a flag announcing to the world that here walked an orthodox Jew. Further uses: an instrument of torture and delight when pressed against the soft ticklish skin of young children, a never empty display window for the entire range of my grandmother's uncompromising cuisine. To complement his beard my grandfather—indoors and out—kept his head covered. His indoor hats were *yarmulkahs* that floated on his bare and powerful skull; the hats he wore outside had brims which kept the sun away and left the skin of his face a soft and strangely attractive waxy white. White, too, were his square-fingered hands, the moons of his nails, his squarish slightly-gapped teeth, the carefully washed and ironed shirts my grandmother supplied for his thrice-daily trips to the synagogue. A typical sartorial moment: on the day before his seventieth birthday I found him outside on a kitchen stepladder wearing slippers but no socks, his suit-pants held up by suspenders, his white shirt complete with what we used to call bicep-pinchers, his outdoors hat—decked out in style, in other words, even though he was sweating rivers while he trimmed the branches of his backyard cherry trees.

Soon after I met him, I began remembering my grandfather. Especially when I lay in bed, the darkness of my room broken by the thin yellow strip of light that filtered through the bottom of my door. Staring at the unwavering strip I would try to make it dance. 'Be lightning,' I would say. 'Strike me dead; prove that God exists.' And then I would cower under my sheets, waiting for the inevitable. That was when I would remember my grandfather. Standing alone with him in the big synagogue in Winnipeg, the same synagogue where he must have sought God's guidance in dealing with Joseph Lucky, looking up at the vaulted ceilings, holding his hand as he led me up the carpeted aisle to the curtained ark where the Torah was kept.

And then he showed me the words themselves. God's words.

Indecipherable squiggles inked onto dried skin not so different from the tough dry calluses on my grandfather's palms. Also full of words was the high bulging forehead of my grandfather. Everything he said to me in English, which he spoke in a gently accented cadence I had difficulty understanding, he would repeat in Hebrew, which I couldn't understand at all. Cave-man talk, I would think, listening to the guttural sounds. He showed me, too, the separate section where the women sat. I was amazed at this concept of the women being put to one side, just as later I was to be amazed to discover that when women had 'the curse' they spent their nights in their own dark beds, left alone to bleed out their shame.

My great-great Uncle Joseph, the one after whom I was named, served in the cavalry of the Russian czar. This is true, and I still have a photograph of a bearded man in full uniform sitting on a horse in the midst of a snowy woods. After two years, during which he was promoted once and demoted twice, my ancestor deserted and made his way across Europe to a boat which took him to Montreal. From there he caught a train on which, the story goes, he endeared himself to a wealthy Jewish woman who owned a large ranch in Alberta. We could pause briefly to imagine the scene: minor-key *War and Peace* played out against a background of railway red velvet, cigar smoke, and a trunk filled with souvenirs. Unfortunately the lady was married, so my uncle ended up not in the castle but out on the range, riding wild mustangs. (Also, it has been claimed, singing Yiddish folk songs to the animals as they bedded down beneath their starry blankets.)

And then my Uncle Joseph struck it rich. Sitting around the camp-fire one night, he reinvented the still with the help of an old horse trough and a few length of hose. All this is according to my father; he was the historian-in-exile, but that is another story. The rest of the family claims he was only trying to make barley soup. Maybe that explains how my uncle became known as Joseph Lucky.

Having made his fortune and his name, Joseph Lucky began sending money to the relatives. We've all heard about those Russian Jews: semi-Cro-Magnon types covered in beards, furs, dense body hair, living without flush toilets or electricity in a post-feudal swamp of bone-breaking peasants, child-snatching witches and wicked land-owners. Having helped his blood relations through the evolutionary gate of the twentieth century—to say nothing of destroying the racial purity of his adopted homeland—my uncle asked only one thing in return: that the newcomers settle in Winnipeg, well away from his field of operations. When they got established, he came to pay a visit. By this time the wealthy Jewess had died and, because of a jealous husband, my uncle Joseph had moved on from his life on the range to 'business interests'. Another photograph I possess: Joseph Lucky standing on the Winnipeg train platform, winter again, wearing matching fur coat and hat and framed by two enormous suitcases which my father tells me were made from 'soft brown leather you could eat'.

This was before the First World War, before my father was born. Also before the War was my uncle's demise. What had happened was that for causes unknown he was put in jail. After a few months he wrote to his nephew, my grandfather. The letter was written in Yiddish, using Hebrew characters — the same formula which my grandmother employed to torture my mother decades later. I've seen the letter; my grandfather showed it to me when I was a child. He opened the envelope and out blew the smell which made a permanent cloud in my grandparents' house, a permanent storm-cloud to be exact, always threatening to rain down the pale greenish soup that my grandmother claimed was all her frail stomach could support.

My grandfather was a strong man. Once, when a neighbour's shed was burning down, he carried out two smoke-damaged pigs. The image of my grandfather, wearing his inevitable satin waistcoat and box *yarmulkah*, walking down the street with a sow over each shoulder, has never seemed improbable to me. I can imagine him, too, poring over the letter from his benefactor. Caught between his duty to help a relative, his distaste for my uncle's way of life and his own poverty. According to my father, my grandfather never answered the letter. Instead, after waiting two weeks he gathered what cash he could and took a train for Edmonton. When he arrived he discovered Joseph Lucky had died of food poisoning and that his body had been claimed by someone whose name had not been recorded. My grandfather always feared that his delay had killed Joseph Lucky. That is why my father felt obliged to give me his name. Also because, he always insisted, Joseph Lucky had likely died not of food poisoning at all, but had been bribed away from the jail (body claimed by an 'unrecorded stranger'! — who could believe that?) by a rich client and spent the rest of his days happily riding some faraway range.

'If you could credit a Jewish cowboy . . . ,' my mother would protest and shake her head. But that was where Joseph Lucky was lucky, I didn't have to be told. Somehow he had escaped being Jewish, wiggled out from under his fate and galloped off into that carefree other world where you were not under a life sentence or, to be more exact, perhaps you were under a life sentence of mortality (even an assimilated Jew finds it hard to believe in Heaven) but you had been promoted to a different part of the sentence: instead of being the object, you were the subject.

'Did you hear the one about the rabbi's wife?'

'No,' I say. We are lying in the centre of the school football field, six of us in a circle, face to face with our bodies extended like the spokes of a wagon-wheel. It is late September, a cool heart-breaking twilight. At the word 'rabbi' my stomach has suddenly tensed up and my hipbones start to press against the hard ground.

'This sausage salesman comes to the door . . . Are you sure you haven't heard it?' The five of us are the offensive backfield of our high-school football team: the wheel of which I am the only Jewish spoke.

'I'm sure,' I say. I look up over at the boy who is talking. The fullback. A power runner known as Willy 'Wild Bill' Higgins. He's the one we need when it's late afternoon, November, and gusts of cold rain are sweeping down the river valley and turning us into sodden little boys who want to go home. That's when Wild Bill — it's me who gave him the name — drives forward with his cleats spitting out gobs of mud, knees pumping up into the face of anyone crazy enough to tackle him.

'All right,' he says, 'forget it. Don't get your cock in a knot.'

All evening, over my homework, I'm left wondering. Something to do with circumcision no doubt. Animal sex? Two weeks ago a girl I asked to a dance told me her father wouldn't let her go out with a Jew. I'm at my sixth school in ten years but I still can't get used to breaking the ice. Can't get used to the fact that it never breaks.

At eleven o'clock the phone rings. It's another spoke of the wheel — a small spoke, like me. 'Don't let dickface get you down,' he says. The first thing I think is how glad I am that this is happening over the telephone, so my friend can't see my eyes swelling up with unwanted tears.

Idiot, I say to myself. *Thin-skinned Jew.* 'Doesn't matter,' I say aloud. 'Except that maybe I missed a good joke.'

Peter Riley laughs. He's a skinny Irish kid whose father has lung cancer. Sometimes, after school, I go home with him and we sit in

the living room with his father, feeding him tea and watching him die. 'She says she only eats kosher,' Peter Riley says.
I start a fake laugh, then stop.
'Not funny?'
'Not funny to me.'
'Join the club,' Peter Riley says.
'What club?'
'You name it.'
'The Wild Bill Fan Club,' I say, a little chunk of the past — another school, another group of boys — jumping unbidden out of my mouth.

Leonard lived above the garage attached to the house my grandfather bought after he moved to Toronto to be nearer the brothers, sisters, aunts, uncles, cousins, etc. The spider's web of relatives in Toronto didn't include my own parents: they had already learned their lesson and were hiding out in Ottawa, on their way to greener fields. As a gesture of family solidarity, however, they had sent me to the University of Toronto. There I was not only to carry my parents' proud banner in the world of higher learning, but to act as unofficial delegate and/or sacrifice. Leonard, not a relative but a paying boarder, was also at the university; ten years older than I, he had the exalted status of a graduate student in religious philosophy. 'He doesn't eat kosher,' my grandmother confided to me in the kitchen, 'you can tell by his smell, but he goes to *shul* every morning and he doesn't make noise.'
In a room with my grandparents, Leonard was so well-behaved and courteous that he hardly seemed to exist. Once out of sight, however, he became the main subject of my grandmother's conversation. 'Did you see how he wiped his mouth?' she always began, as though she had spent the whole time doing nothing but watching Leonard compulsively snatch at the napkin. And then Laura, a cousin slightly older than I who had sealed her reputation by going to a drive-in at age fourteen with a married man (self-made, rich from vending-machine concessions), would point out that once again the insides of Leonard's nostrils were flaming red because — she had seen him at it through his window — every night he spent an hour yanking out his nasal hairs in order to combat his other urges.
'Wanna see my place?' Leonard invited, while we were drinking tea after a sabbath lunch.
I followed him out the back door, along a path worn through the grass, and we arrived at the metal stairway leading up the outside of

the garage to Leonard's room. Immediately I found myself thinking this arrangement was ideal because it allowed Leonard to come and go as he pleased, even bringing company with him if he wanted. Or could. An unlikely possibility I thought, following the shiny seat of Leonard's grey-and-black checked trousers up the final steps.

The first thing I noticed was the mirror where Leonard was reported to carry on with his nose. It hung above a dresser from which the drawers jutted out, each one overflowing. The cartoon chaos of the room continued. Piled over every available surface were dirty clothes, newspapers and magazines, empty pop bottles, wrappings from candy-store food. Even the desk of the graduate philosopher was a tower of babble — unsteady stacks of library books interspersed with sheaves of folded paper. Ostentatiously draped over the back of the chair was a strangely mottled towel. Stepping closer I saw that the towel was, in fact, heavily stained with blood.

'War wounds,' Leonard said.

At lunch I had already noticed Leonard's soft white fingers, his unmuscled arms blotched with freckles and covered with a sparse layer of white-orange fur.

'They're crazy for it then. Ever notice?'

I shook my head.

'Read Freud. The power of taboo. Close your eyes. Imagine it. You're in the dark with the woman of your dreams. The smell of sweat and blood. Smells so strong you can taste it. Get up from the bed and your dick is dripping with it.'

My eyes weren't closed. I was looking at Leonard. His eyes were boring straight into my face. 'You some kind of a pervert?'

Leonard looked puzzled. Encouraged, I continued with a further inspiration: 'If you didn't pick your nose, it wouldn't bleed.'

Leonard shook his head. 'You're going to study philosophy, kid, you need to have an open mind. I told you the truth.'

'Don't make me laugh. No woman in her right mind would come into this rat's nest for more than five minutes.'

At which point Laura opened the door, came and stood by Leonard's chair, practically sticking her chest in his face while he patted her bum. 'Isn't this great? Look, we're going to drive you downtown and then we'll pick you up later for dinner. Isn't this place unbelievable?'

Laura and Leonard are halfway up the greys, exactly at centre ice.

From where I line up on defence I can see the steam billowing from their styrofoam cups of coffee. They grin at me. 'Go get 'em,' Leonard shouts and his voice echoes in the empty arena. This is intra-mural hockey, a house-league game taking place close to midnight. The only other spectators are a few couples who have discovered that the shadowed corners of the varsity rink are good for more than watching hockey.

My legs are tired. There are lines of pain where the blades of the skates, which don't quite fit me, press into the bones of my feet. One of my shoulders has already begun to ache as the result of a collision against the boards. Peter Riley looks back at me. He is our centre. A quick skater with dozens of moves and a hard wrist-shot, he is the only one who really knows how to play. The rest of us make up a supporting cast, trying to feed him the puck and to protect our goalie, a non-skating conscript whose main virtue is that he has the courage to buckle on his armour, slide across the ice in his galoshes and risk his life.

Most games we just give the puck to Peter and he scores with tricky unstoppable shots. Now we're in the finals and they've got the strategy to beat us. Two, sometimes, three, players shadow Peter, sandwiching him every time he tries to dart forward. The rest of us are often left in the open but compared to these other bigger, stronger players, we are ineffectual midgets. Somehow, however, our goalie has risen to the occasion. With a couple of minutes to go in the game we are only one goal behind.

The referee looks back at us. I bend over my stick. My rear end is sore from numerous forced landings. Riley winks at me and then nods his head for good measure. I know what this signal—our only signal—is supposed to mean: when the puck is dropped he will gain control—then I am to skate by at full speed so that he can feed it to me and send me in.

As the puck bounces on the ice I'm already driving forward, and by the time I've crossed centre ice the puck—via Riley—has arrived at my stick. I'm alone, the crowd of two is screaming. I'm going as fast as I can but I can hear the ice being chewed up behind me, long powerful strides gaining on my short choppy ones. The hollow ominous sound of steel carving ice, Laura's amazingly loud voice— I lift my stick back preparing to blast the puck before I'm overtaken— and then something has hooked my ankles and I'm sliding belly-down.

1 MATT COHEN

No whistle so I'm up again. Peter has somehow recovered the puck from the corner and is waiting for me to get in front of the net. This time I'm going to shoot on contact, no waiting: again my stick goes back. Then I'm swinging it forward, towards the puck, already feeling the sweet perfect impact of the hard rubber on the centre of my blade, already seeing the net billow with the tying goal. Suddenly the curtain comes down. A blast to my forehead so intense that I lose consciousness falling to the ice. Get up, dazed, glove held to my head. Start skating again, vision foggy, towards the puck, until I see that everyone else has stopped, and my glove and hockey stick are covered with red, that the clouding of my vision isn't dizziness but a veil of blood over my eye. Leonard and Laura are rushing towards me.

There are words, too. 'Jew. Eat it, Jew,' I thought I heard someone say. The words are rattling in my head like pebbles in a gourd but I'm too confused to know who put them there. Laura's got a handkerchief out of her purse, it's soaked in perfume, soft white cloth with a pink stitched border. The pebbles are still rattling in my skull and I can't stand them, have to do something about them, twist away from Laura and skate towards the big boy with blood on his hockey stick.

But Peter Riley is already there. When the boy hears me coming, turns towards me, Riley twists—twists and straightens his legs as he sends an uppercut deep into the unpadded belly. Mine enemy collapses to the ice retching. His team prepares to rush ours. By now I have felt my cut with my bare finger: a small gash above the left eyebrow that opens and closes every time I move the muscles in my face.

Before anything can happen there is a sharp blast of the whistle. The referee, who is also the Dean of Men and who hands out suspensions for fighting—from the university, not just from hockey—is holding the puck and standing bent over the spot where he wants play to begin again.

'Sir,' Riley says, 'one of our players is bleeding.'

'Have his friends take him to the hospital.'

As I'm clumping along the wooden gangway, Laura's scented hanky pressed to my wound, Leonard is calling my dean a 'Jew-baiting bastard, an anti-Semitic son-of-a-bitch who would have spent his afternoons cracking open teeth to get at their gold fillings'.

By three o'clock in the morning, when I am sharing a mickey of rye with Peter Riley, my wound has been reduced to a small throbbing slice covered by a neat white patch. And Riley is telling me that the dean shook his hand as he left the dressing room. As I fall asleep, the words are still with me. I am lying in the dark. The first time I heard such words, such words said by other than my own, I was ten years old. I was in a new school that year, but friends had come quickly and life seemed suddenly to have grown wide and easy. Then one day, late in the fall, my friends turned on me. There were three of them. 'Jew,' one of them said. 'Jew,' said the other two. We had been standing in a vacant lot on the way home from school. Talking about nothing. One of them pushed me. A nothing push, not really a punch, something I wasn't sure whether or not to ignore.

'Jews are Christ-killers,' one of them said.

'Christ-killers,' the others repeated. The words unfamiliar to all of us. Now I can see they didn't know what to do. Something their parents had said would have put them up to this, probably without intending anything specific.

There were more shoves. I shoved back. 'Christ-killer,' they were saying, still trying to convince themselves. 'Run,' one of them said.

'No.'

'Run,' said the biggest one. He slapped me across the face, knocking my glasses to the grass. When I bent to pick them up, he covered them with his foot. I reached anyway. As I pulled them out from his shoe he stamped on my hand.

'Run.'

I held my glasses tightly. The other two boys, the ones I had thought were my friends, had backed away. Without my glasses their faces were foggy and distorted. I put my glasses on. My friends had pebbles in their hands.

'Run.'

I ran, hating myself from the first step. As I did a shower of rocks fell gently on my back. One boy, the biggest, chased me. I was smaller but faster. I vaulted over the fence — clearing it the way I'd had to in order to become a member of the club they had invented — the Wild Bill Fan Club — then ran to the back door as the one boy still chased after me. As I opened the door, he reached in. To grab? To punch? A reflex action? I slammed the door on his hand.

For a week I walked back and forth from school alone. Stomach broiling. At night I couldn't wait to be in bed, alone, lights out. Then finally the world of fear I'd been containing all day in my belly could expand, spread out, swallow the make-believe theatre of pretend-niceness that surrounded me during the day. In the dark, instead of daring God to show himself as I used to, I listened for the sound of convoy trucks on the road, knocks at the door, policemen's boots on the stairs. And if they weren't going to come? I eventually had to ask myself. Did that mean that in this new world there was safety after all? That my great-great Uncle Joseph Lucky truly had led us out of the wilderness and into the promised land?

One afternoon recess, during the compulsory all-school no-rules soccer game, mine enemy was delivered. Head down, dribbling the ball forward at full speed, running straight at me while being chased by fifty screaming boys. An hour later we were standing on either side of the door of the principal's office. Him with scratched cheeks from the gravel he fell into when I tripped him, plus a swollen lip from the only punch I had managed to land; me with bloody nose and ribs rearranged from the fight-ending bearhug.

I still remember the principal's suit. A blue-grey plaid too long for his short legs, worn cuffs, lapels sporting a maple leaf pin. In his hands, very small, was a thick strap. Without comment he reddened our palms. Then we were out in the hall again, the door closed behind us. No handshakes, no words of mutual consolation, no smiles. But by the time the school day had finished, the underground telegraph had turned us into folk heroes, victims, and survivors of the principal's best, warmly united members of the Wild Bill Fan Club once more.

I am in Laura's bedroom. Laura is in her dressing gown, then takes it off to try on her dress. Laura encased in sterile white brassiere and panties surrounded by tanned skin. The body is untouched, an uninhabited countryside, a national park waiting for its first visitor; but her face is the city. A long curved jaw stubbornly set. Lips painted what Peter Riley called 'North Toronto Red'. Brown eyes, Jewish eyes, eyes which I knew my friend found sympathetic and embracing, but which to me looked hardened with all the calculations they had made.

I am in Laura's bedroom because I have been delegated the task no one wants. Why me? Instead of, for example, my father? The explanation for this lies in other stories, stories too long and inter-twined to tell, stories not about Joseph Lucky and Laura and Leonard, but stories about my parents. Most of all my father who had decided by now to complete his escape and was residing (with my mother, of course—herself a subject not to be broached without lengthy explanations) in Sydney, Australia where he was attempting to unknot the city's bus schedules.

'This is crazy. I'm supposed to talk you out of marrying my best friend.'

'So talk me out.'

'He's a shit. His father's dead and his mother drinks too much. So does he. His brother is a lawyer and makes deals with politicians. His sister goes to church on Sundays. Five years from now he'll be screwing his secretary. How's that?'

'You can do better.'

'He's a Catholic. Secretly he hates Jews but he hasn't got the guts to say it. He's marrying you in order to destroy you. When you have children he'll drag them down the basement to a priest he has hidden in the furnace and baptize them.'

'At least we'll have a house.'

'Tell me,' I suddenly say. As if I'm thinking about it for the first time, and maybe I am. 'Why *are* you marrying outside? Really why?'

Laura looks at me. For a second it seems that my question has truly surprised her, cracked the shell. Then I realize that she's only waiting for me to back down. 'I love him,' she says. Her voice is so wooden as she pronounces this formula that I can't help believing her.

'But answer my question.'

'Crazy boy.'

She crosses the room to where I am sitting on her bed. Bends over me and kisses the scar above my eyebrow. Then my lips. A slow kiss that leaves me bathed in her taste and scent. 'I couldn't marry a Jew. It would be like incest, if you know what I mean. Did I ever show you this? Grandpa gave it to me.'

Dear Nephew,

You will remember me. I am your wicked uncle, Joseph Lucky. A few years ago I came to visit you and the rest of those whom you call your family. As always, I brought gifts. As always, they were greedily snatched and then scorned. His money is dirty, they would like to say, since they have none. You alone wrote to thank me. I kept your letter, nephew, because I, a childless old man, wanted to dream about what might be possible. I imagined such things, nephew, as bringing you to live with me and making you

*a partner in my various enterprises. That is the letter I should
have written you because you might have been the one to change
my fate. Too late now. Now I am in jail, starving because despite
everything you might have heard about me I refuse to eat anything but kosher food. To tell the truth, even the smell of pork
chops is enough to turn this old stomach. Nephew, I beg you to
come and see that I am released, or at least fed. When you arrive
I will give you the name of a lawyer who can arrange things.*

Love from your fond Uncle — —

'What about the other letter? The one my father has?'

'There were lots of letters. Each one written as though the others
had somehow failed to arrive. Not all of them were sent to Grandpa
either.'

'And when he went to Edmonton?'

'He never went. No one did. They let him die because they were
ashamed of him.' Laura puts on her dressing gown and lights a
cigarette. 'You think Peter's cousins are on their knees right now?
Begging Peter not to marry me?'

'They should be.'

An hour later I am at Leonard's. Stiffening the spine so that I can
report the failure of my mission to my grandparents. 'You are the
outsider,' Leonard is explaining to me, 'the perennial third man. You
think it's because of your shiny metal mind. Forget it. You're outside
because you're a Jew. And that's why Laura is marrying your friend.
She grew up being outside and now she wants to be sure she'll be
outside forever. Except that she won't because ten years from now
the whole world will be people like you and Laura, people trying to
get away from themselves. And you know what will happen then?
Laura will decide she's unhappy. She'll start to drink or have an affair
or run away to a kibbutz in Israel. The next time you see her, middle-
aged, she'll say that she wasted ten years of her life. She'll ask you
why you let her get married.'

'Why did I?'

'Because you want to do the same thing.'

Leonard was dressed in his *shul*-going suit. Black without stripes
or flecks. Shiny seat bottom. Pockets padded with *yarmulkahs* and
hankies just in case someone needed an extra. Soon we would be
going to the bride's house, which was where the wedding would
take place — under the supervision of a Unitarian minister who didn't
seem to believe anything overly offensive.

'And you? I thought you were the one who was so hot for her.'
After my grandfather's first heart attack Leonard had evolved from paying boarder to man of the house. Now he even had a job — as a history teacher at the Orthodox Synagogue Hebrew Day School. Leonard the responsible citizen was heavier, jowled and his hair was turning a dull grey at the temples. And then he smiled. With the memory of whatever had transpired between him and Laura, I thought at first, though what could have linked this prematurely middle-aged perpetual bachelor to the ripe and bursting Laura was hard to imagine. 'Never,' Leonard said. 'I promised myself years ago to a young woman of strong character who takes care of her mother in Vancouver.'

'And when did you meet her?'

'The summer I went to study in New York. She was on the Holocaust committee.'

'How romantic.'

Leonard gave me a look I hadn't seen since the day he explained his bloody shirt. 'You're a fool. Helen is the perfect woman for me in every way.' He turned to his desk. In his student days it had been heaped with scholarly texts. But since the summer in New York, the philosophical treatises had been pushed aside first to make room for bulky volumes on the Holocaust and then, more recently, for the history primers he needed for his job. From a drawer stuffed with letters he pulled a picture of a squarish-looking woman with a young smile and a surprising splash of freckles across her nose. 'When her mother dies —'

My grandparents are waiting for me in their parlour. Like Leonard, like my grandfather, like Laura's own father waiting resignedly at home, I am dressed in a suit. An almost new suit, in fact, the one I bought a few months ago when I graduated from law school. Eventually I will wear the same suit, the same white shirt, the same gold cuff-links to my grandfather's funeral. The cuff-links were his gift to me on my Bar Mitzvah. On that occasion, a few weeks after my thirteenth birthday, I had needed new thick-heeled shoes to push me over the five-foot mark. One sideburn had started to grow, but not the other, and this unequal hormonal outburst had been accompanied by the very unmasculine swelling of one of my nipples. For some reason this swollen nipple ached when I sang, especially when my voice cracked in public, which it did dozens of times during the painful delivery of my *moftar*. Afterwards my grandfather, his breath thick with rye, had delivered me a bristly kiss and pinched my arm so lovingly that I carried the bruise for a month.

Now they are sitting stiffly and waiting, elderly patients bracing themselves for the bad news. Stubborn but helpless. I beg them to at least come to the reception, for Laura's sake. This is the compromise everyone has been hoping for—avoiding the wedding but joining the celebration.

My grandfather is looking placidly about the room. His most recent attack seems to have taken away his electricity. He is perpetually serene, almost vacant. Even his shining and muscular skull seems to have lost its power; now the skin is greyer, listless. I try to imagine what might be going on inside. Weather?

My grandmother is twisting her hands. Everything considered, she has big diamonds. 'We'll go,' she announces. 'The mother of those bastard children was born a Jew and so the children can still be rescued, God willing, after the father has left.'

'Assimilated,' Leonard says. He pronounces the word slowly, savouring, then repeats it. First he stares at me—a Leonard who has emerged in the ten years since his own marriage, a Daddy Leonard with a rounded bulldog face, muscular cheeks, blue eyes that have spent so many long nights poring over his Holocaust documents that they have turned the skin surrounding them into dark crater-holes— then he swings his head to Laura for confirmation. She nods. Laura whom I've known forever. Laura who is prettier than ever, but whose face seems more angular because she decided to replace her contact lenses with glasses when she started taking Hebrew lessons again.

I am sitting by the window. It's still open, a souvenir from the golden warmth of the October afternoon. Now it's evening and a cold breeze sucks at the back of my neck, but no one is thinking about the heartbreak of Indian summer.

Laura is kneeling on the floor. Her floor, the floor of the living room of her and Peter Riley's North Toronto house. While she kneels she staples posters to sticks. NAZI JEW KILLER the posters all read.

'I can't believe how *assimilated* you are,' Leonard says, pleased with himself now that he has found the word for me. 'How *typical*. I won't say you're a coward. When it comes to being punched in the face, you're ready. When they call for volunteers to get baked, you'll probably run to the train. *Bravo*. But ask you to stick your neck out and stand up for yourself—all of a sudden you turn into a lawyer for some Jew-baiting creep.'

'Listen to yourself,' I say. 'You're filled with hate. Do you think

Jews are the only people in the world who have ever been killed? Even during the Second World War there were three million Poles who died. Gypsies were sent to concentration camps too. Do you think the Holocaust gave the Jews some sort of moral credit card? Do we get to trade our dead for Palestinians? Is it one for one or do Chosen People get a special rate of exchange?'

'I have never killed anyone. But I am proud of my people when they defend themselves.'

'Violence poisons,' I say.

'God is violent,' Leonard comes back.

Bang-clack, bang-clack, goes Laura's stapler. Now she's finished her signs, a dozen of them. In a few minutes it will be time to carry them out to the family-size station-wagon. While the 'family' — twin four-year-old daughters — sleeps, Peter is to babysit. And while Peter babysits, Laura and Leonard are to drive the signs out to the airport, where Leonard has been tipped off that an East German cabinet minister someone claims was once a concentration-camp guard is to arrive for intergovernmental trade discussions.

Laura and Leonard stand up.

'I'll go with you,' I say.

Leonard's face breaks open. 'I knew you would.' He moves forward, hugs me. All those years living above my grandparents and now he smells like they used to — the same food, the same soap, the same sickly sweet lemon furniture polish. I can't help smiling, thinking about Leonard's youth as I knew it: tortured nasal passages, a white towel soaked with what he claimed was menstrual blood.

We stand around for a moment while Leonard phones home. At the other end, apparently saying little, is his woman of perfect character, the devoted Helen who has borne him four children and seems to make a virtue of obeying Leonard. They live in the main house now — my grandparents left it to them — and the room above the garage is consecrated to books and pamphlets detailing the attempted destruction of the Jews. Lately they've added slides, films, one of those roll-up white screens with little sprinkles on the surface. You know what I mean.

We all drag the posters out the front door to the waiting station-wagon. A few leaves crackle and drift in the cool breeze. Lights are on in all the houses around us. It's the moment when children have gone to bed, tables have been cleared, televisions have been turned on or attaché cases opened. We're on the lawn waiting for Peter to open the back hatch when a neighbour walking his dog stops to talk.

The subject of conversation is, of course, the weather, the growing possibility of snow, the desire to spend one last weekend at the cottage. Only while the neighbour is agonizing over his big decision — whether or not to dig trenches so that he can keep the cottage water turned on until Christmas — does he notice the NAZI JEW KILLER signs. He says he is going to dig the trenches after all, if the weather is good, you have to think of the future, and besides he has always wanted his children to share his own dream, a white Christmas in the country.

At the airport a small band of the faithful were waiting on the fifth floor of the parking garage. We got out of the car, distributed the signs. According to Leonard's information, the former concentration-camp guard was due on an Air Canada flight from London. The plan was to meet him at the Passenger Arrivals gate.

There were ten of us. Too many, with our NAZI JEW KILLER signs, to fit into a single elevator. Laura went with the first group — Leonard too — so I was left with four strangers to descend in the second shift. One of those strangers became you, but only later. Sharing our elevator were two passengers with suitcases. At first they paid us no attention — then, reading our signs, they shrank back.

By the time we had left the elevator and were walking towards the Arrivals gate, Leonard's group was surrounded by airport security officials and police. We raised our own signs and began to approach them. But before we could be noticed Leonard had gotten into a shouting match with one of the officials. 'Never lose your temper needlessly,' Leonard had lectured us in the Riley living room. But, as Laura told me later, Leonard had already called his friends at the television station and promised a confrontation. When photographers with television cameras on their shoulders and assistants carrying portable lights began to run towards the struggling group, Leonard turned towards them. Soon, the official forgotten, he had positioned himself in front of one of the cameras to make a speech about a country that denied its own citizens free expression while protecting foreign 'criminals against humanity'. Then there was one of those incidents that is not supposed to happen, a relic from other countries, other eras: just as Leonard was working himself to a climax, a policeman smashed his truncheon into the back of his head, sending him falling face forward onto the floor.

Later that night I could watch myself on the television news as I entered the circle of light, knelt above Leonard and turned him over so I could see on his face, running with blood, a half-smile of triumph. You weren't in the picture. 'Communist,' shouted a voice from off-camera, but no one laughed.

Driving to the liquor store Peter Riley and I are already drunk. Actually, we have been drinking all afternoon. It's the kind of day that deserves drinking, a Toronto December special that is cold but snowless, a gritty colourless day that merges pavement and sky. Peter's shirt is open. The tuft of red hair at the base of his neck has gone to flat silver; silver too is the colour of the red mop that used to peek out the holes and edge of his football helmet. To heighten the effect he's wearing a leather jacket left over from our university days; U of T 66 is blazoned across the back in white. Looking at him, at myself slumped uncomfortably beneath the seat belt, I am reminded of the men Peter Riley and I used to go and watch during the summer in Ottawa, fat and powerful men with big paunches and thick arms who played evening softball at the high school diamond. Strong but graceless, able to swat the ball a mile, but stumbling around the bases in slow motion, the evening athletes had always seemed an awesome joke to us. 'Battles of the dinosaurs', we called their games, delighting in their strength, the kaleidoscope of grunts and sweat and beer-fed curses.

At the liquor-store parking lot we climb out of the car and stand, side by side, looking up at the clouds. We aren't two baseball players, I am thinking, among other things; we are two middle-aged lawyers, partners in a small firm. We are tense, over-tired, mind-fatigued businessmen taking a day off to drink ourselves into oblivion because it's the only cure we know for the fact that while eating lunch we reminded each other that Leonard had died exactly six weeks before. Not that either of us had ever considered ourselves admirers of Leonard. Still.

'Among other things' includes the sound of the dirt falling onto Leonard's coffin, his family's uncontrolled grief, the talk at the funeral about another martyr to anti-Semitism. You were present, silent, beautiful, though your face was pinched with cold. We started walking towards each other at the same time and before we had even told each other our names, I was asking you for your telephone number. Also at the funeral were the wide circle I see once every few years at such events. Aunts, uncles, cousins at various removes who have come not because they think of Leonard as a martyr or support his politics but because they remember Leonard as the faithful boarder who helped my grandparents through their old age, the daily *shul-goer* who, even when my grandfather was eighty years old, patiently shepherded him back and forth to the synagogue.

Some of the aunts, the uncles, the cousins at various removes are themselves getting old now. Short stocky men and women in their seventies, eighties, even the old shrunken survivor who was born in the last century. Many of them, not all, were born in Russia and came out of the mythic peasant crucible to Canada where they gradually adorned themselves in suits, jewellery, houses, coats, stock-market investments until finally, at this group funeral portrait, they could be seen literally staggering under the weight of their success.

I find myself looking at Peter Riley's open shirt again. 'For Christ's sake, do up the buttons, you'll get arrested.'

'Undo yours,' Peter Riley says. 'In the name of the Wild Bill Fan Club, I formally dare you to undo your buttons.'

'For Christ's sake,' I say again, this time wondering why on this occasion it is Christ I invoke—Leonard must have been right. An occasion, to be precise, on which Peter Riley and I have already emptied one bottle of scotch, to say nothing of a few beer chasers, and now find ourselves at 4:33 P.M. in front of the Yonge Street liquor store in search of a refill. Near the liquor store is a shop where we can buy newspapers, mix, cigarettes, ice, candies. Even twenty years ago, when we were under-age, we went there to buy Coke for our rum.

'I'll go to the liquor store,' I say, 'you get the other.'

The scotch hits me while I am alone in the heated display room. 'The last of the big drinkers I am not' is the sentence that comes into my mind—spoken by my father. But my father is dead, possibly along with whatever part of me is his son. 'Never shit on your own doorstep,' my father also told me. Translation: you can go to bed with non-Jewish girls, but don't bring them home. I move down the counter and settle on a bottle of *The Famous Grouse* scotch whisky. When I present my order the cashier makes a point of staring at my unbuttoned shirt. He has straight oiled hair into which each plastic tine of the comb has dug its permanent trench. My age or older. Skin boiled red by repeated infusions of the product he is selling. Looks a bit like Wild Bill near the end, I finally decide, but not enough for me to tell him about the fan club. I look into his eyes. Tough guy. He doesn't flinch. Meanwhile the store is empty, we could go on staring like this forever. 'I'm having an identity crisis,' I imagine saying to him, 'I mean I was born Jewish but I don't feel comfortable carrying NAZI JEW KILLER signs.'

That night I dream about the hearse, a sleek powerful limousine. You aren't in the dream but the rest of us are. We're sitting behind the driver: Laura in the centre, Peter Riley and I surrounding. Behind us is the coffin and its presence somehow makes us even smaller than we are, reminding us that Death is the queen bee and we humans are just worker bees keeping Death supplied. It is nighttime, the time of night when time does not exist. The hearse is carrying us down University Avenue. Wide, empty, stately, the street conducts us to the American Embassy where there is one other car, an ambulance with its rotating light winking 'He's nuts' into the sky. The attendants, bored, are leaning against the ambulance and talking to the lone policeman.

Crouched on all fours, his weight on his knees and hands, Leonard is howling like a dog at the closed door of the American Embassy. When he sees us he interrupts to wink, then turns back to his howling. After listening for a while I realize that his howl is in fact controlled, a merely moderate howl you can howl until dawn or at least until newspaper reporters arrive. I turn to relay this news to Laura and Peter Riley, but as I turn I see they have been transformed into the ambulance attendants, while I have somehow ended up on my knees, baying at the door. When Leonard tries to arrest me I leap at his throat, bringing him to the ground and tearing at him until I wake myself up with my screams.

At the funeral the men took turns throwing shovelfuls of earth on the coffin. Into the silence small stones and earth rattled against the dull wood. I couldn't help listening, I couldn't help watching, I couldn't help crying at the thought of Leonard dead. At some point I discovered you were still standing beside me. Anonymous in your black coat, bare fingers gripping each other in the frozen air, thin black shoes with the toes pressed together. When the service was over we walked towards the parking lot, climbed into my car, drove to a hotel.

Now this hotel is my train. You are my benefactress, wealthy in the dark cream skin that you inhabit, the mysterious odours of your mysterious places, your eyes that becalm everything they see. Under your protection we ride our wild animals into the twilight. Until

beneath our starry blankets we find a way to sleep — out on the range,
in this room which hovers in an otherwise unmarked universe, which
exists for no other purpose than the mutual exploration of mutual
desire. *Assimilated*, as Leonard used to say; against our non-existent
will we have been assimilated into this compromised situation — two
unrecorded strangers claiming each other with words sight touch
smell until we raise spark enough to join our foreign bodies.

MATT COHEN was born in Kingston, Ontario, in 1942. He was raised
and educated in Ottawa, then attended the University of Toronto
where he graduated in 1964, proceeding to an M.A. in political theory.
In 1967 he joined the faculty of McMaster University as a lecturer in
the department of religion, where he taught the sociology of religion.
The following year he gave up teaching for full-time writing, while
continuing to serve as writer-in-residence or creative-writing instructor at several Canadian universities. Cohen divides his time between
Toronto and his farm near Verona, Ontario. He is married and the
father of two children. His works include *Korsoniloff* (Toronto:
Anansi, 1969); *Johnny Crackle Sings* (Toronto: McClelland and Stew-
art, 1971); *Columbus and the Fat Lady* (Toronto: Anansi, 1972);
The Disinherited (Toronto: McClelland and Stewart, 1974); *Wooden
Hunters* (Toronto: McClelland and Stewart, 1975); *The Colours of
War* (Toronto: McClelland and Stewart, 1977); *Night Flights*
(Toronto: Doubleday, 1978); *The Sweet Second Summer of Kitty
Malone* (Toronto: McClelland and Stewart, 1979); *Flowers of Dark-
ness* (Toronto: McClelland and Stewart, 1981); *Café Le Dog* (Toronto:
McClelland and Stewart, 1983); *The Spanish Doctor* (Toronto:
McClelland and Stewart, 1984); *Nadine* (Markham, Ont.: Viking,
1986); *Living on Water* (Markham, Ont.: Viking, 1988).

MERVIN BUTOVSKY, professor of English at Concordia University,
teaches modern and contemporary literature, with a special interest
in ethnic and minority writing, including North American Jewish
literature. He edited and translated from the Yiddish (with Ode
Garfinkle) *The Far Side of the River*, selected short stories by Yaacov
Zipper (1985), and 'The Journals of Yaacov Zipper 1925-26'. His
essays on Canadian Jewish writing and A.M. Klein have appeared in
Jewish Book Annual. He is also co-editor of a forthcoming volume
of essays on the religion, culture, and politics of Yiddish Montreal.

Canada defines itself officially as a multicultural society. In actuality, however, most writers use either English or French — the designated 'founding' languages of the country — regardless of their mother tongue. Where does that leave the ethnic writer who comes out of a tradition in which neither of these languages is the mother tongue?

First of all, I'm not sure I like the words 'ethnic writer'. Ethnicity in Canada, or multiculturalism, always seems to imply that there are two dominant streams — the English and the French — and in addition a bunch of minorities who occupy marginal positions and run different kinds of restaurants. I'm not sure this any longer reflects the Canadian reality. As for tradition and linguistic background — perhaps these two elements are at odds. English is my first language and the only one I could write in. On the other hand, the culture that goes with being Jewish is not particularly an English-language culture, but is rather more closely bound up with Yiddish, Hebrew, or Middle European languages. So, although I was brought up in English and English is the natural language for me to write in, actual English words and syntax haven't historically been built to accommodate the kinds of experience that I might want to be writing about. So it is definitely different for me to write about being Jewish in English than it is to write about, say, a farmer north of Kingston in English because the actual vocabulary and linguistic structures are more available for one than the other.

What areas of Jewish experience do you find cannot be accommodated by English?

The European Jewish and non-Jewish experience is marked by an ambivalence and uncertainty that is not as natural to English as it is to European languages. In other words, when books written in English are ambiguous, they somehow move to the edge of narrative possibility; whereas ambivalence is at the centre of European narrative. It is not just a matter of language, it is also a question of the kind of novel that has existed in these different languages. For example, in North America the main purpose of most novels is to entertain and to make as much money as possible. Then there is a smaller group of novels whose main purpose is, let's say, to entertain the intellectuals, or more literary people. These entertain both on the levels of so-called commercial plot, character, exposé, etc., but also on the level of doing unexpected things with various literary devices, so the connoisseur of novels sees something different happening. But neither of these kinds of novels is considered essential reading for people who see themselves as intellectuals but not specialists of literature. In other words, novels have no real role in the life of North American intellectuals, just as intellectuals do not have a central role in the imaginative or political life of North America. Whereas in Europe, at least until quite recently, fiction has been central to the collective imagination. Whatever their inner dialogues with themselves, readers expect that fiction at its best will touch and even alter them. Of course such comparisons are generalizations; some Canadian novelists—for example, Margaret Laurence—really have affected the way Canadians see themselves.

Does the ethnic writer have a special role in introducing to Canadian literature the European dimension of cultural seriousness that you find absent? Do such writers bring to fiction a different terrain from the one you are describing?

As Canada fragments into regions, writers have to find their voices not simply in terms of some pan-Canadian identity, but also in terms of their own history and their current interests. In that sense 'ethnic writing'—writing from outside the boundaries of what has been considered Canadian—is now more and more interesting. Because the mainstream—both in terms of politics and literature—is now so weak and fragmented, it's an excellent time for writers of different backgrounds who bring different ideas about language and books. The problem faced by such writers will be the difficulty in finding an audience for their books; a very few writers get a large audience, while the vast majority virtually get only friends and relatives. So there is that dichotomy.

Given the variety of elements that comprise a writer's experience, do you think the direct encounter with his or her ethnic memory is a matter of conscious choice?

There are moments of apparent choice. When I decided to write *The Spanish Doctor* and stop writing the 'Salem' novels, I knew this decision would have important consequences for me as a writer. Yet, when I think back, I can see that the most important consequences were ones that I didn't foresee. In particular, I could not have known that people's view of me would change so radically just because I chose to write about Jewish themes rather than about rural Canada. In fact my books have been received in a completely different way in the last decade than they were in the previous one.

What was the critical response to your novels when you chose to write of Jewish experience?

In Canada it was one of complete puzzlement from most of the critics who had previously read and liked my work. They thought I had gone completely insane. The critic of the *Toronto Star* wrote a piece about 3000 words long—basically an open letter to me—pleading with me to regain my senses and go back to my normal kind of writing! Many other critics assumed that either it was a comedy or I had done it for the money. Yet despite that response, the book found a whole new audience. And beginning with that book, my books began to be widely published abroad. Finally I came to understand that *The Spanish Doctor* had come as such a shock to so many of my readers, especially the critics, because of their sense that I had betrayed my Canadianness by writing about being Jewish. It tells you something uncomfortable about people's conception of what it means to be a Canadian. Even after *Nadine* was published people would say to me: 'Are you going to write about Canada again?' I would reply that most of *Nadine* takes place in Canada, and that her being Jewish does not mean she is not Canadian. Then they would be offended, as if I had made a hostile remark.

Does that imply that ethnic writing in Canada still meets with opposition from critics and readers?

'Ethnic writing' is, as I said earlier, almost by definition writing outside what is supposed to be the mainstream—itself hardly in existence. At this point I think it's fair to say that critics of Canadian literature have no consensus about what either the canon is or what the criteria for 'Canadian literature' are supposed to be. Like the writers, they have fragmented into postmodernists, regionalists, feminists, internationalists, etc. Yet despite its fragmentation and variety, the Canadian literary landscape—at least in fiction—doesn't really represent what's happening here. For example, I live in downtown Toronto and have for a long time. There are over three hundred thousand Italians living here—yet where are the novels about Italians? Where is the novel about Greek life in Toronto? Where are the novels about what is really happening in the centre of our big cities, about all these different people from different places? Where are the novels by native people, by blacks, by Inuit? They don't exist. Many of our cities and much of our countryside are inhabited by people who are not participating in our literary culture. Some may be reading, but their participation must also come through writing and publication.

Your grandparents were immigrants from Eastern Europe who came to Canada in the early years of the century. Can you describe something of the cultural changes that have occurred in the life of your family that distinguishes you from your parents and grandparents? What aspects of the traditions that your grandparents once lived have been transmitted to you: which do you retain; which compel your commitment; which have you neglected or abandoned?

First of all, my two sets of grandparents were quite different from each other. All four grandparents were Jewish but one set was relatively agnostic, though they did belong to a synagogue and they must have kept kosher to some extent. To my child's eyes they seemed very low-key about the religious observances of Judaism. Their children – including my mother – did not know very much about being Jewish in the formal sense. They spoke a little Yiddish, but for their generation they did not have a real Jewish education. At the same time, they were ardent Zionists and two of the three children lived in Israel for long periods – one has made her life there – and *their* children live there or have spent many years there. So while that side of my family was not very religious, they expressed their Jewish identity through Zionism and attachment to Israel. On my father's side, my grandfather went to *yeshiva* and they were extremely orthodox. They kept a strictly kosher home, were observant, and were deeply involved in synagogue life. My grandfather went to synagogue every day. He practiced Jewish rituals and was involved in raising money to support synagogues. The religious and communal side of Judaism were the central facts of his existence. He was also a very gentle and ethical man. My grandmother was also extremely strict in her observances – perhaps even more so than her husband – and disapproved very strongly of any deviation from strict observance, which meant that she had a very hard time with her grandchildren, all of whom were considerably more lax than herself.

Your account of the pattern of your parents' Jewish belonging suggests that your mother's family identified with a type of modern Jewish nationalism in contrast to your father's upbringing in a traditional religious home. How do you see yourself in relation to this dual heritage?

I got a sort of minimum Jewish education enforced with equally minimum authority. Of course we were completely aware of the half-hearted nature of the whole thing. Most of the students who went to Hebrew school in Ottawa regarded the studies as something of a joke; the teachers were there to be tortured, knowledge was there to be evaded. It was only at around the age of thirty that I realized that questions about my identity as a Jew were totally unresolved, and that I simply wasn't going to be able to discard them. But neither could I become a strictly religious Jew. So I was left with this half-loaf, as it were. Yet, these questions have turned out to be far more important than I thought at the time.

How does the question of your Jewish identity affect your personal life and your life as a writer?

Jewishness for me has become a lot more interesting. In a sense it is partly an obsession which I'm trying to work through in my writing; I pursue it because I have no choice. It's also partly a lens – a changing lens – through which I see the world, and finally it is something that I keep exploring and learning about. For example, whereas it was unthinkable twenty years ago that I would spend days reading about Jewish history or some related subject, now I often do. I learned a lot about Jewish history in Europe through researching *The Spanish Doctor*, *Nadine*, and the novel I'm now working on. I'm gradually discovering what it is I want to get to the centre of: I feel I have to understand – although I know I won't – what happened to the Jew-ish-European dream. Not simply because it ended in a tragedy greater than all other tragedies – perhaps it wasn't – but because it is in some way the life I was meant to inherit. Also, of course, if we cannot understand what in us has been destroyed then we can't understand how other peoples suffer in similar circumstances.

Does your introspection stem from the sense of responsibility the Holocaust imposes on every Jew – no matter how alienated from Judaism they may have been? Do you think the post-Holocaust era demands a more radical form of self-definition if one is to be serious about one's self? Perhaps, the need to locate oneself within the whole historic scheme of modern Jewish peoplehood, whereas in the past one might have remained indifferent to that relationship?

Obviously I do desire to locate myself—though I often think that the idea of self-knowledge is completely ridiculous. Certainly I have no intention of becoming a scholar on the Holocaust. Frankly, I wish I could get it off my mind, it was such a horrible event.

In retrospect, would you consider your 'Salem' novels—set in rural Ontario and dealing with family relationships of a decidedly non-Jewish nature—to represent, at that stage of your life, an avoidance or displacement of your Jewish identity?

Not at all. I wrote about those characters because I found them and their way of life both attractive and tragic. I suppose I saw them as fragments of a dream the rest of the world had stopped dreaming. They were living out a mythology which the majority had already forgotten; I was living in the country and becoming a writer and just couldn't help writing about them. But—it has to be said—many Jews are also living out a forgotten mythology. What has traditionally been the Jewish idea of what Jews are doing in history is completely at odds with what anyone else thinks.

Would you ever consider as subject the portrait of a Canadian Jewish artist?

It's not impossible that there would be a writer as my fictional subject, although writer-characters generally serve as observers, not as participants. Nadine, on the other hand, is the writer of the novel *Nadine*.

And is it a portrait of the artist?

It's a portrait of Nadine—not of me. In fact, to tell the truth, I don't know if I even regard myself as a 'Canadian Jewish artist'. It seems like a very ambiguous role to take on.

Do you find it an interesting role?

I don't know. Maybe one of the problems with literature in Canada is that writers are known for their roles rather than their books.

MICHAEL ONDAATJE b. 1943

The Bridge

A truck carries fire at five A.M. through central Toronto, along Dundas Street and up Parliament Street, moving north. Aboard the flatbed three men stare into passing darkness — their muscles relaxed in this last half-hour before work — as if they don't own the legs or the arms jostling against their bodies and the backboard of the Ford. Written in yellow over the green door is DOMINION BRIDGE COMPANY. But for now all that is visible is the fire on the flatbed burning over the three-foot by three-foot metal dish, cooking the tar in a cauldron, leaving this odour on the streets for anyone who would step out into the early morning and swallow the air.

The truck rolls burly under the arching trees, pauses at certain intersections where more workers jump onto the flatbed, and soon there are eight men, the fire crackling, hot tar now and then spitting onto the back of a neck or an ear. Soon there are twenty, crowded and silent.

The light begins to come out of the earth. They see their hands, the textures on a coat, the trees they had known were there. At the top of Parliament Street the truck turns east, passes the Rosedale fill, and moves towards the half-built viaduct.

The men jump off. The unfinished road is full of ruts and the fire and the lights of the truck bounce, the suspension wheezing. The truck travels so slowly the men are walking faster, in the cold dawn air, even though it is summer.

Later they will remove coats and sweaters, then by eleven their shirts, bending over the black rivers of tar in just their trousers, boots, and caps. But now the thin layer of frost is everywhere, coating the machines and cables, brittle on the rain puddles they step through. The fast evaporation of darkness. As light emerges they see their breath, the clarity of the air being breathed out of them. The truck finally stops at the edge of the viaduct, and its lights are turned off.

The bridge goes up in a dream. It will link the east end with the centre of the city. It will carry traffic, water, and electricity across the Don Valley. It will carry trains that have not even been invented yet. Night and day. Fall light. Snow light. They are always working— horses and wagons and men arriving for work on the Danforth side at the far end of the valley.

There are over 4,000 photographs from various angles of the bridge in its time-lapse evolution. The piers sink into bedrock fifty feet below the surface through clay and shale and quicksand—45,000 cubic yards of earth are excavated. The network of scaffolding stretches up.

Men in a maze of wooden planks climb deep into the shattered light of blond wood. A man is an extension of hammer, drill, flame. Drill smoke in his hair. A cap falls into the valley, gloves are buried in stone dust.

Then the new men arrive, the 'electricals', laying grids of wire across the five arches, carrying the exotic three-bowl lights, and on October 18, 1918 it is completed. Lounging in mid-air.

The bridge. The bridge. Christened 'Prince Edward'. The Bloor Street Viaduct.

During the political ceremonies a figure escaped by bicycle through the police barriers. The first member of the public. Not the expected show car containing officials, but this one anonymous and cycling like hell to the east end of the city. In the photographs he is a blur of intent. He wants the virginity of it, the luxury of such space. He circles twice, the string of onions that he carries on his shoulder splaying out, and continues.

But he was not the first. The previous midnight the workers had arrived and brushed away officials who guarded the bridge in preparation for the ceremonies the next day, moved with their own flickering lights—their candles for the bridge dead—like a wave of civilization, a net of summer insects over the valley.

And the cyclist too on his flight claimed the bridge in that blurred movement, alone and illegal. Thunderous applause greeted him at the far end.

On the west side of the bridge is Bloor Street, on the east side is Danforth Avenue. Originally cart roads, mud roads, planked in 1910, they are now being tarred. Bricks are banged into the earth and narrow creeks of sand are poured in between them. The tar is spread.

Bitumiers, bitumatori, tarrers, get onto their knees and lean their weight over the wooden block irons, which arc and sweep. The smell of tar seeps through the porous body of their clothes. The black of it is permanent under the nails. They can feel the bricks under their kneecaps as they crawl backwards towards the bridge, their bodies almost horizontal over the viscous black river, their heads drunk within the fumes.

Hey, Caravaggio!

The young man gets up off his knees and looks back into the sun. He walks to the foreman, lets go of the two wooden blocks he is holding so they hang by the leather thongs from his belt, bouncing against his knees as he walks. Each man carries the necessities of his trade with him. When Caravaggio quits a year later he will cut the thongs with a fish knife and fling the blocks into the half-dry tar. Now he walks back in a temper and gets down on his knees again. Another fight with the foreman.

All day they lean over tar, over the twenty yards of black river that has been spread since morning. It glistens and eases in sunlight. Schoolkids grab bits of tar and chew them, first cooling the pieces in their hands then popping them into their mouths. It concentrates the saliva for spitting contests. The men plunk cans of beans into the blackness to heat them up for their lunch.

In winter, snow removes the scent of tar, the scent of pitched cut wood. The Don River floods below the unfinished bridge, ice banging at the feet of the recently built piers. On winter mornings men fan out nervous over the whiteness. Where does the earth end? There are flares along the edge of the bridge on winter nights — worst shift of all — where they hammer the nails in through snow. The bridge builders balance on a strut, the flares wavering behind them, aiming their hammers towards the noise of a nail they cannot see.

* * *

The last thing Rowland Harris, Commissioner of Public Works, would do in the evening during its construction was have himself driven to the edge of the viaduct, to sit for a while. At midnight the half-built bridge over the valley seemed deserted — just lanterns tracing its outlines. But there was always a night shift of thirty or forty men. After a while Harris removed himself from the car, lit a cigar, and walked onto the bridge. He loved this viaduct. It was his first child as head of Public Works, much of it planned before he took over but he had bullied it through. It was Harris who envisioned that it could carry not just cars but trains on a lower trestle. It could also transport water from the east-end plants to the centre of the city. Water was Harris' great passion. He wanted giant water mains travelling across the valley as part of the viaduct.

He slipped past the barrier and walked towards the working men. Few of them spoke English but they knew who he was. Sometimes he was accompanied by Pomphrey, an architect, the strange one from England who was later to design for Commissioner Harris one of the city's grandest buildings — the water filtration plant in the east end.

For Harris the night allowed scope. Night removed the limitations of detail and concentrated on form. Harris would bring Pomphrey with him, past the barrier, onto the first stage of the bridge that ended sixty yards out in the air. The wind moved like something ancient against them. All men on the bridge had to buckle on halter ropes. Harris spoke of his plans to this five-foot-tall Englishman, struggling his way into Pomphrey's brain. Before the real city could be seen it had to be imagined, the way rumours and tall tales were a kind of charting.

One night they had driven there at eleven o'clock, crossed the barrier, and attached themselves once again to the rope harnesses. This allowed them to stand near the edge to study the progress of the piers and the steel arches. There was a fire on the bridge where the night workers congregated, flinging logs and other remnants onto it every so often, warming themselves before they walked back and climbed over the edge of the bridge into the night.

They were working on a wood-facing for the next pier so that concrete could be poured in. As they sawed and hammered, wind shook the light from the flares attached to the side of the abutment. Above them, on the deck of the bridge, builders were carrying huge Ingersoll-Rand air compressors and cables.

An April night in 1917. Harris and Pomphrey were on the bridge, in the dark wind. Pomphrey had turned west and was suddenly stilled. His hand reached out to touch Harris on the shoulder, a gesture he had never made before.

—Look!

Walking on the bridge were five nuns.

Past the Dominion Steel castings wind attacked the body directly. The nuns were walking past the first group of workers at the fire. The bus, Harris thought, must have dropped them off near Castle Frank and the nuns had, with some confusion at that hour, walked the wrong way in the darkness.

They had passed the black car under the trees and talking cheerfully stepped past the barrier into a landscape they did not know existed—onto a tentative carpet over the piers, among the night labourers. They saw the fire and the men. A few tried to wave them back. There was a mule attached to a wagon. The hiss and jump of machines made the ground under them lurch. A smell of creosote. One man was washing his face in a barrel of water.

The nuns were moving towards a thirty-yard point on the bridge when the wind began to scatter them. They were thrown against the cement mixers and steam shovels, careening from side to side, in danger of going over the edge.

Some of the men grabbed and enclosed them, pulling leather straps over their shoulders, but two were still loose. Harris and Pomphrey at the far end looked on helplessly as one nun was lifted up and flung against the compressors. She stood up shakily and then the wind jerked her sideways, scraping her along the concrete and right off the edge of the bridge. She disappeared into the night by the third abutment, into the long depth of air which held nothing, only sometimes a rivet or a dropped hammer during the day.

Then there was no longer any fear on the bridge. The worst, the incredible had happened. A nun had fallen off the Prince Edward Viaduct before it was even finished. The men covered in wood shavings or granite dust held the women against them. And Commissioner Harris at the far end stared along the mad pathway. This was his first child and it had already become a murderer.

The man in mid-air under the central arch saw the shape fall towards him, in that second knowing his rope would not hold them both. He reached to catch the figure while his other hand grabbed the metal pipe edge above him to lessen the sudden jerk on the rope. The new weight ripped the arm that held the pipe out of its socket and he screamed, so whoever might have heard him up there would have thought the scream was from the falling figure. The halter thulked, jerking his chest up to his throat. The right arm was all agony now— but his hand's timing had been immaculate, the grace of the habit, and he found himself a moment later holding the figure against him dearly.

He saw it was a black-garbed bird, a girl's white face. He saw this in the light that sprayed down inconstantly from a flare fifteen yards above them. They hung in the halter, pivoting over the valley, his broken arm loose on one side of him, holding the women with the other. Her body was in shock, her huge eyes staring into the face of Nicholas Temelcoff.

Scream, please, Lady, he whispered, the pain terrible. He asked her to hold him by the shoulders, to take the weight off his one good arm. A sway in the wind. She could not speak though her eyes glared at him bright, just staring at him. *Scream, please*. But she could not.

During the night, the long chutes through which wet concrete slid were unused and hung loose so the open spouts wavered a few feet from the valley floor. The tops of these were about ten feet from him now. He knew this without seeing them, even though they fell outside the scope of light. If they attempted to slide the chute their weight would make it vertical and dangerous. They would have to go fur-ther — to reach the lower-deck level of the bridge where there were structures built for possible water mains.

We have to swing. She had her hands around his shoulders now, the wind assaulting them. The two strangers were in each other's arms, beginning to swing wilder, once more, past the lip of the chute which had tempted them, till they were almost at the lower level of the rafters. He had his one good arm free. Saving her now would be her responsibility.

She was in shock, her face bright when they reached the lower level, like a woman with a fever. She was in no shape to be witnessed, her veil loose, her cropped hair open to the long wind down the valley. Once they reached the catwalk she saved him from falling back into space. He was exhausted. She held him and walked with him like a lover along the unlit lower parapet towards the west end of the bridge.

Above them the others stood around the one fire, talking agitat-edly. The women were still tethered to the men and not looking towards the stone edge where she had gone over, falling in darkness. The one with that small scar against her nose . . . she was always falling into windows, against chairs. She was always unlucky.

The Commissioner's chauffeur slept in his car as Temelcoff and the nun walked past, back on real earth away from the bridge. Before they reached Parliament Street they cut south through the cemetery. He seemed about to faint and she held him against a gravestone. She forced him to hold his arm rigid, his fist clenched. She put her hands underneath it like a stirrup and jerked upwards so he screamed out again, her whole body pushing up with all of her strength, groaning as if about to lift him and then holding him, clutching him tight. She had seen the sweat jump out of his face. *Get me a shot. Get me.* . . . She removed her veil and wrapped the arm tight against his side. *Parliament and Dundas . . . few more blocks.* So she went down Parliament Street with him. Where she was going she didn't know. On Eastern Avenue she knocked at the door he pointed to. All these abrupt requests—scream, swing, knock, get me. Then a man opened the door and let them into the Ohrida Lake Restaurant. *Thank you, Kosta. Go back to bed, I'll lock it.* And the man, the friend, walked back upstairs.

She stood in the middle of the restaurant in darkness. The chairs and tables were pushed back to the edge of the room. Temelcoff brought out a bottle of brandy from under the counter and picked up two small glasses in the fingers of the same hand. He guided her to a small table, then walked back and, with a switch behind the zinc counter, turned on a light near her table. There were crests on the wall.

She still hadn't said a word. He remembered she had not even screamed when she fell. That had been him.

* * *

Nicholas Temelcoff is famous on the bridge, a daredevil. He is given all the difficult jobs and he takes them. He descends into the air with no fear. He is a solitary. He assembles ropes, brushes the tackle and pulley at his waist, and falls off the bridge like a diver over the edge of a boat. The rope roars alongside him, slowing with the pressure of his half-gloved hands. He is burly on the ground and then falls with terrific speed, grace, using the wind to push himself into corners of abutments so he can check driven rivets, sheering valves, the drying of the concrete under bearing plates and padstones. He stands in the air banging the crown pin into the upper cord and then shepherds the lower cord's slip-joint into position. Even in archive photographs it is difficult to find him. Again and again you see vista before you and the eye must search along the wall of sky to the speck of burned paper across the valley that is him, an exclamation mark, somewhere in the distance between bridge and river. He floats at the three hinges of the crescent-shaped steel arches. These knit the bridge together. The moment of cubism.

He is happiest at daily chores—ferrying tools from pier down to trestle, or lumber that he pushes in the air before him as if swimming in a river. He is a spinner. He links everyone. He meets them as they cling—braced by wind against the metal they are riveting or the wood sheeting they hammer into—but he has none of their fear. Always he carries his own tackle, hunched under his ropes and dragging the shining pitons behind him. He sits on a coiled seat of rope while he eats his lunch on the bridge. If he finishes early he cycles down Parliament Street to the Ohrida Lake Restaurant and sits in the darkness of the room as if he has had enough of light. Enough of space.

His work is so exceptional and time-saving he earns one dollar an hour while the other bridge workers receive forty cents. There is no jealousy towards him. No one dreams of doing half the things he does. For night work he is paid $1.25, swinging up into the rafters of a trestle holding a flare, free-falling like a dead star. He does not really need to see things, he has charted all that space, knows the pier footings, the width of the crosswalks in terms of seconds of movement—281 feet and 6 inches make up the central span of the bridge. Two flanking spans of 240 feet, two end spans of 158 feet. He slips into openings on the lower deck, tackles himself up to bridge level. He knows the precise height he is over the river, how long his ropes are, how many seconds he can free-fall to the pulley. It does not matter if it is day or night, he could be blindfolded. Black space is time. After swinging for three seconds he puts his feet up to link with the concrete edge of the next pier. He knows his position in the air as if he is mercury slipping across a map.

* * *

A South River parrot hung in its cage by the doorway of the Ohrida Lake Restaurant, too curious and interested in the events of the night to allow itself to be blanketed. It watched the woman who stood dead centre in the room in darkness. The man turned on one light behind the counter. Nicholas Temelcoff came over to the bird for a moment's visit after getting the drinks. 'Well, Alicia, my heart, how are you?' And walked away not waiting for the bird's reply, the fingers of his left hand delicately holding the glasses, his arm cradling the bottle.

He muttered as if continuing his conversation with the bird, in the large empty room. From noon till two it was full of men, eating and drinking. Kosta the owner and his waiter performing raucous shows for the crowd—the boss yelling insults at the waiter, chasing him past customers. Nicholas remembered the first time he had come there. The dark coats of men, the arguments of Europe.

He poured a brandy and pushed it over to her. 'You don't have to drink this but you can if you wish. Or see it as a courtesy.' He drank quickly and poured himself another. 'Thank you,' he said, touching his arm curiously as if it were the arm of a stranger.

She shook her head to communicate it was not all right, that it needed attention.

'Yes, but not now. Now I want to sit here.' There was a silence between them. 'Just to drink and talk quietly. . . . It is always night here. People step in out of sunlight and must move slow in the darkness.'

He drank again. 'Just for the pain.' She smiled. 'Now music.' He stood up free of the table as he spoke and went behind the counter and turned the wireless on low. He spun the dial till there was bandstand. He sat down again opposite her. 'Lot of pain. But I feel good.' He leaned back in his chair, holding up his glass. 'Alive.' She picked up her glass and drank.

'Where did you get that scar?' He pointed his thumb to the side of her nose. She pulled back.

'Don't be shy . . . talk. You must talk.' He wanted her to come out to him, even in anger, though he didn't want anger. Feeling such ease in the Ohrida Lake Restaurant, feeling the struts of the chair along his back, her veil tight on his arm. He just wanted her there near him, night all around them, where he could look after her, bring her out of the shock with some grace.

'I got about twenty scars,' he said, 'all over me. One on my ear here.' He turned and leaned forward so the wall-light fell onto the side of his head. 'See? Also this under my chin, that also broke my jaw. A coiling wire did that. Nearly kill me, broke my jaw. Lots more. My knees. . . .' He talked on. Hot tar burns on his arm. Nails in his calves. Drinking up, pouring her another shot, the woman's song on the radio. She heard the lyrics underneath Temelcoff's monologue as he talked and half mouthed the song and searched into her bright face. Like a woman with a fever.

This is the first time she has sat in a Macedonian bar, in any bar, with a drinking man. There is a faint glow from the varnished tables, the red checkered tablecloths of the day are folded and stacked. The alcove with its serving counter has an awning hanging over it. She realizes the darkness represents a Macedonian night where customers sit outside at their tables. Light can come only from the bar, the stars, the clock dressed in its orange and red electricity. So when customers step in at any time, what they are entering is an old courtyard of the Balkans. A violin. Olive trees. Permanent evening. Now the arbour-like wallpaper makes sense to her. Now the parrot has a language.

He talked on, slipping into phrases from the radio songs which is how he learned his words and pronunciations. He talked about himself, tired, unaware his voice split now into two languages, the woman hearing everything he said and trying to remember it all. He could see her eyes were alive, interpreting the room. He noticed the almost-tap of her finger to the radio music.

The blue eyes stayed on him as he moved, leaning his head against the wall. He drank, his breath deep into the glass so the fumes would hit his eyes and the sting of it keep him awake. Then he looked back at her. How old was she? Her brown hair so short, so new to the air. He wanted to coast his hand through it.

'I love your hair,' he said. 'Thank you . . . for the help. For taking the drink.'

She leaned forward earnestly and looked at him, searching out his face now. Words just on the far side of her skin, about to fall out. Wanting to know his name which he had forgotten to tell her. 'I love your hair.' His shoulder was against the wall and he was trying to look up. Then his eyes were closed. So deeply asleep he would be gone for hours. She could twist him around like a puppet and he wouldn't waken.

She felt as if she were the only one alive in this building. In such formal darkness. There was a terrible taste from that one drink still on her tongue, so she walked behind the zinc counter, turning on the tap to wash out her mouth. She moved the dial of the radio around a bit but brought it back securely to the same station. She was looking for that song he had half sung along with earlier, the voice of the singer strangely powerful and lethargic. She saw herself in the mirror. A woman whose hair was showing, caught illicit. She did what he had wanted to do. She ran her hand over her hair briefly. Then turned from her image.

Leaning forward she lay her face on the cold zinc, the chill there even past midnight. Upon her cheek, her eyelid. She let her skull roll to cool her forehead. The zinc was an edge of another country. She put her ear against the grey ocean of it. Its memory of a day's glasses. The spill and the wiping cloth. Confessional. Tabula Rasa.

At the table she positioned the man comfortably so he would not fall on his arm. *What is your name?* she whispered. She bent down and kissed him, then began walking around the room. This orchard. Strangers kiss softly as moths, she thought.

* * *

In certain weather, when fog fills the valley, the men stay close to each other. They arrive for work and walk onto a path that disappears into whiteness. What country exists on the other side? They move in groups of three or four. Many have already died during the building of the bridge. But especially on mornings like this there is a prehistoric fear, a giant bird lifting one of the men into the air. . . .

Nicholas has removed his hat, stepped into his harness, and dropped himself off the edge, falling thirty feet down through fog. He hangs under the spine of the bridge. He can see nothing, just his hands and the yard of pulley-rope above him. Six in the morning and he's already lost to that community of men on the bridge who are also part of the fairy tale.

He is parallel to the lattice-work of hanging structures. Now he enters the cages of steel and wood like a diver entering a sunken vessel that could at any moment tip over into deeper fracture zones of the sea floor. Nicholas Temelcoff works as the guy derricks raise and lower the steel — assembling it further out towards the next pier. He directs the steel through the fog. He is a fragment at the end of the steel bone the derrick carries on the end of its sixty-foot boom. The steel and Nicholas are raised up to a temporary track and from there the 'travellers' handle it. On the west end of the viaduct a traveller is used to erect the entire 150-foot span. The travellers are twin derricks fitted with lattice-work booms that can lift twelve tons into any position, like a carrot off the nose of the most recently built section of the bridge.

Nicholas is not attached to the travellers, his rope and pulleys link up only with the permanent steel of a completed section of the bridge. Travellers have collapsed twice before this and fallen to the floor of the valley. He is not attaching himself to a falling structure. But he hangs beside it, in the blind whiteness, slipping down further

within it until he can shepherd the new ribs of steel onto the end of
the bridge. He bolts them in, having to free-fall in order to use all of
his weight for the final turns of the giant wrench. He allows ten feet
of loose rope on the pulley, attaches the wrench, then drops onto
the two-foot handle, going down with it, and jars with the stiffening
of the bolt, falling off into the air, and jars again when he reaches
the end of the rope. He pulleys himself up and does it again. After
ten minutes every bone feels broken — the air he stops in feels hard
as concrete, his spine aching where the harness pulls him short.

He rises with the traveller from the lower level, calling out numbers
to the driver above him through the fog, alongside the clattering of the
woodwork he holds onto, the creaks and bends of the lattice drowning
out his call of *one — two — three — four* which is the only language he
uses. He was doing this once when a traveller collapsed at night — the
whole structure — the rope shredding around him. He let go, swinging
into the darkness, *anywhere* that might be free of the fifteen tons of
falling timber which crashed onto the lower level and then tumbled
down into the valley, rattling and banging in space like a trolley full of
metal. And on the far end of the swing, he knew he had escaped the
timber, but not necessarily the arm-thick wires that were now uncoiling
free, snaking powerfully in every direction through the air. On his return
swing he curled into a ball to avoid them, hearing the wires whip
laterally as they completed the energy of the break. His predecessor
had been killed in a similar accident, cut, the upper half of his body
found an hour later, still hanging in the halter.

By eight A.M. the fog is burned up and the men have already been
working for two hours. A smell of tar descends to Nicholas as workers
somewhere pour and begin to iron it level. He hangs waiting for the
whistle that announces the next journey of the traveller. Below him
is the Don River, the Grand Trunk, the CN and CP railway tracks, and
Rosedale Valley Road. He can see the houses and work shacks, the
beautiful wooden sheeting of the abutment which looks like a revival
tent. Wind dries the sweat on him. He talks in English to himself.

* * *

She takes the first step out of the Ohrida Lake Restaurant into the
blue corridor — the narrow blue lane of light that leads to the street.
What she will become she becomes in that minute before she is
outside, before she steps into the six-A.M. morning. The parrot Alicia
regards her departure and then turns its attention back to the man

asleep in the chair, one arm on the table, palm facing up as if awaiting donations, his head against the wall beside a crest. He is in darkness now, the open palm callused and hard. Five years earlier or ten years into the future the woman would have smelled the flour in his hair, his body having slept next to the dough, curling around it so his heat would make it rise. But now it was the hardness of his hands, the sound of them she would remember like wood against glass.

* * *

Commissioner Harris never speaks to Nicholas Temelcoff but watches often as he hooks up and walks at the viaduct edge listening to the engineer Taylor's various instructions. He appears abstracted but Harris knows he listens carefully. Nicholas never catches anyone's eye, as if he must hear the orders nakedly without seeing a face around the words.

His eyes hook to objects. Wood, a railing, a rope clip. He eats his sandwiches without looking at them, watching instead a man attaching a pulley to the elevated railings or studying the expensive leather on the shoes of the architects. He drinks water from a corked green bottle and his eyes are focused a hundred feet away. He never realizes how often he is watched by others. He has no clue that his gestures are extreme. He has no portrait of himself. So he appears to Harris and the others as a boy: say, a fanatic about toy cars, some stage they all passed through years ago.

Nicholas strides the parapet looking sideways at the loops of rope and then, without pausing, steps into the clear air. Now there is for Harris nothing to see but the fizzing rope, a quick slither. Nicholas stops twenty feet down with a thud against his heart. Sometimes on the work deck they will hear him slowly begin to sing various songs, breaking down syllables and walking around them as if laying the clauses out like tackle on a pavement to be checked for worthiness, picking up one he fancies for a moment then replacing it with another. As with sight, because Nicholas does not listen to most conversations around him, he assumes no one hears him.

For Nicholas language is much more difficult than what he does in space. He loves his new language, the terrible barriers of it. ' *"Does she love me?—Absolutely! Do I love her?—Positively!"* ' Nicholas sings out to the forty-foot pipe he ferries across the air towards the traveller. *He* knows Harris. He *knows* Harris by the time it takes him to walk the sixty-four feet six inches from sidewalk to sidewalk on the bridge and by his expensive tweed coat that cost more than the combined weeks' salaries of five bridge workers.

The event that will light the way for immigration in North America is the talking picture. The silent film brings nothing but entertainment—a pie in the face, a fop being dragged by a bear out of a department store—all events governed by fate and timing, not language and argument. The tramp never changes the opinion of the policeman. The truncheon swings, the tramp scuttles through a corner window and disturbs the fat lady's ablutions. These comedies are nightmares. The audience emits horrified laughter as Chaplin, blindfolded, rollerskates near the edge of the unbalconied mezzanine. No one shouts to warn him. He cannot talk or listen. North America is still without language, gestures and work and bloodlines are the only currency.

But it was a spell of language that brought Nicholas here, arriving in Canada without a passport in 1914, a great journey made in silence. Hanging under the bridge, he describes the adventure to himself, just as he was told a fairy tale of Upper America by those who returned to the Macedonian villages, those first travellers who were the judas goats to the west.

Daniel Stoyanoff had tempted them all. In North America everything was rich and dangerous. You went in as a sojourner and came back wealthy—Daniel buying a farm with the compensation he had received for losing an arm during an accident in a meat factory. Laughing about it! Banging his other hand down hard onto the table and wheezing with laughter, calling them all fools, sheep! As if his arm had been a dry cow he had fooled the Canadians with.

Nicholas had been stunned by the simplicity of the contract. He could see Stoyanoff's body livid on the killing floor—standing in two inches of cow blood, screaming like nothing as much as cattle, his arm gone, his balance gone. He had returned to the village of Oschima, his sleeve flapping like a scarf, and with cash for the land. He had looked for a wife with two arms and settled down.

In ten years Daniel Stoyanoff had bored everyone in the village with his tall tales and he couldn't wait for children to grow up and become articulate so he could thrill them with his sojourner's story of Upper America. What Daniel told them was that he had in fact lost both arms in the accident, but he happened to be rooming with a tailor who was out of work and who had been, luckily, on the killing floors of Schnaufer's that morning. Dedora the tailor had pulled gut out of a passing cat, stitched Daniel's right arm back on, and then turned for the other but a scrap dog had run off with it, one of those dogs that lounged by the doorway. Whenever you looked up from cutting and slicing the carcasses you would see them, whenever you left work at the end of the day in your blood-soaked overalls and boots they followed you, licking and chewing your cuffs.

Stoyanoff's story was told to all children of the region at a certain age and he became a hero to them. *Look*, he would say stripping off his shirt in the Oschima high street, irritating the customers of Petroff's outdoor bar once more, *look at what a good tailor Dedora was—no hint of stitches*. He drew an imaginary line around his good shoulder and the kids brought their eyes up close, then went over to his other shoulder and saw the alternative, the grotesque stump.

Nicholas was twenty-five years old when war in the Balkans began. After his village was burned he left with three friends on horseback. They rode one day and a whole night and another day down to Trikala, carrying food and a sack of clothes. Then they jumped on a train that was bound for Athens. Nicholas had a fever, he was delirious, needing air in the thick smoky compartments, wanting to climb up onto the roof. In Greece they bribed the captain of a boat a napoleon each to carry them over to Trieste. By now they all had fevers. They slept in the basement of a deserted factory, doing nothing, just trying to keep warm. There had to be no hint of illness before trying to get into Switzerland. They were six or seven days in the factory basement, unaware of time. One almost died from the high fevers. They slept embracing each other to keep warm. They talked about Daniel Stoyanoff's America.

On the train the Swiss doctor examined everyone's eyes and let the four friends continue over the border. They were in France. In Le Havre they spoke to the captain of an old boat that carried animals. It was travelling to New Brunswick.

Two of Nicholas' friends died on the trip. An Italian showed him how to drink blood in the animal pens to keep strong. It was a French boat called *La Siciliana*. He still remembered the name, remembered landing in Saint John and everyone thinking how primitive it looked. How primitive Canada was. They had to walk half a mile to the station where they were to be examined. They took whatever they needed from the sacks of the two who had died and walked towards Canada.

Their boat had been so filthy they were covered with lice. The steerage passengers put down their baggage by the outdoor taps near the toilets. They stripped naked and stood in front of their partners as if looking into a mirror. They began to remove the lice from each other and washed the dirt off with cold water and a cloth, working down the body. It was late November. They put on their clothes and went into the Customs sheds.

Nicholas had no passport, he could not speak a word of English. He had ten napoleons which he showed them to explain he wouldn't be dependent. They let him through. He was in Upper America.

He took a train for Toronto where there were many from his village; he would not be among strangers. But there was no work. So he took a train north to Copper Cliff, near Sudbury, and worked there in a Macedonian bakery. He was paid seven dollars a month with food and sleeping quarters. After six months he went to Sault Ste Marie. He still could hardly speak English and decided to go to school, working nights in another Macedonian bakery. If he did not learn the language he would be lost.

The school was free. The children in the class were ten years old and he was twenty-six. He used to get up at two in the morning and make dough and bake till 8:30. At nine he would go to school. The teachers were all young ladies and were very good people. During this time in the Sault he had translation dreams—because of his fast and obsessive studying of English. In the dreams trees changed not just their names but their looks and character. Men started answering in falsettos. Dogs spoke out fast to him as they passed him on the street.

When he returned to Toronto all he needed was a voice for all this language. Most immigrants learned their English from recorded songs or, until the talkies came, through mimicking actors on stage. It was a common habit to select one actor and follow him throughout his career, annoyed when he was given a small part, and seeing each of his plays as often as possible—sometimes as often as ten times during a run. Usually by the end of an east-end production at the Fox or Parrot Theatres the actors' speeches would be followed by growing echoes as Macedonians, Finns, and Greeks repeated the phrases after a half-second pause, trying to get the pronunciation right.

This infuriated the actors, especially when a line such as 'Who put the stove in the living room, Kristin?' — which had originally brought the house down — was now spoken simultaneously by a least seventy people and so tended to lose its spontaneity. When the matinee idol Wayne Burnett dropped dead during a performance, a Sicilian butcher took over, knowing his lines and his blocking meticulously, and money did not have to be refunded.

Certain actors were popular because they spoke slowly. Lethargic ballads, and a kind of blues where the first line of a verse is repeated three times, were in great demand. Sojourners walked out of their accent into regional American voices. Nicholas, unfortunately, would later chose Fats Waller as his model and so his emphasis on usually unnoticed syllables and the throwaway lines made him seem high-strung or dangerously anti-social or too loving.

But during the time he worked on the bridge, he was seen as a recluse. He would begin sentences in his new language, mutter, and walk away. He became a vault of secrets and memories. Privacy was the only weight he carried. None of his cohorts really knew him. This man, awkward in groups, would walk off and leave strange clues about himself, like a dog's footprints on the snowed roof of garage.

                                        * * *

Hagh! A doctor attending his arm, this is what woke him, brought him out of his dream. *Hab!* It was six hours since he had fallen asleep. Kosta was there. He saw that the veil and his shirt had been cut open by the doctor. Somehow, they said, he had managed to get his arm back into the socket.

He jerked his hand to the veil, looking at it closely.

She had stayed until Kosta came down in the early morning. She talked to him about the arm, to get a doctor, she had to leave. She spoke? Yes yes. What did she sound like? Hah? What more did Kosta know about her? He mentioned her black skirt. Before he left, Nicholas looked around the bar and found strips of the black habit she had cut away to make a skirt for the street.

When he walks into the fresh air outside the Ohrida Lake Restaurant, on the morning after the accident on the bridge, he sees the land-scape as something altered, no longer so familiar that it is invisible to him. Nicholas Temelcoff walks now seeing Parliament Street from the point of view of the woman — who had looked through his belt-satchel while he slept, found his wide wire shears, and used them to cut away the black lengths of her habit. When he walks out of the Ohrida Lake Restaurant that morning it is her weather he grows aware of. He knows he will find her.

There are long courtships which are performed in absence. This one is built perhaps on his remark about her hair or her almost-silent question as he was falling off some tower or bridge into sleep. The verge of sleep was always terrifying to Nicholas so he would drink himself into it blunting out the seconds of pure fear when he could not use his arms, would lie there knowing he'd witness the half-second fall before sleep, the fear of it greater than anything he felt on the viaduct or any task he carried out for the Dominion Bridge Company.

As he fell, he remembers later, he felt a woman's arm reaching for him, curious about his name.

He is aware of her now, the twin. What holds them together is not the act which saved her life but those moments since. The lost song on the radio. His offhand and relaxed flattery to a nun with regard to her beauty. Then he had leaned his head back, closed his eyes for too long, and slept.

A week later he rejoins the flatbed truck that carries the tar and fire, jumps on with the other men, and is back working at the bridge. His arm healed, he swings from Pier D to Pier C, ignores the stories he hears of the nun who disappeared. He lies supine on the end of his tether looking up towards the struts of the bridge, pivoting slowly. He knows the panorama of the valley better than any engineer. Like a bird. Better than Edmund Burke, the bridge's architect, or Harris, better than the surveyors of 1912 when they worked blind through the bush. The panorama revolves with him and he hangs in this long silent courtship, her absence making him look everywhere.

In a year he will open up a bakery with the money he has saved. He releases the catch on the pulley and slides free of the bridge.

MICHAEL ONDAATJE was born in 1943 in Colombo, Ceylon (now Sri Lanka) and moved to England in 1954 before immigrating to Canada in 1962. He attended Bishop's University, the University of Toronto (B.A.), and Queen's University (M.A.). He has taught English literature at the University of Western Ontario (1967-70) and at Glendon College, York University (since 1971), all the while writing poetry and fiction, making films, working with Coach House Press, and editing *Brick*. His works include *The Dainty Monsters* (Toronto: Coach House, 1967); *the man with seven toes* (Toronto: Coach House, 1969); *The Collected Works of Billy the Kid: Left Handed Poems* (Toronto: Anansi, 1970); *Rat Jelly* (Toronto: Coach House, 1973); *Coming Through Slaughter* (Toronto: Anansi, 1976); *There's a Trick with a Knife I'm Learning To Do: Poems 1963-1978* (Toronto: McClelland and Stewart, 1979); *Running in the Family* (Toronto: McClelland and Stewart, 1982); *Secular Love* (Toronto: Coach House, 1985); *In the Skin of a Lion* (Toronto: McClelland and Stewart, 1987).

LINDA HUTCHEON is the daughter and granddaughter of Italian immigrants from Bagni di Lucca, Tuscany (to Toronto, 1925) and Maiano, Friuli (to Viscount, Saskatchewan, 1910). She teaches English and Comparative Literature at the University of Toronto. She is the author of *Narcissistic Narrative* (1980); *Formalism and the Freudian Aesthetic* (1984); *A Theory of Parody* (1985); *A Poetics of Postmodernism: History, Theory, Fiction* (1988); *The Canadian Postmodern* (1988); and *The Politics of Postmodernism* (1989).

Do you feel like a 'Sri Lankan Canadian' writer? Does that designation even mean anything to you?

Sure, I guess I feel I'm *that* more than anything else. I grew up in Sri Lanka and lived in England for about eight years, and then came here. But I don't feel much of 'England' in me. I *do* feel I have been allowed the migrant's double perspective, in the way, say, someone like Gertrude Stein was 're-focused' by Paris. I came here at the age of nineteen when everyone changes, when everyone wants to remake themselves. I was lucky to come then and go to university then. It is much more difficult to arrive at thirty or forty and begin again.

Your work has recently come under some scrutiny in places like The Toronto South Asian Review *for being more concerned with 'aesthetic' issues — art, art's design, or the artist — than with the specific social and cultural conditions of being a Sri Lankan writing in Canada. Do you feel this response is a refusal to 'allow you your subject', so to speak? What's your reaction to that kind of criticism?*

As a writer I don't think I'm concerned with art and aesthetic issues, any more than I would want to be just concerned with making the subject of being a Sri Lankan in Canada my one and only subject. I go to writing to discover as many aspects of myself and the world around me as I can. I go to discover, to explore, not to state the case I already know. *Running in the Family* is a book about a family and a father, essentially. It would have been very easy to make the whole thing an ironic or even sarcastic look at a generation. But why bother? When characters in books are 'lesser' than the writer, there seems to be a great loss in the subtleties and truths being discovered or discussed. Obviously the politics of the time is important. But it *is* a book about a family. Also the thing about writing is that you want to represent or make characters who are believable, who are fully rounded, and that stops you from making them just politically good or politically vicious. I'm more interested, I guess, in making people as believable and complex and intricate as possible than in making an argument in a novel or even a memoir—which is also a kind of political statement, I think. I think if you enter a novel with just an argument, you reduce the book.

And maybe your reader's options too.

Right.

At the risk of grossly oversimplifying, I've always thought that one of your major concerns—even if displaced or distanced from the personal or at least the autobiographical—was that experience of 'otherness' and the political consciousness that goes with awareness of racial and ethnic difference. I mean this whether you are writing about Buddy Bolden in Coming Through Slaughter *or about an American outlaw in* The Collected Works of Billy the Kid. *There seems to be a desire to explore the state of being 'different' within a dominant culture.*

That is certainly what I'm drawn to, especially the unspoken and unwritten stories—the 'un-historical' stories. That's one of the areas I think writers should write about. The media have created a kind of false surface of content in which they loll around, and they have to be reminded of the other side.

You once said you liked Stuart MacKinnon's The Interval *because 'it starts from the personal and moves out'. Would that process also describe your own relation to your own 'otherness'?*

Yes, I think so. When I began *In the Skin of a Lion*, for instance, I didn't have a plan for what it would become. I didn't have a concept of writing about immigrants in Toronto in 1917; it just happened. No one will quite believe me, but I became interested in the characters, and the characters turned out to be immigrants who worked on things like bridges. The writing was a learning process, as the writing of books often is for me. I don't go into the book with a full set of ideas: this is going to be a book about this issue or that period of time. For me *that*'s the pleasure of writing: learning about things, discovering the work of Lillian Petroff, and so learning about where the Macedonians were living in Toronto and how they lived in this city. That moving out from the self and into a wider sphere is what I enjoy. In *Lion* and in *Running* I wanted to move out from the focus on one individual as in *Slaughter*, for instance.

Why the Macedonian community?

That evolved. I came to that community through the character of Nicholas Temelcoff, who was one of the bridge-builders. I went to an evening of Macedonian celebrations where there was a reference to a bridge builder named Temelcoff and so I asked and found out about him. And so, through his story, I discovered more and more. And then all kinds of strange coincidences happened: the typist I gave the manuscript to—Donya Peroff—was Macedonian and she is also a baker's daughter. She helped me too, giving me advice about Macedonian recipes. Everywhere I went, I was sort of guided. I got caught up in the whole political range of Macedonians, from left to right.

In the period of time the book covers, the main immigration influx was European, not Asian as it is today. And at the same time, I didn't want to write an Asian story for the very reason it would have been interpreted as a personal saga. I wanted to step away from a private story into a public one, a social one—although obviously much of the emotion that the migrants feel in the book has a personal source.

I just didn't want to limit this story, which I think is important, to one which would have been seen as a sort of self-portrait.

This novel, In the Skin of a Lion, *seems to address the Canadian aspect of the ethnic experience most directly. But other works come at the same issues from different angles. For example,* Running in the Family *seems to me the investigation of a* writer—*as much as that of a son or a Sri Lankan*—*into a personal and now physically foreign past, much as is Rushdie's* Midnight's Children. *In both cases, how these works are written cannot be separated from what they are about: that is, it's a matter of what you once called 'the architecture'*—*of form, meaning, tone, rhythm*—*as well as the building bricks themselves. Could the South Asian or the transplanted-immigrant experience you share, at least to some extent, with Rushdie account in any way for this common integration of the formal and the personal-historical?*

Certainly. One of the things I really like about Rushdie's work is his language—and also his ambition. I greatly admire him for both. He's one of these writers who takes on the world and talks seriously and personally about major issues. I think the form in something like *Midnight's Children* or *The Satanic Verses* is splendid, but it's the kind of form that is created by a juggler with fifteen balls in the air and three of them fall down and bounce in the wrong direction. One of those bad bounces would ruin a Jane Austen novel. And yet, there are twelve other balls up still in the air. I like that sense of a book being rather like a creaking ship carrying everything it can take across the ocean.

You don't write novels like that, though.

No, but I like the kind of book I can't write. In that sense, I'm amazed. When I write, at first I write in a kind of loose, random, sort of accidental way to try to catch everything that's happening around me or around the story, going down roads that end up nowhere and so forth. And the form and shape for me emerge out of that. I'm in the middle of a book right now and I have no idea what I'm going to find at the end. I still have to shape and gather and find a sort of form that represents all those emotions and all those explorations and pull them into a whole.

Was Running in the Family *different, harder to write than your other books, because of the closeness of the material?*

Yes, but *In the Skin of a Lion* was the closest emotionally to me, in some odd way. I finished that book and immediately I missed all the characters. I think that was partly the fact that they were totally my creations, in spite of the fact that some were partly based on real people. In the other books, there really was a Billy the Kid; there really was a Buddy Bolden. What I had to do there was a 'version' of Buddy Bolden. In that sense, I also did a 'version' of my father in *Running in the Family*. In *Skin* I was writing more of a normal kind of novel; the characters were more invented and therefore much more a part of myself.

In Running in the Family, *you offer much about the geographical and historical background of Sri Lanka itself—which is very important for the reader. Was it also important for you?*

Again, that was something I learned, or re-learned, as I wrote. I hadn't been back for a number of years and that gap allowed me a certain objectivity; yet at the same time I was totally caught up in rediscovering my childhood. I guess that's what drew me to the memoir form. So here I was writing about a group of people that seemed utterly separate in some ways from the world around them, unaware of what was going on around them politically or whatever. So I wanted to establish a kind of map; I wanted to make clear that this was just part of a long tradition of invasions and so forth. So the map and the history and the poetry made a more social voice, became the balance to the family story, the other end of the see-saw.

This reflecting of the public in the private, and vice versa, makes this more than a memoir, then, doesn't it? Is it memoir? fiction? history? autobiography? biography?

I'm not quite sure what form that book is. I think all those things are there.

Many of the authors in this anthology have first written autobiographical fiction, though, where you have written this sort of postmodern memoir . . . and done so later.

I suppose *Running* should have been a first book, but I wasn't ready early on—emotionally or technically—to write it.

Aritha Van Herk says she has been trying for nine years to write her novel about her family's Dutch immigrant experience in Can-

ada. She wants it to be right—I assume, emotionally and techni-
cally—so she has had to apprentice herself, in a sense, and write
other works first.

I think that's very true. I feel very lucky in some ways because I had
already done a kind of wonky historical novel and then I had worked
with Paul Thompson on a documentary of the play *The Farm Show*.
That's essentially a play about Paul and where he grew up in Ontario,
though it's also about a farming community. It seemed to me, though,
to be about Paul going back and talking to his relatives again and
telling *us* where *he* came from. Working on a documentary film like
that, where you can go back and rewind and look at this guy's
reactions and see the evasiveness and all these tricks, that was a
tremendous thing for me to witness and share. I don't think I could
have written *Running* without going through that kind of experience.
You'd think that producing a play about a farm community in Ontario
and writing about a family in Sri Lanka would be different. But our
influences today come from all over the world. The recent novels
from Africa and Australia influence us as much as books from Ontario.
I think this has had a major impact on our generation of writers.
Graham Swift's *Waterland* is a wonderful regional novel [about the
fen country of England] but I don't think it could have been written
without his having read the contemporary North Americans and the
Rushdies. And he takes all that in and he goes and writes a fabulous
English regional novel. Ishiguro's new book is the same sort of thing:
he goes all the way around being Japanese living in England and
then comes back and writes a novel about a butler. I think it's just
remarkable. It seems odd to say these writers are influenced by
Achebe or Calvino, but they are.

How do you feel about readers and critics who don't want you to
write in this kind of international context, who want you to write
'Canadian' or 'ethnic' novels?

I guess I like being a writer because of the freedom that is allowed
me: I can write about whatever I want to write about. Those demands
seem to be more to do with the world of sociologists or motivated by
political usefulness. I feel little responsibility to that sort of demand.

MARILÚ MALLET b. 1944

How Are You?

We're both refugees. Neither of us has a passport. Our coats were both rescued from the garbage. We're trying to adapt. Casimir was sponsored by a Jewish group looking for a tax write-off. I, by a committee of former priests who had lived in Latin America. He was given a TV set and a black suit. I got a mattress complete with bedbugs. He talks about synagogues, I talk about the priests and their committee. We have something in common. Something that oozes out of our pores: a touch of scepticism, a vestige of bitterness.

We met at language class. An inadvertent glance and some words about the weather. Seven months of snow. The freezing, cutting wind.

'And the people here, they're so simple-minded, they're interested in nothing and nobody, they just don't want their lives complicated. . . .'

He is tall, blond and blue-eyed, with an aquiline nose—the face of a movie actor. But there's something more about it, a certain interesting hardness. I'm short, thin and pale, with black, curly hair. Seen together, we're nothing but contrasts.

Our subway car was late. I asked Casimir:

'What's the matter?'

A man in a beige raincoat answered with the indifference so common here:

'They're cleaning up the blood.'

Perhaps it all happened because we realized at the same time, from that chilling remark, that in the next station there had been another suicide.

'That's February for you,' said Casimir.

We got off at Berri and took the Longueuil subway line. There we changed to a bus full of Greeks, Pakistanis, Arabs, Portuguese and I don't know what else, all blue as mulberries from the cold. They pay us forty-five dollars a week for going to these courses and learning English. He said he came from Lodz. I'm from Valparaiso. He left Poland because he is a Jew. I told him about the military putsch.

The learning system is simple but effective. The teacher says, 'How
are you?' and we repeat it after him, taking turns, just like real
schoolchildren but grown tall or bearded or fat or depressed. The
first day he said 'How are you' about a hundred times until I was
dizzy. Not counting how often I heard it from our side. Casimir
winked at me and tapped his temple with his finger. He was going
crazy too. I smiled at him across the room. Twenty weeks of this just
to get money for the rent.

There's a half-hour break for lunch. No more How-are-you's for a
while. But we hear the deafening noise of Coca-Cola and soup
machines in the large cafeteria. Casimir and I sit down with the five
thousand other immigrant pupils in this language school. Each one
has his little packed lunch, 'ethnic' lunches, rice or shishkebab,
goulash or meat pie, pasta or marzipan. Wrapped in aluminum foil
or plastic bags. Neither of us had ever tried soup from a machine
before, or coffee that tasted like gasoline.

'I think I have a fever,' I told him.

'It's the language course,' he said. 'It's as if they erased your power
of reason, the way you wipe out a tape when you record on top of
the message.'

It's funny how a clever remark, coming from an attractive person,
seems even more convincing. And when the conversation is in a new
language, you feel as if you're rediscovering words. In that moment
we looked at each other as if we belonged. Two lonely people who
have found someone at last, to their surprise. He asked me if I had
any family. One sister and my father, I replied. He was an only son,
and his widowed mother was still in Poland.

A strident bell put an end to the break, and the cafeteria emptied.
The garbage containers were stuffed with papers and wrappers.
Crumbs and overflowing ashtrays littered the tables. The afternoon
was the same as the morning, with its How-are-you's.

We went back together in the subway. He lives on St Lawrence
Boulevard, near Waldman's, half a block from the Portuguese store
where they pluck the chickens live before the customer's eyes. That's
where he buys the chicken feet and necks to make his Jewish barley
soup. He's also just a stone's throw from Four Brothers and War-
shaw's supermarkets, and cheese stores and all those little ethnic
shops that sell unusual products at cheap prices.

I live on Van Horne near the post office, the supermarket, the drug store, the bank, and the bus-stop. I keep telling myself it's not such a bad neighbourhood. Casimir rents a room above a delicatessen that sells bagels and cream cheese and smoked-meat sandwiches. I, oddly enough, live above a pizzeria. That explains why my building is infested with cockroaches. Sometimes at night when I go in the bathroom I see them running in the tub or the wash-basin. These cockroaches are pale, long, and yellowish, not like the Chilean ones which are black and round.

'Are Polish cockroaches different?' I asked him.

'Perhaps,' he replied.

He says that there are lots of them in his kitchen. They are actually frightening at times. The exterminator who came there two weeks ago told him each cockroach lays eighty eggs, and the eggs take twenty-eight days to turn into active creatures with legs. His landlord is stingy and saves oil by turning down the heat. Like Casimir, he is a Polish Jew, one of the community. I'm lucky by comparison. I can't say that my house is freezing. On the contrary, I almost suffocate in the stifling heat. I live on the fourth floor, and there's an elevator. That gives a little class to the building. The elevator locks, and there's a different key for each floor. The landlady, a Greek dressmaker with a blond wig, lives across from me. At times I pay her an angry visit, trying with gestures to make her understand that somebody forgot to shut the inside grill of the lift and I've had to climb the hundred and twenty-two steps, exhausted. Another small but mysterious detail about this elevator: every Monday some unidentified tenant with idle hands draws a gigantic male sex in coloured chalk on its wall. The Greek woman's son comes home drunk and discovers the drawing, and never fails to hammer on every door in a vain attempt to find the guilty artist.

'Not easy to get to sleep, Casimir!'

Every day the trip from Berri to Longueuil, from Longueuil to La Prairie. One class after the other, with Casimir. We get to know other students. A Bulgarian ballet dancer who escaped from a plane during its landing in Ghent; Mahmala, a Lebanese industrialist who despises the rest of us; three Haitians, refugees from Duvalier; a Greek worker; a quiet Portuguese girl who works nights; Alberto, a Colombian schoolteacher; and the professor, a Hindu, a coffee-coloured ringer for an upper-class Englishman. Altogether there are twelve human beings in the overheated room where we can see snow through the window and the distant white horizon. We sit very close to each other, Casimir and I. Sometimes I look at him, sometime he looks my way. He often sighs deeply and rolls his eyes toward the ceiling, showing his impatience.

On Mondays we usually start the class with the sentence, 'What did you do during the weekend?' We hear Mahmala recount in broken English how his wife bathed him on Saturday night. Lakis, the Greek, is a night watchman for Canadian National Railways. The Portuguese girl's name is Ilda, she lives with her mother and seven sisters. The Colombian arrived in Canada with his whole family and the maid and is trying to scrape together the money for a house. I don't talk much. Casimir says he's the only Jew who eats herring seven days a week. Oh yes, I forgot to mention Félix, a Spaniard and formerly a priest. He was a late starter in the course. He's trying desperately to make up for his years of abstinence. He makes his approach to the girls in the class on the slimmest pretext — apparently without success. After each failed attempt he laughs to himself, glassy-eyed and happy, his mind filled with what might have been.

During breaks we talk to each other. Almost always it's about some bad news from one of our countries. Murders, military coups, sometimes wars, new economic crises, or exotic disasters like flood, earthquakes, hurricanes, or unexpected droughts.

At noon Casimir and I go for walks. He says Siberia isn't as cold as Montreal. I had never seen snow, and I can't get used to the stalactites hanging from the moustaches of people with colds. He's used to the cold in Poland. He shows me how to wear my scarf and toque and gloves, and explains how I mustn't press my nose against store windows. It might stick and I'd go away with open nostrils like a skull. Casimir says the cold acts as a local anaesthetic. You feel nothing, but your cartilage is solidifying, your ears can fall off and silently sink into the snow. For me so many things are new: being careful on the slippery sidewalks, with my heavy coat and big boots. Here everything is provided for, he says. If you slip and break a bone you can sue the city for not clearing the way in time. That's nice to know. Some people get pensions. The ones who unthinkingly and involuntarily were hurt this way and can't work. Night and day the snow removal goes on, with blowers that from time to time suck in a pedestrian.

'People have to be very careful about their children,' Casimir explained.

The other students don't attract much of our attention. They are shy and introverted and monotonously repeat anything they are told. Their weekend activities are also not very exciting. Shopping, washing clothes, cooking, watching TV (for those who have one). We listen to detailed descriptions of their apartments, the nearby park, the stores where they shop, and the buses they take to come to the school.

We eat together, and very quickly. It's always an egg sandwich that we've made at home. In the few minutes left we go skating. We've bought used skates for fifty cents, from a Jewish shoemaker Casimir knew about, on St Lawrence. Casimir was a champion skater on the frozen rivers of Poland. I can barely stay on my feet. He helps by taking my arm. From time to time he lets me go and turns to look at me, his frosted breath steaming out of his mouth. We don't talk during these times. The silence is comfortable, almost intimate. Sometimes he rearranges my scarf, and I let him do it. I wait for these small, familiar gestures, observing his handsome face, saying nothing, as if something secret had made a delicate landing between us.

After class we take the subway together. We go for a coffee at a restaurant in one of the stations. He has all kinds of strategies for living cheaply. He buys leftover fish and greens, and old cheese. He checks out the garbage cans of food stores. He steals his electricity from the hydro line in the street with a special device he made himself. He even has a stove that was donated by his Jewish association. When we go our separate ways we kiss each other on both cheeks. He gives me a hug, and holds me a second or two longer than necessary. Just imperceptibly: I notice it but no one else would.

Perhaps it was our previous education that brought us closer. That's what I think now when I try to find what lay behind our relationship. He had studied economics, and I was in social sciences. We feel that we're the educated ones in the class. We're the ones that speak English best. The language of success, of work, of the opportunity everyone came here in search of. Many of the other pupils hang around us to improve or practise the little they have mastered. This gives us a certain feeling of power in the school for immigrants. Sometimes the texts we have to repeat start with phrases like 'Try me!' or 'Give me a chance!' I suppose it's to stimulate our ambition. And we also make up written dialogues. We're divided up in groups according to our level, and Casimir and I always end up together. We write stories as if they were for a real play. He is a

Strindberg fan, I like Ibsen. He talks about Grotowski, I about Polanski. He's a bit like Polanski. Something about his manner. . . . Not long ago we did a parody of Romeo and Juliet. We rehearsed it in a café, and when we parted he kissed me on the lips. I tried to avoid it, I was afraid, I had a sense of foreboding. He seemed surprised at himself. Later he called me up and tried to explain. I went to sleep unconcerned, thinking of his nice-boy face.

Class after class, break after break, glance after glance, the weeks went past. The course was coming to an end. The teacher, always enthusiastic about life in Canada, showed us films like 'The Story of a Lumberman', 'The Life of a Tractor Driver', or 'The Weekend of a Worker on the Snow Removal Team'. All the films were optimistic, and dealt with the joys of productive labour. He taught us songs like 'Jingle Bells' which we sang off key in a smiling chorus, each with his indigenous accent. Above all, he taught us to fill out forms and make phone calls in our search for work. Work? Had it come to that! Work. The word provoked anxious frowns and long faces.

'Marcia, let's leave together,' Casimir said during the break.

So we took the bus together to Longueuil station, with its shops and lottery stand. I was going to pay my fare, but he said:

'No, no, I'm paying.'

But we didn't move. We stood waiting in front of the turnstile as the crowd went by. Suddenly he exclaimed:

'Did you see that?'

The machines had rejected two subway tickets.

'I always have to wait, but I eventually get through free.'

Penny-pinching, saving a bit here, a bit there—I hated it. He was Jewish through and through. In the subway he said:

'I've been wanting to invite you for so long. I've got some really good soup, wait till you see. Leftovers—that's my specialty!'

I thought it over for a moment, then started laughing. Was I going to refuse my first invitation in this town?

His apartment was small. One room, with a distinct atmosphere. He shared a bathroom and toilet with the owner. We ate some smoked herring and soup. Leftovers or not, it wasn't too bad. We had some wine and I felt a little tipsy. The place was empty, with no decorations on its white walls. There were no chairs, and we had to sit on the edge of the bed. He asked me about the military putsch. He couldn't get into his head that such a thing had happened. Such an exemplary country, so unique. I explained the usual things about multinationals and imperialism. A small, poor country hasn't the right to make its own decisions. He told me about Poland. For centuries it had been divided, dismembered, invaded. For a time it had been wiped right off the map. He became aggressive, saying that socialism wasn't worth the trouble, it led to a paranoid daily life and the new ruling class of bureaucrats. I was sick of the whole discussion. But he went on:

'The multinationals are one thing, but on the other hand you simply copied our mistakes.'

He stopped and came near me, kissed my right hand.

I drew back a little, thinking of other things.

'It's been months and months since I had anybody near me. Come and lie down beside me for a minute.'

'No!' I said, apprehensive.

'Why should we deny ourselves a few moments of tenderness?'

His eyes were like crystal.

He cuddled close to my shoulder.

'It's snowing,' he said.

He held my face and said very slowly:

'You're beautiful!'

I said nothing. I floated in the moment, imagining the snow and the freezing wind outside, thinking about the two of us there on the edge of the bed, refugees for opposite reasons. I wanted to run away, but we kissed interminably, mingling our despairs and solitudes. I was trembling.

'What's the matter?' Casimir asked, stroking my hair.

I was weeping softly. He repeated,

'Come, please?'

I almost gave in, but I was overcome by a terrible sadness. I gathered my courage and whispered:

'I can't.'

He put out the light. We undressed, little by little. Awkwardly, we embraced. Suddenly I pulled back and, in spite of myself, told him how I had been arrested.

'I was in a police station,' I said. 'Two policemen beat me . . .'

He switched on the lamp again. Through my tears I saw Casimir, naked, and realized that he had great scars on one shoulder and arm. And he discovered the marks on my breast and back.

'This too?' he asked, pointing to the burn mark on my breast.

I nodded and closed my eyes for a moment. I didn't want to talk.

I didn't want to remember. Then I opened them, and saw his grave face. His blond hair was tousled. His expression was hard and tragic. 'I'll tell you a secret,' he said softly, playing with my fingers. Was he afraid someone would hear him?

'I'm not Jewish.'

He paused for a second, then went on in the same hushed voice: 'I had to learn Yiddish and go to the synagogue. I got these marks trying to escape from prison.' He showed me his arm. 'For years I tried to get out of Poland. At last I discovered an organization that helped Jews leave the country. I spent seven years telling lies, appearing before one tribunal after another. I swore my mother had a Jewish lover during the time of the Nazis. I went around with a cyanide pill in my pocket, just in case they . . .'

We were both melancholy now. He was frowning, his eyes half-closed. Nervously, he took my hand. He ran a finger over my face, shyly, barely touching. He kissed me on the cheek. We held each other tight, searching for more marks of pain and violence on the other's body.

He turned off the light again, and the darkness drove us under the covers. We kissed in silence, side by side, together and alone, two prisoners in a single trap.

The next day was Saturday. We woke early. Casimir made coffee, and said in his usual tone:

'What are you going to do next week when the course ends? How will you pay the rent?'

'I don't know. Work in a factory. Or a restaurant.'

'You're young, you're pretty, forget about building socialism, I know some businessmen in their fifties, they'd be delighted to marry you. The Town of Mount Royal is a good neighbourhood, people with money and Cadillacs and big houses. Maybe money doesn't make you happy, but it helps. I'll introduce you to some of them.'

I laughed, but it must have looked more like a grimace.

'Are you crazy?'

'Crazy? I'm just fed up with being a candidate for living, I'm fed up being poor. Hanging around with people that are run-of-the-mill mediocrities. I want dough. Whatever I have to do for it.'

I looked at him attentively. He was excited.

'I'm going to Toronto,' he added. 'There's nothing doing here. The political situation is too unstable. Quebec's going to be a big problem.'

He went over to his bed and took out a shoe-box from beneath it.

He removed the lid and showed me what was inside: the photo of a very ugly woman. He paused for a moment to see my reaction, then exclaimed:

'I'm going to marry her!'

After a second he went on:

'Her father owns a factory.'

I was aghast.

'You never told me!'

'It was through the synagogue,' he said.

And he offered me a second cup of coffee, saying:

'So there's an end to romance. I'd like to believe in it, but . . .'

I didn't want coffee. I put on my overcoat, my boots, my scarf, and my toque.

'Hey, we're going skating Monday, aren't we?'

I nodded. As I crossed the threshold I saw some enormous cockroaches, yellowish like mine. The only thing we have in common, I thought. The exhaust from the buses soiled the snow, turning it beige or even coffee-coloured. People bent over forward to escape the bitter wind.

That Monday Casimir didn't come to the course. I phoned him at home but there was no answer. Then the course was over.

A month later I got a card from him. From Toronto. It said, 'Married and manager.' Then came a few details of his plans: 'When I get my citizenship I'm changing my name again. Casimir Davis or better Henry Davis. There's a lot of prejudice against Jews here. I'll be able to visit Poland and see my mother. And some day I'll be a wheel on Wall Street.' Below, in capitals, he added:

HOW ARE YOU?

I re-read the card with care. No, there was no return address.

MARILÚ MALLET is a Chilean writer and filmmaker, born in 1944, who came to Canada as a political refugee after the *coup d'état* against President Salvador Allende in 1973. She has directed a number of films, television programs, and documentaries about Latin America and the immigrant experience in Canada for Radio-Québec and the National Film Board. Her film *Journal inachevé* won the Prix de la critique québécoise and the Prix spécial du Jury at the Biarritz Film

Festival in 1983. Her short stories, originally published in French, have appeared in many Quebec magazines and have received wide critical attention. She currently teaches cinema at the Collège Bois-de-Boulogne and works as a freelance film director in Montreal. Her first collection, *Les Compagnons de l'horloge-pointeuse* (Montréal: Editions Québec/Amérique, 1981) was translated from French into English by Alan Brown as *Voyage to the Other Extreme* (Montreal: Véhicule Press, 1985) and her second, *Miami trip*, appeared in French in 1986 (Montréal: Editions Québec/Amérique).

HUGH HAZELTON is a Montreal writer and translator who immigrated to Canada from Chicago in 1969. He has published three books of poetry and is currently working on an anthology of Canadian writing on Latin America. He teaches Spanish translation at Concordia University.

You were one of the first Latin American women writers, and certainly one of the first Chilean exiles, to become known in Quebec, weren't you?

Well, I work in film, and first established myself here as a film director. Later I sent out the manuscript of my first collection of short stories to publishers that I'd chosen from the telephone directory. The book was finally accepted by a small publishing house that burnt down a few months later. I'd just photocopied the manuscript the day before. Luckily, Québec/Amérique, a larger Montreal publisher, was looking for young authors at the time, and they brought out the book. There were quite a few authors who weren't Québécois by birth who began publishing in French about then: Désirée Sucshny, who was Hungarian, and Fulvio Caccia and Antonio D'Alfonso, who were Italian. There was a whole generation of authors who had grown up in other languages, but were writing in French. I'd come to Canada later and wrote in Spanish, so my work had to be translated.

Do you think that being Chilean had anything to do with the excellent reception that your books had here? Was there still a lot of concern and solidarity with Chile at that time?

No. People had been very interested in Chile ten years before, after the *coup d'état* against President Allende in 1973. Quebec welcomed Chilean exiles and gave us space to make films about Chile and adapting to life here; there was a lot of solidarity. But by the time I began publishing, we had been forgotten. I think that what the publisher liked was that the tone of my stories was more ironic than usual in Quebec, and that the world they described seemed strange. People liked the characters, especially when I satirized the Chilean bureaucracy, because there was also plenty of bureaucracy here. 'How Are You?' was quite popular. I think that people enjoyed finding stories which were written here in Quebec but were not about the Québécois. The book was a curiosity for them.

Had you travelled much outside Chile before coming to Canada?

Yes, I had; in fact, I'd only actually lived in Chile for about half my life. I was born there, but when I was five, my family moved to France and then to Italy. I returned to Chile when I was about ten, and finished high school there. Then I went to college in the United States, first in Los Angeles, and then at the University of California in Davis.

How did you feel about living in the States at the time?

I didn't like Los Angeles. It was difficult living there; the city struck me as being extremely violent. I didn't really get to know many Americans there; I just stayed with my family all the time. In Los Angeles, Hispanics were not treated well; there's a huge Mexican population there with a long historical relationship with the US. As a Chilean of French descent, I didn't physically fit the American stereotype of a Hispanic. Americans associate Spanish with people with Mexican features. I looked like any other person of European descent, so I never felt any racial prejudice. Discrimination is based on colour in the US. They thought I was a rarity, but in fact there are a lot of people like me in Latin America. I was outside of their frame of reference, and a bit confusing to them.

When did you return to Chile?

I went back to finish my studies in architecture and cinema. Then, in the late sixties, I went to Cuba for a few years to work. When Salvador Allende and the socialists were elected in Chile in 1971, I came back to help and participate in the changes that were taking place. After Allende was killed in the military *coup* in 1973, I sought asylum in the Canadian embassy in Santiago, and then came to Canada as a political refugee.

Had you ever thought of coming to Canada before that?

No, never. But after the *coup*, it seemed like a good choice. I had to leave the country, but the question was where to go. I didn't want to return to Europe, because women's lives are more restricted there than they are here. I knew the work of the National Film Board and that Canada was one of the only places in the world in which film production was financed by the state. I also knew that it had a social-democratic tradition. Of course, I knew that part of the country was French-speaking, which also made it easier and more accessible, and that Canada was similar to the United States, where I'd already lived. I wanted to go to a country more in keeping with my own ideals.

When you were writing 'How Are You?', what were your feelings toward refugees from the communist countries? Did you feel their interests coincided with yours? I'm thinking of Casimir, for example. There seems to be a gulf between him and the narrator.

That's true. My first impression was that the world was completely different from the way I'd imagined it in Chile. I'd always thought that a few developed countries decided everything among themselves, and that they just divided up the refugees if there were any problems. Real national independence seemed to be out of the question; it was just a question of which economic block your country happened to be in. Casimir was based on a person I knew then, and this person was really quite like me. He was Polish, and came from a world without a future for the young: a poor country, with a large bureaucracy.

How did you feel toward economic immigrants from other parts of the world?

Basically we didn't have anything in common, either ideologically or culturally. Most of them weren't interested in culture. They were from another social class.

Do you think that you, as a Latin American and Chilean refugee, were more idealistic, that you thought social change was still possi-

ble? Did you feel that economic immigrants had come basically because of material factors, simply to improve their standard of living?

Yes, because they were from a social class in which they hadn't even been able to educate their children. They'd come for the American Dream. I think that the immigration policy here favours the poorer, less-educated economic immigrant over the better-educated professional. People like me are seen as competing for middle-class jobs with those who were born here. The policy is based first on cheap manpower, and second on attracting capital and bringing in people with money to invest.

Have you maintained much contact with the Chilean community?

No. If you really want to become a part of the country here, you don't have time to participate in all that. Canada's a bit of an abstraction for me to say I feel a part of, but I do feel that I'm a Montrealer now. It's hard to integrate into life in this city. The climate is severe; people are individualistic. In North America you've got to work all the time if you want to have a decent life. There's always unemployment insurance and welfare to fall back on if you want to live on the margin of society, but I've tried to live with dignity and avoid that. I chose the Left in Chile because I wanted to work toward a more just society, not because I wanted to opt out of the one that already exists.

Have you ever felt any prejudice toward yourself as an immigrant?

Yes, but not directly. Only two people have ever treated me in an obviously racist way, and they were both immigrants themselves, from France. I've never been treated like that by a Canadian or Québécois. Maybe people here are too repressed to make racist remarks, even though they feel like it.

Does Québécois culture seem introverted to you?

It did, but young people are different now. They're more curious. I think that things have opened up a lot lately; in the seventies and early eighties the culture was more closed in on itself. Now we'll see if a more cosmopolitan world-view and imagination can really be accepted as part of the Québécois and Canadian psyches, which have definitely been limited in the past.

Do you find that readers and critics here usually suppose that you're going to deal with Latin America or the immigrant experience?

Yes. They always think I'm going to write or make films about immigrants. I have my own interests, though. And the people I feel closest to at the moment are writers.

Has living in Canada helped you, in economic terms, to continue developing as a writer?

Well, I do have more access to cultural activities here. Chile is poorer when it comes to financing cultural projects. Television is certainly of lower quality there; maybe that's why Chileans read more and buy more books. But the truth is that if I were living in Chile, I'd probably be better off economically than I am here. In Chile, I belong to an economic élite, because there are so many people worse off than I am. Here, I'm on a lower economic level.

Do you think you've changed a lot since you've been in Canada? I noticed a real shift in tone between your first and second collections of short stories. Have your values changed, too? Do you still believe in the same ideals that caused you to come up here?

Yes, but I'm not at all the same person who left Chile. The world of 'How Are You?' is far behind me now. I'm in a different stage of life, another world. I still have the same ideals, though I may not think, or write, or see things in the same way. But that new tone in my writing is mine just the same.

Do you ever feel that you're falling between the two cultures, the Latin American and the Québécois?

No. I just feel that I'm myself. The only thing that's really important to me is that I write well. Whether my stories are considered Canadian, Québécois, or Chilean isn't really important to me. I only want them to be as good as possible.

Do you think it's harder to assimilate into the mainstream culture here than in the US?

Yes. There are people whose families have lived here for a hundred years, and yet they still feel closer to their original ethnic group than to Quebec or Canada. I think there's a tendency here toward division and ghettoization; there's not enough mixing and intermarriage between ethnic groups. In Latin America and even in the US there's more of a mingling of nationalities and races, which can be very powerful. In Canada many people don't mix even in the second generation. Some have been here for years and still don't know either of the official languages. They only speak and read the language of the country where they grew up. A Pole who immigrates to Argentina will be calling himself Argentine within five years, but a Pole who comes to Canada will continue to think of himself as being Polish.

Do you see the policy of multiculturalism as being divisive or cohesive?

It divides, and goes against what forms a people. I think that the countries that are the most interesting are the ones that have had the greatest mixing of ethnic groups. Brazil, for instance, has an incredible cultural mix of Portuguese, Germans, Japanese, Africans, and Amerindians; the result has been something completely different. There is a certain pressure to assimilate here, but the problem is that people don't know what to assimilate into, so they end up not identifying with anything. Canada has a weak national identity, but it isn't the only country in the Americas like that: other nations, including Chile and Uruguay, have the same problem.

How do you perceive the future here?

I think that the foreseeable future will be quite difficult: Quebec will have to take hold of itself and decide its own future, or it will disappear. Young people today watch television in English; they go to films in English; they play Nintendo games in English. The language debate has become completely irrelevant. The population has become American.

Do you see Quebec becoming assimilated into the United States?

Yes, and it's happening fast.

Is it inevitable? Unstoppable?

It seems so, because the rate of assimilation is increasing every day, and people are still totally passive about it. One day they're going to wake up and find that the place has turned into another Puerto Rico. The fact that Puerto Ricans speak Spanish doesn't make much difference, does it? Quebec has some difficult choices ahead of it. Politics always follow economics, and a people's best defence is its cultural identity. You've got to have a forceful cultural policy, and what Quebec has now just isn't strong enough.

But doesn't it bother you to think that you might end up a citizen of the United States?

No, not any more, because things have changed. There are already almost thirty million Latin Americans in the US.

But there are also large Latin American communities in Montréal and Toronto. Aren't you interested in them?

Yes, but most of the Hispanic people up here have arrived fairly recently. In the US, Spanish-speaking people already have careers and kids studying in university. We Chilean Canadians, for instance, are the product of a single historical event, the *coup d'état* in 1973. In the US, Hispanic immigration is a permanent factor. A lot of Latin American intellectuals now spend half the year in the US and the other half in Latin America. They're painters and writers who live in the North but are working on Latin American themes.

But don't you want to see Canada continue its social-democratic tradition? Wouldn't it matter to you if it were absorbed by the States?

Of course it would. I consider Canada to be an ideal country in many ways. I think that its social structures and institutions are excellent. The problem is that there's an increasing pressure to assimilate into American culture, and Canadian institutions don't have people who are prepared to deal with it.

FRANK PACI b. 1948

The Stone Garden

Our usual meeting place was The Circle—a collection of five-foot
high boulders that had been excavated in making the gully for the
east-west line. Left on the ridge, they formed an irregular circle. You
could sit on top of the boulders—all of them five feet high—and
pretend you were on horses or on the high seats of a Grand Council.
Over a year ago we had built our fort out of burlap and boards and
corrugated tin siding over the boulders, but some older kids had
wrecked it. Story had it that the Ojibway Indians had formed the
circle in protest against Francis H. Clergue who had built the original
paper mill in the 1890s over a vast Indian burial ground. The Indians
and *coureurs de bois* used to portage the rapids at the lock site just
south of the rapids where Clergue, an enterprising American lawyer,
had built his vast industrial empire of paper mill, iron works, power
and light plant, railways, mines, and steel plant. It was these industries
that would eventually bring the Italians to settle in the West End,
brought them at the turn of the century, later between the wars, and
even later after the Second World War like my father. I didn't know
that at the time, of course, but only learned it much later. Just as I
didn't know that the old blockhouse we used to pass in order to get
to the pulp mill offices where we used to get stacks of newsprint had
been Clergue's home for a while. It was an ordinary log cabin
mounted on a rock and cement base for protection. On the way back
I used to smell the freshly made paper and notice the grains of pulp
that undoubtedly came from those same logs that I'd hear thudding
against each other every day.

. . . Rico called the meeting in the middle of the afternoon and everyone came—the five of us perched atop the boulders in the Circle
like a Grand Council.

'I'm so bored this summer,' Rico announced. 'Let's do something.
Let's rob the Stone Garden.'

We had robbed gardens before, the small back gardens of the

neighbourhood which were easily accessible, taking small amounts of peas and carrots and horseradish—but the Stone Garden was different. It was like a fortress, a place beyond our powers. We had played beside it for years and had never seen what was inside. A high and thick stone wall surrounded it. No garden was this protected. And the other peculiarity was that no bracing or mortar of any kind had been used to keep the stones together. The irregular shaped stones had simply been fitted so expertly together that their weight and placement formed an impenetrable wall. No two stones looked alike. It seemed a fantastic feat of architecture.

'The Calabrese do that,' my father told me one day when I had mentioned the wall. 'Those ones from the rocky hilly regions in the Mezzogiorno. The *contadini*. They make fences like that where there are more rocks than money.'

'But who owns the garden?'

'Some old guy . . . is called Vecchio. He doesn't live here no more. He used to own land in the West End. Then the steel plant, she bought him out. Very rich now. Some people on George Street watch his garden for him. You stay away from there. *Il a i cane.*'

We all knew about the dogs. We had heard them barking inside. But this Vecchio guy we had never seen. Just like we had never seen the actual inside of the garden. For all we knew, it could've been empty.

'It's not empty,' Rico told us, after I had expressed my doubts. 'I saw someone yesterday come out with bags of stuff. Imagine what's in there.'

'What did he look like?' I said.

'It was just DiLabbio from George Street.'

'It wasn't the old guy?'

'Naw. It was little DiLabbio. I can handle him.'

'What about the dogs?' Perry said.

Rico's face beamed. 'Here's what we'll do. Perry, you get some fresh meat from home. There're only two dogs in there. You climb the wall and throw the meat right at them. Me and Markie'll climb at the other end with bags. You whistle when the dogs are at the meat. We jump in and grab as much as we can. Katie, you and Maria can stand guard outside the door in case DiLabbio shows up. When I give the secret signal we meet at the tracks and make a run for it to the locks. It'll be a piece of cake.'

'No way,' Katie said. 'I want to go in too.'

'*Che cazz*',' Rico said. 'You're crazy.'
'Just think of the extra stuff we'd get.'
'Yeah, and think what good the stuff'll be if we get caught. No girls inside.'
'Girl? Reeko, you amaze me. You know I won't get caught. I can run as fast as Markie and Perry.'
'And I say no.'
'Why, may I ask?'
'Because.'
'Because why?'
'Because I say so.'
'Let's vote on it then.'
'No vote. What I say goes.'
'Who says?'
'I say.'
'Tell me why then.'
'You really want to know?'
'Yes.' She raised her head high like a proud rider.
'Because you're a *mungia-cake*.'
'I am not!' Katie raised her voice, sliding off the boulder and standing in the middle of the Circle.
'You are so!' Rico said. 'You're Scottish.'
'My parents are Scottish,' Katie's eyes narrowed. 'I believe I'm as much a member of this gang as you are, Mr Stocco.'
'Yeah, but you're still a *mungia-cake*.'
'You take that back, Reeko,' she braced her body, left foot forward, fists clenched. In her patched overalls and red shirt she looked ready to take him on.

I observed her closely. It was odd how people became so taken up in their emotions, losing control of their senses. In my quietness, in my growing reserve with people, I was beginning to establish a distance between myself and what was happening in front of me, as if I could retreat from an incident and let it unreel before me like a two-dimensional scene. My silence also allowed wider latitude for my inner voice, which was talking to me more and more—as if giving me commentary to the scenes unfolding before me.

'C'mon, Katie,' Maria said. 'Put the lid on.'
'Do you think I'm afraid of him?' Katie snarled at Maria. 'If this is a gang, we should all have equal say.'
'What I say goes,' Rico's face was starting to flare up.

'Who says you're the leader?'
'Shut up and get back to your seat.'
'Who's going to make me?'
'Me.'
'You and whose army, dumbo?'
Rico's eyes assumed that blank and pitiless look of an animal approaching its kill. 'Shut the fuck up,' he said calmly. 'You're just a fucken *mungia-cake*. Sit down – or go home and bake a cake.'
We could see he wasn't fooling anymore. Katie got the message too. Later she would tell me she hated Rico's guts, that he was a dummy – a brainless dodo-bird, a dumbo farmer from the remotest regions of Italy. But now she backed off and went to the other side of her boulder, where she sulked for the rest of the meeting.

Around us the smoke rose into the sky – the large white and black cumulous billows of the Steel Plant, the white showery ash of the Chrome Plant, and the wispy foul-smelling chemicals of the Paper Mill. Now, looking back, I can see how that smoke delineated the boundaries of our world. We weren't as aware of it then, of course, because it was always there – an omnipresent screen. Sometimes I'd stare at the billowing smoke of the Steel Plant, see the first dense plumes come out in a torrent, then rise high in the air like a bomb cloud, then thin out as it reached the apex of the neighbourhood, and finally trail away over the city, evaporating into nothingness. When watching movies later in life, I rarely saw this aspect of reality. I saw mainly my comic-book reality transposed into the screen. And even the art films of the European directors never showed me this world, this reality, which seemed wiped out from the face of the earth – except in my memory.

And when I would later work in the Steel Plant and be at the very cause of the smoke, in the various tiers of the inferno of steelmaking – the Blast Furnace, the Coke Ovens, the Open Hearth, the Strip and Rolling Mills – I'd think back to the times we'd view the smoke from a distance and only see its splendour and power. For to us the smoke was an indistinct place into which our fathers disappeared every day, the place they came home from tired and dirty, smelling of stale sweat and graphite they could never get out of the pores of their skin. This reality I had also never seen on the screen or in paintings, or heard in operas, or seen on a stage, or read in the pages of a book – as if it never existed beyond my world.

Later in the afternoon we robbed the Stone Garden as Rico had planned it. Rico and I slunk through the high grass as Perry and the girls took up their positions. When Rico and I got nearer we had to hide in the chokecherry bushes. The inside reeked of urine and excrement. Furtively I let my eyes find the exact spot where Mary Hiller had lain on the grass, letting me commit my most secret sin on her. It seemed so long ago, I could hardly picture what she looked like under her dress. Most of what I remembered was the smell of her and what she felt like between her legs. One of my most secret fantasies was to see her — a woman with full breasts and luscious legs — coming up to me at my fence and saying — Markie, want to play?

Now that we were actually going to scale the high wall, it didn't appear as impregnable as it did in my imaginary fears. From the bushes I saw it in a different light. The stones were actually easy to scale since they protruded like rungs of a ladder. Isn't it curious, Father, how the real actual world of fact is never quite as difficult or fearful or exciting, for that matter, as you make it to be in your imagination? Isn't it odd how afraid you are to perform a certain feat and then when it comes time to do it, you realize how all your fears are unfounded?

Isn't it curious, this difference between the factual world of actual places and things and people — and your transformation of them in your mind into meaningful things of your experience?

Presently we heard dogs barking, followed by a moment of silence and then a clear sharp whistle, such as a cowboy would make across the plains. Rico and I looked at each other and smiled. The plan was going along beautifully. But my mind wasn't entirely on the task at hand. I was struck by the nature of coincidence, of difference and similarity through time. These chokecherry bushes that Rico was using as a hideout to rob the garden, Mary Hiller had used before as a hideout, but for a different purpose. Outwardly they seemed the same, if my memory served me correctly — with the worn pathways and the trampled grass and the debris of many a night of debauch, along with the lingering smell of shit and wine bottles. But they seemed smaller and less mysterious to my older eyes. I had the sense that I was about to do something bad — and the sense of danger and excitement that came with doing bad things.

Rico gave the signal and we made a dash for the wall, just like in the movies and comics, with the good guys risking their lives in the heat of danger. How beautiful reality was when mixed with the unclear vision of imagination and wonder! My fingers clutched the sharp rocks like talons, my feet punched into the small gaps. It felt like scaling the side of a cliff with jagged edges. But our bodies were strong and limber, and we weren't afraid of anything.

Once on the top I was stilled by the sight that met my eyes. A lush garden more beautiful than I had ever seen lay before me like a Shangri-la. I could hardly believe my eyes.

'Man!' Rico blurted out. 'Just like Italia.'

But I was speechless. My eyes couldn't get over the fact that all this had been hidden to me for so long. I saw small apple and pear trees, their branches bending with ripe fruit. Rows and rows of green vegetables were in the middle. Cucumber and zucchini. Peas and cabbage and *fave*. Different kinds of lettuce. Red ripe tomatoes. Celery and horseradish. Green peppers and rhubarb. Over in the far corner we saw a small greenhouse with dwarf trees and a small vineyard.

My father's garden was good enough when compared with the other small vegetable gardens of the West End. A few tomatoes. Some beans and peas. Potatoes and lettuce. But this was a veritable paradise, a dense luxurious oasis with fruit trees and sculptured hedges and gravelled walkways and beautiful flowers throughout — all hidden, all kept under wraps, as if the owner didn't give a hoot for the recognition of others, as if he had kept this oasis hidden in the most unlikely place imaginable to better keep it from prying eyes.

'What're those fruit in the greenhouse?' I asked Rico.

'Apricots and cherries and grapes,' he said, his eyes large with wonder. 'We had those in the Abruzzi. I used to eat them all the time.'

I looked more closely at him, saw the fleshy mottled face, red splotched whenever he became excited, and seemed to see him for the first time. He must've known much more about the old country than me, must've known directly what it meant to live there, must've seen gardens like this often with older eyes. While I only had vague images and memories. I, too, had eaten from cherry trees and vineyards. And I remembered distinctly the taste of green juicy figs in our backyard in the stucco house at the bottom of the hill in Novilara where my mother cried when she was pregnant with Lianna. But I had been uprooted when I was too young. The sights and tastes were too deep in my unconscious.

'I'll get the stuff in the greenhouse,' Rico said. 'You get the apples and pears. Don't forget to tie the bags at the top and sling them over your shoulder. C'mon, before the dogs get wind of us.'

I couldn't see the dogs anywhere. Going down was harder than going up. It was so easy to slip and get impaled on the jagged rocks. Rico ran to the greenhouse. In the still humid air I could smell the rich earth and lush vegetation. It was in the late afternoon. The sun beat down on me. There seemed thousands of crickets chirping in the foliage. I had a sense of having stepped into a sacred place that had been long forbidden me. My senses were alive to the wonder of it all, that such a beautiful place could've been hidden so long in the middle of an industrial neighbourhood. I seemed to walk in a daze to the apple trees, which weren't even tall enough to scale. Their branches laden with hundreds of red McIntosh hung down within reach.

I started filling my bags hurriedly, my mind a jumble of sensations. With each apple I picked, for example, I was so self-conscious of sin that I thought I wasn't so much filling my bag with fruit as filling my time in Purgatory with years of torture. At the same time, however, my senses were so absorbed in the smells and sights of the garden that I couldn't get over the initial shock that this place could have remained hidden so long. For a moment I felt like dropping my bags and walking through the other parts of the garden and soaking in all it had to offer. It seemed so peaceful, so cloistered from the rest of the West End. I couldn't see the paper mill or steel plant over the high walls, couldn't even smell the sulphur or graphite. It was as if a canopy of glass enclosed it, making it a huge greenhouse where all beautiful things could grow on their own and not be afraid of cold and wind and snow. I could live here and be myself—and not have to worry about sins and nightmares and suffering. I could sleep under the stars without a blanket and pick the fruit from the trees as my sole food. Maybe I'd let Katie and Maria visit me—and we'd play in the grass through the day without care of school or parents or priests. We wouldn't let Mary Hiller in, of course. Or Rico, either, because Rico would lose his temper or want to steal things and Mary Hiller would want to do dirty things in the grass, but Perry could come and play too, I thought.

It was strange, Father. It was as if I had found my true home—and I became oblivious of what I was doing. So that when Rico's shouts got through to me, I was momentarily disoriented.

Fear gripped me. In my haste I bumped my head against a low lying branch and scraped my forehead. This seemed to wake me up to the danger of the dogs—and I remembered thinking that I deserved the stinging pain for stealing.

We got to the wall just in time. Rico was already halfway up. With the bags of booty slung over my shoulder I hastily clambered up the protruding stones. But just when I thought I was clear of danger, a German shepherd's snout came out of nowhere and scared the shit out of me. The dog tore into my pant cuff—luckily the thick part rolled at the bottom.

'Rico!' I cried out for help.

'Kick him, stupid!'

Holding on for dear life, I kicked viciously at the snout. We heard a yelp, and I was free.

But on the way down the other side I was so excited that I slipped and fell halfway down, scraping my side and shoulder. Rico laughed. The whole side of my body was throbbing with pain and he was laughing.

'You got too excited,' he said. 'Stay calm and you'll never fall.'

Just then we heard the whistle of the four-thirty Canadian Pacific. It had already passed Albert and was chugging towards the fields. Perry and the girls came running from around the corner.

'Let's go!' Rico shouted. 'We'll hop it.'

I saw the look of fear on Maria's face. There was no way she was going to hop the train. She was a girl. Instead, she turned and ran to the street. The rest of us made a run for it to the tracks. I half expected the dogs to be loosed after us, their vicious snouts snapping at our heels. The loaded bags of stolen goods were heavy and cumbersome. Dogs were barking behind us. I was sweating, my heart beating fiercely. Without thinking, I ran along the closest boxcar, grabbed hold of the metal ladder, felt the pull of the train jerk me forward, let it run me faster, and then jumped onto the lowest rung.

Only then did I turn to see behind me. All three of them had managed to hop the train. We were all breathing heavily.

Suddenly, as if by the magic of train and track, the magic of coincidence, we were free of danger. We had done it. Rico broke out into song.

'*Quand' i' faccio grande, quand' i' faccio grande . . .*'

Perry gave a rebel yell, Katie laughed in such a joyous way that she looked beautiful to me.

Rico shouted, 'You all should've seen Markie's eyes when that dog bit into him! *Madonna mia*,' he laughed. 'But he sure kicked him good. You must've eaten plenty of pasta yesterday, *paisan*?'

Katie shouted, 'Markie Trecoci, head of gnocchi!'

And then they all chanted it, as we rode over the fields, the train rumbling under my hands, the boxcars swaying slightly, the ground moving under me quickly.

A sudden rush of adrenalin spread through my body. Feeling the rumble of the train under my feet and in my hands, the weight of the bags of apples secure on my shoulder, the sight of my friends so happy over my prowess, I felt the most indescribable joy and freedom I had ever felt in my life — a moment of being to rival Mary Hiller.

The hair prickled at my neck, the blood rushed to my head. I felt so keenly that rush of being, that total joy when all the separations of our being — the secret you and the social you and the religious you — merge into one rapturous being. I was riding the train, safe and beautiful, as if I had conquered the world. The West End was receding beneath my feet as we passed over the first train-bridge, past the Circle where we had made our plans, and past the Paper Mill. I felt I could do anything and everything, that a powerful surge of energy was in my body. That nothing was impossible to me.

I, Markie Trecoci, had been inside the Stone Garden and gotten away with it. And inside me was this warm feeling, as if I had been allowed to see not just the garden but something deep inside me which I had never seen before, something I wasn't fully conscious of just then — but which would flower later in my life when I would return to Italy.

'Hold on tight!' Rico shouted to us. 'We'll go over the water-bridge!'

Fear gripped me again. Our bodies hung precariously over the bridge. There was no trestle. A slip and we'd be plunged into the swirling waters of the power canal. Our bodies would be carried to the Power Plant and drive the turbines that would light the street lamps of Sault Ste Marie. Beside me Perry looked as if he was going to panic.

'Don't look down!' I shouted to him. 'Stay calm.'

At the end of the bridge we let go and fell joyously onto safe ground.

Later we lay silently on the red sandstone rocks close to the water, breathing heavily, letting the sun dry our bodies. No one spoke. The feeling I had experienced on the train returned to me, was less pronounced, but at the same time suffused through my body, now that we were definitely safe. The tiredness left me and was replaced by a warm lassitude. Katie-with-the-dark-eyes lay beside me on the flat rocks. I could smell her girl's warmth, her hair and flushed skin. Rico and Perry were on the other rock. Carelessly, as if by instinct, my hand fell onto her stomach and lay there, palm up. I half expected her harsh Scottish accent to break the silence and chastise me. But no word escaped her lips. I could feel her heavy breathing, her pulse, the indescribable sense of a girl's body that was so different from mine. My hand didn't move a muscle. It was as if I was connected to her body, her pulse and breathing going through my hand into my arm and into my own body. That way we remained — and I knew pure joy such as I've never felt.

When we sat up afterwards Katie didn't look at me and I didn't look at her. But I knew something had happened.

Later we all sat up and started chatting excitedly. Somehow there was a sense that we had all experienced the same feeling on that train — each in his own way — and a sort of indescribable wave of understanding spread over us. We were friends. We were joined in some sort of compact of experience. Perry, Rico, Katie McAndrew and me, Markie Trecoci, head of gnocchi.

When we ate some of our booty, I felt, sitting on the topmost pile of stone and watching the fast eddying water of the St Mary's River close to my feet, the happiest human being in the world. No food — nothing in the restaurants of Rome or Paris or North America — has ever tasted so good as the fruit we ate that day.

◆ ◆ ◆

FRANK PACI, born in Pesaro, Italy, in 1948, immigrated with his family to Canada in 1952 and grew up in Sault Ste Marie. While he attended the University of Toronto, earning a B.A. (1970) and B.Ed. (1975), he spent the summers working in the steel plant in the Soo. Paci has an M.A. in English from Carleton University (1980) and has taught school in Sault Ste Marie and in Toronto. In 1988-89 he was writer-in-residence (holding the Mariano Elia Chair in Italian-Canadian Studies) at York University. The years he did not teach Paci devoted to full-time writing. His first three novels, set in Sault Ste Marie and

Toronto, deal with Italian immigrant families and reflect Paci's general experiences. All his writing explores the trauma of immigration; however, it also examines the process of self-discovery and the search for personal meaning. His novels (all first published by Oberon Press) are *The Italians* (1978; New York: New American Library, 1980; translated into French as *Les Gaetano* [Montreal: Guernica, 1989]); *Black Madonna* (1982); *The Father* (1984). He also has three novels in manuscript, which are being considered for publication.

JOSEPH PIVATO was born near Vicenza, Italy, and grew up in Toronto. He has a B.A. (English and French) from York University and an M.A. and Ph.D. in comparative literature from the University of Alberta. Since 1977 he has taught Canadian and comparative literature at Athabasca University in Edmonton. In 1987-88 he held the Mariano Elia Chair in Italian-Canadian Studies at York University. Since 1973 he has published many articles on Canadian, comparative, and Renaissance literature and on ethnic-minority writing. He has edited *Contrasts: Comparative Essays on Italian-Canadian Writing* (1985) and co-edited *Literatures of Lesser Diffusion* (1990).

Growing up in Toronto as an Italian immigrant child I sometimes had bad experiences. Canadian boys would beat me up; grade-school teachers thought I was a slow learner because I could not speak or spell English well. What was your experience in Sault Ste Marie?

Well, it wasn't exactly like yours because my parents immigrated when I was four years old. By the time I had started school I was speaking passable English, I suppose, and I had started to fit in already. What I remember most distinctly, however, was this tremendous pressure to transform myself by repudiating my Italian background. It didn't occur to me that the two cultures and languages could co-exist within me. One of the effects of this pressure of assimilation — which, of course, is experienced by all immigrants in varying degrees — is that it made me very much ashamed of my parents and their ways. In my teen years the shame became contempt. I was very much influenced by school and the media to view my parents and their ways as foreign to my true sensibility. I was only disowning part of myself, of course. So, I wasn't so much struggling with others for acceptance as struggling within myself.

After so many years in Canada, do you still feel that questions of ethnic duality are relevant to you?

Yes, they are. I'm still investigating who I am. This duality has played a large role in shaping me. The post-World-War-II era has seen great migrations of people. So it's in the blood of many others as well.

Other Italian Canadian authors — Mary di Michele, Dino Minni and Pier Giorgio Di Cicco — also try to come to terms with their duality: the trauma of dislocation, the early separation from immigrant parents, the alienation from both the old world and the new. It seems that they will always remain sensitive to their ethnic background and to others who are different. Do you agree with this?

Yes, this sensitivity is in our blood. It plays a central role in the lived experiences that formed our characters. For example, when I was growing up, the English would always mispronounce my name — which still happens with people who have never heard it. This is natural enough. But I grew up thinking it was somehow my fault — I was different. I couldn't fit into the English world and I didn't want to fit into the Italian world of my parents.

Similar feelings of shame over one's parents are dealt with by the character Marie Barone in Black Madonna. *It's a major problem for immigrant children. Many never find ways of dealing with this self-hatred, and as adults they feel guilty for having been ashamed of their parents.*

Yes, writing then becomes a way of re-examining the past, of correcting, in a sense, its errors, and of making up to its ghosts. We must keep in mind, however, that being an immigrant has its advantages — being able to see the new country with fresh eyes, and, of course, having more than one culture to draw from.

\When and how did you discover you wanted to be a writer?

I'm trying to investigate this very question in my current novel in progress. It could've been an entire fluke, that someone like me emerged from such an unlikely environment. It undoubtedly has to do with my subjective constitution or frame of mind — too delicate and tangled an issue to go into here. The facts, however, can speak a little. I was fascinated with comic books as a child—and later with books in general. Then I sustained an athletic injury in high school, which put a serious dent in my athletic ambitions, and I became a more committed reader. Another fact was that my father, out of the blue, bought me a typewriter. My parents didn't read and there were no books whatsoever in the house. I reacted strongly against my family, wanting to be exactly the opposite of what they were. In my adolescent years I experienced some sort of Cartesian turn of consciousness where my safe secure world came crashing down on me, including my faith. You can make a pretty good argument that writing is a form of mythologizing to compensate for the loss of the old myths. Another fact has been my lifelong fascination with language, the power of language to give meaning and transform factuality. But the ultimate reason for my turning to writing was that for me it seemed the only way to find out who I was and why I was on earth. These things build up slowly, of course, but by my second year in university, when I wrote my first story and carried it around in my back pocket, I seemed to jump from one level of being into another—and the path opened for me.

Who influenced your early writing?

Well, after writing a number of short stories, I enrolled in Dave Godfrey's creative writing course at the University of Toronto in my third year at St Michael's. Godfrey was the first published creative writer I ever met. At that time he was writing *The New Ancestors*, which won the Governor General's Award. He seemed to like my work. I was, so to speak, on cloud eight. And that was the very year that Margaret Laurence was writer-in-residence at the U of T. She was the second living author I met. And when she expressed kindness towards my work—I was about halfway through my first unpublished novel—I was lifted up to cloud nine. The thing was, though, that both these people made me think I was better than I actually was. It took me about eight years to go through the painful experiences of learning my craft through trial and error—after I lost contact with both of them—before I could stand on my own two feet as a writer.

Some writers rediscover their immigrant roots when they make a trip back to the old country. The act of reverse migration seems profoundly to affect their sense of personal identity. What were the effects on your work of your first return trip to Italy?

I was four years old when my parents emigrated and I went back the first time when I was twenty-four, in 1972. I was the first in my family to go back. For twenty years I had been nurtured away from Italy in a house that I took to be representative of Italy. It was as if I had been asleep for twenty years. I woke up. I saw that Italy was in my blood; I came to see my parents more clearly and to appreciate them for the first time. Before, I little understood or respected them. The trip made me see them from a different angle. I saw the soil they came from, and, from a larger perspective, the grandeur and age of a culture that made Canada rough and dark by comparison. Don't get me wrong, though. I'm much more Canadian than I'll ever be Italian. From that trip I realized that I had to write from the deepest roots of my being, from the concretely felt experiences of the family.

While some immigrant writers are nostalgic about the past, I find Italian Canadian writers, like di Michele and Micone too, critically re-examining the past. Your writing is not nostalgic.

We should approach the past with great anticipation and with great foreboding—but approach it we must. In my novels is a sense of homage to the sacrifices of the first-generation immigrant parents. There is very little nostalgia. Most of these parents are maimed or die badly. There is a dark streak of doom in these works. At the same time, there is a note that the sacrifices of the parents have not been in vain, although these sacrifices may have been disproportionate to what has been gained. I reinterpret the past, I suppose, to make sense of the present, and vice versa.

In the last two decades there has been a great deal of discussion about a 'Canadian literary tradition', a canon of novels, the main-stream. The rivalry between anglophone and francophone cultures seems to leave little room for other ethnic groups. Would you describe Italian Canadian writing as a marginal literature?

Well, the very designation 'Italian Canadian' is a problem because by referring to a body of work as Italian Canadian we are automatically ascribing marginality to it. That's our fault. And, of course, if some of these writers write in Italian, then they are again automatically cutting off the mainstream reader. I don't think of myself as an Italian Canadian writer. I'm simply a writer, who lives in Canada, uses English, and is of Italian descent. There's a big difference. I don't know, but does Joy Kogawa think of herself as a Japanese Canadian writer? Or does Michael Ondaatje think of himself as a Sri Lankan Canadian writer? If you mean marginal in the sense that this body of work is not accepted as mainstream, then probably yes. But that's not the fault of the writers. It's rather the fault of the readers, mostly those who aren't ready to concede their mainstream ethnic biases — i.e., British — to 'marginal' ethnic cultures. There's an understandable fear here of displacement, and, of course, the mainstream ethnic culture has the grip on the channels of cultural power — the CBC, newspapers, publishing, etc. But if by marginal you mean unimportant, then I would answer that future readers will decide what is important.

I have noted how carefully your writing avoids Italian stereotypes. This is also true of many other Italian Canadian writers: Antonio D'Alfonso, Mary di Michele, Caterina Edwards, Dino Minni, and Marco Micone.

When I wrote my first novel, *The Italians*, I was well aware that Mario Puzo's *The Godfather* [1969] was very popular. I wanted to show readers that there were other types of Italian 'heroes', that you don't have to be a gangster to be a hero. The vast majority of Italian immigrants lead very quiet lives. I am writing about these quiet heroic people. I am trying to show readers a different slant.

In addition to fighting stereotypical views about ethnic people, minority writing is challenging the assumptions about mainstream English Canada. In this way Italian Canadian writing is a minority literature like black, native, or feminist literature. Do you see your work playing this role?

Minority writing can't but present different points of view, different characters with different concerns. The Italian peasants in my novels are such characters. Assunta Barone, the 'black madonna', is almost voiceless. That is an unusual condition and readers must ask why is she this way? This woman character raises questions both about the immigrant world and about Canadian society.

Would you agree that this minority literature shares in the postmodern movement of attacking centralizing views of culture?

In the sense that this writing tries to undercut prevailing values and questions long-held ideas, then it is part of what some call postmodernism. But I must point out that there is very little self-conscious experimentation in this writing. There is no parody of previous forms, no play with language. The language problems in Italian-Canadian writing are not the creation of the writers but the real condition of miscommunication and silence among immigrants. The revolutionary aspect of the writing here is that the author is giving these people a voice for the first time, and creating a language for them, and with them.

Are ethnic writers overly concerned with realism, with the chronicle of the immigrant experience?

How do you see 'realism'? I see it as the narrator being more concerned with the object of his narration than the consciousness observing the object. The writer certainly has to be concerned with the way the story and characters must best be rendered. The subject matter itself finds its best method, as Faulkner would say. This made him at times an 'experimentalist', but only in the sense that he was passionately concerned with the subject matter. My writing so far has dealt with certain people, who, in a large measure, represent a 'simple' state of consciousness. In order to be true to them I have to render them in a certain way, in the so-called 'naïve' realistic way, I suppose. But keep in mind that fiction is never real. It's always a fabrication of a different world, a mimetic world, in which all levels of consciousness have a place. Every story tries to be 'real' by being 'unreal'.

ROHINTON MISTRY b. 1952

Swimming Lessons

The old man's wheelchair is audible today as he creaks by in the hallway: on some days it's just a smooth whirr. Maybe the way he slumps in it, or the way his weight rests has something to do with it. Down to the lobby he goes, and sits there most of the time, talking to people on their way out or in. That's where he first spoke to me a few days ago. I was waiting for the elevator, back from Eaton's with my new pair of swimming-trunks.

'Hullo,' he said. I nodded, smiled.

'Beautiful summer day we've got.'

'Yes,' I said, 'it's lovely outside.'

He shifted the wheelchair to face me squarely. 'How old do you think I am?'

I looked at him blankly, and he said, 'Go on, take a guess.'

I understood the game; he seemed about seventy-five although the hair was still black, so I said, 'Sixty-five?' He made a sound between a chuckle and a wheeze: 'I'll be seventy-seven next month.' Close enough.

I've heard him ask that question several times since, and everyone plays by the rules. Their faked guesses range from sixty to seventy. They pick a lower number when he's more depressed than usual. He reminds me of Grandpa as he sits on the sofa in the lobby, staring out vacantly at the parking lot. Only difference is, he sits with the stillness of stroke victims, while Grandpa's Parkinson's disease would bounce his thighs and legs and arms all over the place. When he could no longer hold the *Bombay Samachar* steady enough to read, Grandpa took to sitting on the veranda and staring emptily at the traffic passing outside Firozsha Baag. Or waving to anyone who went by in the compound: Rustomji, Nariman Hansotia in his 1932 Mercedes-Benz, the fat ayah Jaakaylee with her shopping-bag, the *kuchrawalli* with her basket and long bamboo broom.

The Portuguese woman across the hall has told me a little about the old man. She is the communicator for the apartment building.

To gather and disseminate information, she takes the liberty of unabashedly throwing open her door when newsworthy events transpire. Not for Portuguese Woman the furtive peerings from thin cracks or spyholes. She reminds me of a character in a movie, *Barefoot in The Park* I think it was, who left empty beer cans by the landing for anyone passing to stumble and give her the signal. But PW does not need beer cans. The gutang-khutang of the elevator opening and closing is enough.

The old man's daughter looks after him. He was living alone till his stroke, which coincided with his youngest daughter's divorce in Vancouver. She returned to him and they moved into this low-rise in Don Mills. PW says the daughter talks to no one in the building but takes good care of her father.

Mummy used to take good care of Grandpa, too, till things became complicated and he was moved to the Parsi General Hospital. Parkinsonism and osteoporosis laid him low. The doctor explained that Grandpa's hip did not break because he fell, but he fell because the hip, gradually growing brittle, snapped on that fatal day. That's what osteoporosis does, hollows out the bones and turns effect into cause. It has an unusually high incidence in the Parsi community, he said, but did not say why. Just one of those mysterious things. We are the chosen people where osteoporosis is concerned. And divorce. The Parsi community has the highest divorce rate in India. It also claims to be the most westernized community in India. Which is the result of the other? Confusion again, of cause and effect.

The hip was put in traction. Single-handed, Mummy struggled valiantly with bedpans and dressings for bedsores which soon appeared like grim spectres on his back. *Mamaiji*, bent double with her weak back, could give no assistance. My help would be enlisted to roll him over on his side while Mummy changed the dressing. But after three months, the doctor pronounced a patch upon Grandpa's lungs, and the male ward of Parsi General swallowed him up. There was no money for a private nursing home. I went to see him once, at Mummy's insistence. She used to say that the blessings of an old person were the most valuable and potent of all, they would last my whole life long. The ward had rows and rows of beds; the din was enormous, the smells nauseating, and it was just as well that Grandpa passed most of his time in a less than conscious state.

But I should have gone to see him more often. Whenever Grandpa went out, while he still could in the days before parkinsonism, he would bring back pink and white sugar-coated almonds for Percy and me. Every time I remember Grandpa, I remember that; and then I think: I should have gone to see him more often. That's what I also thought when our telephone-owning neighbour, esteemed by all for that reason, sent his son to tell us the hospital had phoned that Grandpa died an hour ago.

The postman rang the doorbell the way he always did, long and continuous; Mother went to open it, wanting to give him a piece of her mind but thought better of it, she did not want to risk the vengeance of postmen, it was so easy for them to destroy letters; workers nowadays thought no end of themselves, strutting around like peacocks, ever since all this Shiv Sena agitation about Maharashtra for Maharashtrians, threatening strikes and Bombay bundh *all the time, with no respect for the public; bus drivers and conductors were the worst, behaving as if they owned the buses and were doing favours to commuters, pulling the bell before you were in the bus, the driver purposely braking and moving with big jerks to make the standees lose their balance, the conductor so rude if you did not have the right change.*

But when she saw the airmail envelope with a Canadian stamp her face lit up, she said wait to the postman, and went in for a fifty paisa piece, a little baksheesh *for you, she told him, then shut the door and kissed the envelope, went in running, saying my son has written, my son has sent a letter, and Father looked up from the newspaper and said, don't get too excited, first read it, you know what kind of letters he writes, a few lines of empty words, I'm fine, hope you are all right, your loving son — that kind of writing I don't call letter-writing.*

Then Mother opened the envelope and took out one small page and began to read silently, and the joy brought to her face by the letter's arrival began to ebb; Father saw it happening and knew he was right, he said read aloud, let me also hear what our son is writing this time, so Mother read: My dear Mummy and Daddy, Last winter was terrible, we had record-breaking low temperatures all through February and March, and the first official day of spring was colder than the first official day of winter had been, but it's getting warmer now. Looks like it will be a nice warm summer. You asked about my new apartment. It's small, but not bad at all. This is just a quick note to let you know I'm fine, so you won't worry about me. Hope everything is okay at home.

After Mother put it back in the envelope, Father said everything

*about his life is locked in silence and secrecy, I still don't under-
stand why he bothered to visit us last year if he had nothing to say;
every letter of his has been a quick note so we won't worry – what
does he think we worry about, his health, in that country everyone
eats well whether they work or not, he should be worrying about
us with all the black market and rationing, has he forgotten already
how he used to go to the ration-shop and wait in line every week;
and what kind of apartment description is that, not bad at all; and
if it is a Canadian weather report I need from him, I can go with
Nariman Hansotia from A Block to the Cawasji Framji Memorial
Library and read all about it, there they get newspapers from all
over the world.*

The sun is hot today. Two women are sunbathing on the stretch of
patchy lawn at the periphery of the parking lot. I can see them clearly
from my kitchen. They're wearing bikinis and I'd love to take a closer
look. But I have no binoculars. Nor do I have a car to saunter out to
and pretend to look under the hood. They're both luscious and
gleaming. From time to time they smear lotion over their skin, on
the bellies, on the inside of the thighs, on the shoulders. Then one
of them gets the other to undo the string of her top and spread some
there. She lies on her stomach with the straps undone. I wait. I pray
that the heat and haze make her forget, when it's time to turn over,
that the straps are undone.

But the sun is not hot enough to work this magic for me. When
it's time to come in, she flips over, deftly holding up the cups, and
reties the top. They arise, pick up towels, lotions, and magazines,
and return to the building.

This is my chance to see them closer. I race down the stairs to the
lobby. The old man says hullo. 'Down again?'

'My mailbox,' I mumble.

'It's Saturday,' he chortles. For some reason he finds it extremely
funny. My eye is on the door leading in from the parking lot.

Through the glass panel I see them approaching. I hurry to the
elevator and wait. In the dimly lit lobby I can see their eyes are having
trouble adjusting after the bright sun. They don't seem as attractive
as they did from the kitchen window. The elevator arrives and I hold
it open, inviting them in with what I think is a gallant flourish. Under
the fluorescent glare in the elevator I see their wrinkled skin, aging
hands, sagging bottoms, varicose veins. The lustrous trick of sun and
lotion and distance has ended.

I step out and they continue to the third floor. I have Monday night to look forward to, my first swimming lesson. The high school behind the apartment building is offering, among its usual assortment of macramé and ceramics and pottery classes, a class for non-swimming adults.

The woman at the registration desk is quite friendly. She even gives me the opening to satisfy the compulsion I have about explaining my non-swimming status.

'Are you from India?' she asks. I nod. 'I hope you don't mind my asking, but I was curious because an Indian couple, husband and wife, also registered a few minutes ago. Is swimming not encouraged in India?'

'On the contrary,' I say. 'Most Indians swim like fish. I'm an exception to the rule. My house was five minutes walking distance from Chaupatty beach in Bombay. It's one of the most beautiful beaches in Bombay, or was, before the filth took over. Anyway, even though we lived so close to it, I never learned to swim. It's just one of those things.'

'Well,' says the woman, 'that happens sometimes. Take me, for instance. I never learned to ride a bicycle. It was the mounting that used to scare me, I was afraid of falling.' People have lined up behind me. 'It's been very nice talking to you,' she says, 'hope you enjoy the course.'

The art of swimming had been trapped between the devil and the deep blue sea. The devil was money, always scarce, and kept the private swimming clubs out of reach; the deep blue sea of Chaupatty beach was grey and murky with garbage, too filthy to swim in. Every so often we would muster our courage and Mummy would take me there to try and teach me. But a few minutes of paddling was all we could endure. Sooner or later something would float up against our legs or thighs or waists, depending on how deep we'd gone in, and we'd be revulsed and stride out to the sand.

Water imagery in my life is recurring. Chaupatty beach, now the high-school swimming pool. The universal symbol of life and regeneration did nothing but frustrate me. Perhaps the swimming pool will overturn that failure.

When images and symbols abound in this manner, sprawling or rolling across the page without guile or artifice, one is prone to say, how obvious, how skilless; symbols, after all, should be still and gentle as dewdrops, tiny, yet shining with a world of meaning. But what happens when, on the page of life itself, one encounters the ever-moving, all-engirdling sprawl of the filthy sea? Dewdrops and oceans both have their rightful places; Nariman Hansotia certainly knew that when he told his stories to the boys of Firozsha Baag. The sea of Chaupatty was fated to endure the finales of life's everyday functions. It seemed that the dirtier it became, the more crowds it attracted: street urchins and beggars and beachcombers, looking through the junk that washed up. (Or was it the crowds that made it dirtier? — another instance of cause and effect blurring and evading identification.)

Too many religious festivals also used the sea as repository for their finales. Its use should have been rationed, like rice and kerosene. On Ganesh Chaturthi, clay idols of the god Ganesh, adorned with garlands and all manner of finery, were carried in processions to the accompaniment of drums and a variety of wind instruments. The music got more frenzied the closer the procession got to Chaupatty and to the moment of immersion.

Then there was Coconut Day, which was never as popular as Ganesh Chaturthi. From a bystander's viewpoint, coconuts chucked into the sea do not provide as much of a spectacle. We used the sea, too, to deposit the leftovers from Parsi religious ceremonies, things such as flowers, or the ashes of the sacred sandalwood fire, which just could not be dumped with the regular garbage but had to be entrusted to the care of Avan Yazad, the guardian of the sea. And things which were of no use but which no one had the heart to destroy were also given to Avan Yazad. Such as old photographs.

After Grandpa died, some of his things were flung out to sea. It was high tide; we always checked the newspaper when going to perform these disposals; an ebb would mean a long walk in squelchy sand before finding water. Most of the things were probably washed up on shore. But we tried to throw them as far out as possible, then waited a few minutes; if they did not float back right away we would pretend they were in the permanent safekeeping of Avan Yazad, which was a comforting thought. I can't remember everything we sent out to sea, but his brush and comb were in the parcel, his *kusti*, and some Kemadrin pills, which he used to take to keep the parkinsonism under control.

Our paddling sessions stopped for lack of enthusiasm on my part. Mummy wasn't too keen either, because of the filth. But my main concern was the little guttersnipes, like naked fish with little buoyant penises, taunting me with their skills, swimming underwater and

emerging unexpectedly all around me, or pretending to mastur-
bate—I think they were too young to achieve ejaculation. It was
embarrassing. When I look back, I'm surprised that Mummy and I
kept going as long as we did.

I examine the swimming-trunks I bought last week. Surf King, says
the label, Made in Canada-Fabriqué Au Canada. I've been learning
bits and pieces of French from bilingual labels at the supermarket
too. These trunks are extremely sleek and streamlined hipsters, the
distance from waistband to pouch tip the barest minimum. I wonder
how everything will stay in place, not that I'm boastful about my
endowments. I try them on, and feel the tip of my member lingers
perilously close to the exit. Too close, in fact, to conceal the exigen-
cies of my swimming lesson fantasy: a gorgeous woman in the class
for non-swimmers, at whose sight I will be instantly aroused, and
she, spying the shape of my desire, will look me straight in the
eye with her intentions; she will come home with me, to taste the
pleasures of my delectable Asian brown body whose strangeness has
intrigued her and unleashed uncontrollable surges of passion inside
her throughout the duration of the swimming lesson.

I drop the Eaton's bag and wrapper in the garbage can. The
swimming-trunks cost fifteen dollars, same as the fee for the ten
weekly lessons. The garbage bag is almost full. I tie it up and take it
outside. There is a medicinal smell in the hallway; the old man must
have just returned to his apartment.

PW opens her door and says, 'Two ladies from the third floor were
lying in the sun this morning. In bikinis.'

'That's nice,' I say, and walk to the incinerator chute. She reminds
me of Najamai in Firozsha Baag, except that Najamai employed a bit
more subtlety while going about her life's chosen work.

PW withdraws and shuts her door.

*Mother had to reply because Father said he did not want to write
to his son till his son had something sensible to write to him, his
questions had been ignored long enough, and if he wanted to keep
his life a secret, fine, he would get no letters from his father.*

*But after Mother started the letter he went and looked over her
shoulder, telling her what to ask him, because if they kept on writing
the same questions, maybe he would understand how interested
they were in knowing about things over there; Father said go on,
ask him what his work is at the insurance company, tell him to*

take some courses at night school, that's how everyone moves ahead over there, tell him not to be discouraged if his job is just clerical right now, hard work will get him ahead, remind him he is a Zoroastrian: manashni, gavashni, kunashni, *better write the translation also: good thoughts, good words, good deeds—he must have forgotten what it means, and tell him to say prayers and do* kusti *at least twice a day.*

Writing it all down sadly, Mother did not believe he wore his sudra *and* kusti *anymore, she would be very surprised if he remembered any of the prayers; when she had asked him if he needed new* sudras *he said not to take any trouble because the Zoroastrian Society of Ontario imported them from Bombay for their members, and this sounded like a story he was making up, but she was leaving it in the hands of God, ten thousand miles away there was nothing she could do but write a letter and hope for the best.*

Then she sealed it, and Father wrote the address on it as usual because his writing was much neater than hers, handwriting was important in the address and she did not want the postman in Canada to make any mistake; she took it to the post office herself, it was impossible to trust anyone to mail it ever since the postage rates went up because people just tore off the stamps for their own use and threw away the letter, the only safe way was to hand it over the counter and make the clerk cancel the stamp before your own eyes.

Berthe, the building superintendent, is yelling at her son in the parking lot. He tinkers away with his van. This happens every fine-weathered Sunday. It must be the van that Berthe dislikes because I've seen mother and son together in other quite amicable situations.

Berthe is a big Yugoslavian with high cheekbones. Her nationality was disclosed to me by PW. Berthe speaks a very rough-hewn English, I've overheard her in the lobby scolding tenants for late rents and leaving dirty lint screens in the dryers. It's exciting to listen to her, her words fall like rocks and boulders, and one can never tell where or how the next few will drop. But her Slavic yells at her son are a different matter, the words fly swift and true, well-aimed missiles that never miss. Finally, the son slams down the hood in disgust, wipes his hands on a rag, accompanies mother Berthe inside.

Berthe's husband has a job in a factory. But he loses several days of work every month when he succumbs to the booze, a word Berthe uses often in her Slavic tirades on those days, the only one I can understand, as it clunks down heavily out of the tight-flying formation of Yugoslavian sentences. He lolls around in the lobby, submitting passively to his wife's tongue-lashings. The bags under his bloodshot eyes, his stringy moustache, stubbled chin, dirty hair are so vulnerable to the poison-laden barbs (poison works the same way in any language) emanating from deep within the powerful watermelon bosom. No one's presence can embarrass or dignify her into silence. No one except the old man who arrives now. 'Good morning,' he says, and Berthe turns, stops yelling, and smiles. Her husband rises, positions the wheelchair at the favourite angle. The lobby will be peaceful as long as the old man is there.

It was hopeless. My first swimming lesson. The water terrified me. When did that happen, I wonder, I used to love splashing at Chaupatty, carried about by the waves. And this was only a swimming pool. Where did all that terror come from? I'm trying to remember.

Armed with my Surf King I enter the high school and go to the pool area. A sheet with instructions for the new class is pinned to the bulletin board. All students must shower and then assemble at eight by the shallow end. As I enter the showers three young boys, probably from a previous class, emerge. One of them holds his nose. The second begins to hum, under his breath: Paki Paki, smell like curry. The third says to the first two: pretty soon all the water's going to taste of curry. They leave.

It's a mixed class, but the gorgeous woman of my fantasy is missing. I have to settle for another, in a pink one-piece suit, with brown hair and a bit of a stomach. She must be about thirty-five. Plain-looking.

The instructor is called Ron. He gives us a pep talk, sensing some nervousness in the group. We're finally all in the water, in the shallow end. He demonstrates floating on the back, then asks for a volunteer. The pink one-piece suit wades forward. He supports her, tells her to lean back and let her head drop in the water.

She does very well. And as we all regard her floating body, I see what was not visible outside the pool: her bush, curly bits of it, straying out at the pink Spandex v. Tongues of water lapping against her delta, as if caressing it teasingly, make the brown hair come alive in a most tantalizing manner. The crests and troughs of little waves, set off by the movement of our bodies in a circle around her, dutifully irrigate her; the curls alternately wave free inside the crest, then adhere to her wet thighs, beached by the inevitable trough. I could watch this forever, and I wish the floating demonstration would never end.

Next we are shown how to grasp the rail and paddle, face down in the water. Between practising floating and paddling, the hour is almost gone. I have been trying to observe the pink one-piece suit, getting glimpses of her straying pubic hair from various angles. Finally, Ron wants a volunteer for the last demonstration, and I go forward. To my horror he leads the class to the deep end. Fifteen feet of water. It is so blue, and I can see the bottom. He picks up a metal hoop attached to a long wooden stick. He wants me to grasp the hoop, jump in the water, and paddle, while he guides me by the stick. Perfectly safe, he tells me. A demonstration of how paddling propels the body.

It's too late to back out; besides, I'm so terrified I couldn't find the words to do so even if I wanted to. Everything he says I do as if in a trance. I don't remember the moment of jumping. The next thing I know is, I'm swallowing water and floundering, hanging on to the hoop for dear life. Ron draws me to the rails and helps me out. The class applauds.

We disperse and one thought is on my mind: what if I'd lost my grip? Fifteen feet of water under me. I shudder and take deep breaths. This is it. I'm not coming next week. This instructor is an irresponsible person. Or he does not value the lives of non-white immigrants. I remember the three teenagers. Maybe the swimming pool is the hangout of some racist group, bent on eliminating all non-white swimmers, to keep their waters pure and their white sisters unogled.

The elevator takes me upstairs. Then gutang-khutang. PW opens her door as I turn the corridor of medicinal smells. 'Berthe was screaming loudly at her husband tonight,' she tells me.

'Good for her,' I say, and she frowns indignantly at me.

The old man is in the lobby. He's wearing thick wool gloves. He wants to know how the swimming was, must have seen me leaving with my towel yesterday. Not bad, I say.

'I used to swim a lot. Very good for the circulation.' He wheezes. 'My feet are cold all the time. Cold as ice. Hands too.'

Summer is winding down, so I say stupidly, 'Yes, it's not so warm any more.'

The thought of the next swimming lesson sickens me. But as I comb through the memories of that terrifying Monday, I come upon the straying curls of brown pubic hair. Inexorably drawn by them, I decide to go.

It's a mistake, of course. This time I'm scared even to venture in the shallow end. When everyone has entered the water and I'm the only one outside, I feel a little foolish and slide in.

Instructor Ron says we should start by reviewing the floating technique. I'm in no hurry. I watch the pink one-piece pull the swim-suit down around her cheeks and flip back to achieve perfect flotation. And then reap disappointment. The pink Spandex triangle is perfectly streamlined today, nothing strays, not a trace of fuzz, not one filament, not even a sign of post-depilation irritation. Like the airbrushed parts of glamour magazine models. The barrenness of her impeccably packaged apex is a betrayal. Now she is shorn like the other women in the class. Why did she have to do it?

The weight of this disappointment makes the water less manageable, more lung-penetrating. With trepidation, I float and paddle my way through the remainder of the hour, jerking my head out every two seconds and breathing deeply, to continually shore up a supply of precious, precious air without, at the same time, seeming too anxious and losing my dignity.

I don't attend the remaining classes. After I've missed three, Ron the instructor telephones. I tell him I've had the flu and am still feeling poorly, but I'll try to be there the following week.

He does not call again. My Surf King is relegated to an unused drawer. Total losses: one fantasy plus thirty dollars. And no watery rebirth. The swimming pool, like Chaupatty beach, has produced a stillbirth. But there is a difference. Water means regeneration only if it is pure and cleansing. Chaupatty was filthy, the pool was not. Failure to swim through filth must mean something other than failure of rebirth—failure of symbolic death? Does that equal success of symbolic life? death of a symbolic failure? death of a symbol? What is the equation?

The postman did not bring a letter but a parcel, he was smiling because he knew that every time something came from Canada his baksheesh *was guaranteed, and this time because it was a parcel Mother gave him a whole rupee, she was quite excited, there were so many stickers on it besides the stamps, one for Small Parcel, another Printed Papers, a red sticker saying Insured; she showed it to Father, and opened it, then put both hands on her cheeks, not able to speak because the surprise and happiness was so great, tears came to her eyes and she could not stop smiling, till Father became impatient to know and finally got up and came to the table.*

When he saw it he was surprised and happy too, he began to grin, then hugged Mother saying our son is a writer, and we didn't even know it, he never told us a thing, here we are thinking he is still clerking away at the insurance company, and he has written a book of stories, all these years in school and college he kept his talent hidden, making us think he was just like one of the boys in the Baag, shouting and playing the fool in the compound, and now what a surprise; then Father opened the book and began reading it, heading back to the easy chair, and Mother so excited, still holding his arm, walked with him, saying it was not fair him reading it first, she wanted to read it too, and they agreed that he would read the first story, then give it to her so she could also read it, and they would take turns in that manner.

Mother removed the staples from the padded envelope in which he had mailed the book, and threw them away, then straightened the folded edges of the envelope and put it away safely with the other envelopes and letters she had collected since he left.

The leaves are beginning to fall. The only ones I can identify are maple. The days are dwindling like the leaves. I've started a habit of taking long walks every evening. The old man is in the lobby when I leave, he waves as I go by. By the time I'm back, the lobby is usually empty.

Today I was woken up by a grating sound outside that made my flesh crawl. I went to the window and saw Berthe raking the leaves in the parking lot. Not in the expanse of patchy lawn on the periphery, but in the parking lot proper. She was raking the black tarred surface. I went back to bed and dragged a pillow over my head, not releasing it till noon.

When I return from my walk in the evening, PW, summoned by the elevator's gutang-khutang, says, 'Berthe filled six big black garbage bags with leaves today.'

'Six bags!' I say. 'Wow!'

Since the weather turned cold, Berthe's son does not tinker with his van on Sundays under my window. I'm able to sleep late.

Around eleven, there's a commotion outside. I reach out and switch on the clock radio. It's a sunny day, the window curtains are bright. I get up, curious, and see a black Olds Ninety-Eight in the parking lot, by the entrance to the building. The old man is in his wheelchair, bundled up, with a scarf wound several times round his neck as though to immobilize it, like a surgical collar. His daughter and another man, the car-owner, are helping him from the wheelchair into the front seat, encouraging him with words like: that's it, easy does it, attaboy. From the open door of the lobby, Berthe is shouting encouragement too, but hers is confined to one word: yah, repeated at different levels of pitch and volume, with variations on vowel-length. The stranger could be the old man's son, he has the same jet black hair and piercing eyes.

Maybe the old man is not well, it's an emergency. But I quickly scrap that thought—this isn't Bombay, an ambulance would have arrived. They're probably taking him out for a ride. If he is his son, where has he been all this time, I wonder.

The old man finally settles in the front seat, the wheelchair goes in the trunk, and they're off. The one I think is the son looks up and catches me at the window before I can move away, so I wave, and he waves back.

In the afternoon I take down a load of clothes to the laundry room. Both machines have completed their cycles, the clothes inside are waiting to be transferred to dryers. Should I remove them and place them on top of a dryer, or wait? I decide to wait. After a few minutes, two women arrive, they are in bathrobes, and smoking. It takes me a while to realize that these are the two disappointments who were sunbathing in bikinis last summer.

'You didn't have to wait, you could have removed the clothes and carried on, dear,' says one. She has a Scottish accent. It's one of the few I've learned to identify. Like maple leaves.

'Well,' I say, 'some people might not like strangers touching their clothes.'

'You're not a stranger, dear,' she says, 'you live in this building, we've seen you before.'

'Besides, your hands are clean,' the other one pipes in. 'You can touch my things any time you like.'

Horny old cow. I wonder what they've got on under their bathrobes. Not much, I find, as they bend over to place their clothes in the dryers.

'See you soon,' they say, and exit, leaving me behind in an erotic wake of smoke and perfume and deep images of cleavages. I start the washers and depart, and when I come back later, the dryers are empty.

PW tells me, 'The old man's son took him out for a drive today. He has a big beautiful black car.'

I see my chance, and shoot back: 'Olds Ninety-Eight.'

'What?'

'The car,' I explain, 'it's an Oldsmobile Ninety-Eight.'

She does not like this at all, my giving her information. She is visibly nettled, and retreats with a sour face.

Mother and Father read the first five stories, and she was very sad after reading some of them, she said he must be so unhappy there, all his stories are about Bombay, he remembers every little thing about his childhood, he is thinking about it all the time even though he is ten thousand miles away, my poor son, I think he misses his home and us and everything he left behind, because if he likes it over there why would he not write stories about that, there must be so many new ideas that his new life could give him.

But Father did not agree with this, he said it did not mean that he was unhappy, all writers worked in the same way, they used their memories and experiences and made stories out of them, changing some things, adding some, imagining some, all writers were very good at remembering details of their lives.

Mother said, how can you be sure that he is remembering because he's a writer, or whether he started to write because he is unhappy and thinks of his past, and wants to save it all by making stories of it; and Father said that is not a sensible question, anyway, it is now my turn to read the next story.

The first snow has fallen, and the air is crisp. It's not very deep, about two inches, just right to go for a walk in. I've been told that immigrants from hot countries always enjoy the snow the first year, maybe for a couple of years more, then inevitably the dread sets in, and the approach of winter gets them fretting and moping. On the other hand, if it hadn't been for my conversation with the woman at the swimming registration desk, they might now be saying that India is a nation of non-swimmers.

Berthe is outside, shovelling the snow off the walkway in the parking lot. She has a heavy, wide pusher which she wields expertly. The old radiators in the apartment alarm me incessantly. They continue to broadcast a series of variations on death throes, and go from hot to cold and cold to hot at will, there's no controlling their temperature. I speak to Berthe about it in the lobby. The old man is there too, his chin seems to have sunk deeper into his chest, and his face is a yellowish grey.

'Nothing, not to worry about anything,' says Berthe, dropping rough-hewn chunks of language around me. 'Radiator no work, you tell me. You feel cold, you come to me, I keep you warm,' and she opens her arms wide, laughing. I step back, and she advances, her breasts preceding her like the gallant prows of two ice-breakers. She looks at the old man to see if he is appreciating the act: 'You no feel scared, I keep you safe and warm.'

But the old man is staring outside, at the flakes of falling snow. What thoughts is he thinking as he watches them? Of childhood days, perhaps, and snowmen with hats and pipes, and snowball fights, and white Christmases, and Christmas trees? What will I think of, old in this country, when I sit and watch the snow come down? For me, it is already too late for snowmen and snowball fights, and all I will have is thoughts about childhood thoughts and dreams, built around snowscapes and winter-wonderlands on the Christmas cards so popular in Bombay; my snowmen and snowball fights and Christmas trees are in the pages of Enid Blyton's books, dispersed amidst the adventures of the Famous Five, and the Five Find-Outers, and the Secret Seven. My snowflakes are even less forgettable than the old man's, for they never melt.

It finally happened. The heat went. Not the usual intermittent coming and going, but out completely. Stone cold. The radiators are like ice. And so is everything else. There's no hot water. Naturally. It's the hot water that goes through the rads and heats them. Or is it the other way around? Is there no hot water because the rads have stopped circulating it? I don't care, I'm too cold to sort out the cause and effect relationship. Maybe there is no connection at all.

I dress quickly, put on my winter jacket, and go down to the lobby. The elevator is not working because the power is out, so I take the stairs. Several people are gathered, and Berthe has announced that she has telephoned the office, they are sending a man. I go back up the stairs. It's only one floor, the elevator is just a bad habit. Back in Firozsha Baag they were broken most of the time. The stairway enters the corridor outside the old man's apartment, and I think of his cold feet and hands. Poor man, it must be horrible for him without heat. As I walk down the long hallway, I feel there's something different but can't pin it down. I look at the carpet, the ceiling, the wallpaper: it all seems the same. Maybe it's the freezing cold that imparts a feeling of difference.

PW opens her door: 'The old man had another stroke yesterday. They took him to the hospital.'

The medicinal smell. That's it. It's not in the hallway any more.

In the stories that he'd read so far Father said that all the Parsi families were poor or middle-class, but that was okay; nor did he mind that the seeds for the stories were picked from the sufferings of their own lives; but there should also have been something positive about Parsis, there was so much to be proud of: the great Tatas and their contribution to the steel industry, or Sir Dinshaw Petit in the textile industry who made Bombay the Manchester of the East, or Dadabhai Naoroji in the freedom movement, where he was the first to use the word swaraj, *and the first to be elected to the British Parliament where he carried on his campaign; he should have found some way to bring some of these wonderful facts into his stories, what would people reading these stories think, those who did not know about Parsis—that the whole community was full of cranky, bigoted people; and in reality it was the richest, most advanced and philanthropic community in India, and he did not need to tell his own son that Parsis had a reputation for being generous and family-oriented. And he could have written something also about the historic background, how Parsis came to India from Persia because of Islamic persecution in the seventh century, and were the descendants of Cyrus the Great and the magnificent Persian Empire. He could have made a story of all this, couldn't he?*

Mother said what she liked best was his remembering everything so well, how beautifully he wrote about it all, even the sad things, and though he changed some of it, and used his imagination, there was truth in it.

My hope is, Father said, that there will be some story based on his Canadian experience, that way we will know something about our son's life there, if not through his letters then in his stories; so far they are all about Parsis and Bombay, and the one with a little bit about Toronto, where a man perches on top of the toilet, is shameful and disgusting, although it is funny at times and did make me laugh, I have to admit, but where does he get such an imagination from, what is the point of such a fantasy; and Mother said that she would also enjoy some stories about Toronto and the people there; it puzzles me, she said, why he writes nothing about it, especially since you say that writers use their own experience to make stories out of.

Then Father said this is true, but he is probably not using his Toronto experience because it is too early; what do you mean, too early, asked Mother and Father explained it takes a writer about ten years time after an experience before he is able to use it in his writing, it takes that long to be absorbed internally and understood, thought out and thought about, over and over again, he haunts it and it haunts him if it is valuable enough, till the writer is comfortable with it to be able to use it as he wants; but this is only one theory I read somewhere, it may or may not be true.

That means, said Mother, that his childhood in Bombay and our home here is the most valuable thing in his life just now, because he is able to remember it all to write about it, and you were so bitterly saying he is forgetting where he came from; and that may be true, said Father, but that is not what the theory means, according to the theory he is writing of these things because they are far enough in the past for him to deal with objectively, he is able to achieve what critics call artistic distance, without emotions interfering; and what do you mean emotions, said Mother, you are saying he does not feel anything for his characters, how can he write so beautifully about so many sad things without any feelings in his heart?

But before Father could explain more, about beauty and emotion and inspiration and imagination, Mother took the book and said it was her turn now and too much theory she did not want to listen to, it was confusing and did not make as much sense as reading the stories, she would read them her way and Father could read them his.

My books on the windowsill have been damaged. Ice has been forming on the inside ledge, which I did not notice, and melting when the sun shines in. I spread them in a corner of the living room to dry out.

The winter drags on. Berthe wields her snow pusher as expertly as ever, but there are signs of weariness in her performance. Neither husband nor son is ever seen outside with a shovel. Or anywhere else, for that matter. It occurs to me that the son's van is missing, too.

The medicinal smell is in the hall again, I sniff happily and look forward to seeing the old man in the lobby. I go downstairs and peer into the mailbox, see the blue and magenta of an Indian aerogramme with Don Mills, Ontario, Canada in Father's flawless hand through the slot.

I pocket the letter and enter the main lobby. The old man is there, but not in his usual place. He is not looking out through the glass door. His wheelchair is facing a bare wall where the wallpaper is torn in places. As though he is not interested in the outside world any more, having finished with all that, and now it's time to see inside. What does he see inside, I wonder? I go up to him and say hullo. He says hullo without raising his sunken chin. After a few seconds his grey countenance faces me. 'How old to do you think I am?' His eyes are dull and glazed; he is looking even further inside than I first presumed.

'Well, let's see, you're probably close to sixty-four.'

'I'll be seventy-eight next August.' But he does not chuckle or wheeze. Instead, he continues softly, 'I wish my feet did not feel so cold all the time. And my hands.' He lets his chin fall again.

In the elevator I start opening the aerogramme, a tricky business because a crooked tear means lost words. Absorbed in this while emerging, I don't notice PW occupying the centre of the hallway, arms folded across her chest: 'They had a big fight. Both of them have left.'

I don't immediately understand her agitation. 'What . . . who?'

'Berthe. Husband and son both left her. Now she is all alone.'

Her tone and stance suggest that we should not be standing here talking but do something to bring Berthe's family back. 'That's very sad,' I say, and go in. I picture father and son in the van, driving away, driving across the snow-covered country, in the dead of winter, away from wife and mother; away to where? how far will they go? Not son's van nor father's booze can take them far enough. And the further they go, the more they'll remember, they can take it from me.

All the stories were read by Father and Mother, and they were sorry when the book was finished, they felt they had come to know their son better now, yet there was much more to know, they wished there were many more stories; and this is what they mean, said

Father, when they say that the whole story can never be told, the whole truth can never be known; what do you mean, they say, asked Mother, who they, and Father said writers, poets, philosophers. I don't care what they say, said Mother, my son will write as much or as little as he wants to, and if I can read it I will be happy. The last story they liked the best of all because it had the most in it about Canada, and now they felt they knew at least a little bit, even if it was a very little bit, about his day-to-day life in his apartment; and Father said if he continues to write about such things he will become popular because I am sure they are interested there in reading about life through the eyes of an immigrant, it provides a different viewpoint; the only danger is if he changes and becomes so much like them that he will write like one of them and lose the important difference.

The bathroom needs cleaning. I open a new can of Ajax and scour the tub. Sloshing with mug from bucket was standard bathing procedure in the bathrooms of Firozsha Baag, so my preference now is always for a shower. I've never used the tub as yet; besides, it would be too much like Chaupatty or the swimming pool, wallowing in my own dirt. Still, it must be cleaned.

When I've finished, I prepare for a shower. But the clean gleaming tub and the nearness of the vernal equinox give me the urge to do something different today. I find the drain plug in the bathroom cabinet, and run the bath.

I've spoken so often to the old man, but I don't know his name. I should have asked him the last time I saw him, when his wheelchair was facing the bare wall because he had seen all there was to see outside and it was time to see what was inside. Well, tomorrow. Or better yet, I can look it up in the directory in the lobby. Why didn't I think of that before? It will only have an initial and a last name, but then I can surprise him with: hullo Mr Wilson, or whatever it is.

The bath is full. Water imagery is recurring in my life: Chaupatty beach, swimming pool, bathtub. I step in and immerse myself up to the neck. It feels good. The hot water loses its opacity when the chlorine, or whatever it is, has cleared. My hair is still dry. I close my eyes, hold my breath, and dunk my head. Fighting the panic, I stay under and count to thirty. I come out, clear my lungs and breathe deeply.

I do it again. This time I open my eyes under water, and stare blindly without seeing, it takes all my will to keep the lids from closing. Then I am slowly able to discern the underwater objects. The drain plug looks different, slightly distorted; there is a hair trapped between the hole and the plug, it waves and dances with the movement of the water. I come up, refresh my lungs, examine quickly the overwater world of the washroom, and go in again. I do it several times, over and over. The world outside the water I have seen a lot of, it is now time to see what is inside.

The spring session for adult non-swimmers will begin in a few days at the high school. I must not forget the registration date.

The dwindled days of winter are now all but forgotten; they have grown and attained a respectable span. I resume my evening walks, it's spring, and a vigorous thaw is on. The snowbanks are melting, the sound of water on its gushing, gurgling journey to the drains is beautiful. I plan to buy a book of trees, so I can identify more than the maple as they begin to bloom.

When I return to the building, I wipe my feet energetically on the mat because some people are entering behind me, and I want to set a good example. Then I go to the board with its little plastic letters and numbers. The old man's apartment is the one on the corner by the stairway, that makes it number 201. I run down the list, come to 201, but there are no little white plastic letters beside it. Just the empty black rectangle with holes where the letters would be squeezed in. That's strange. Well, I can introduce myself to him, then ask his name.

However, the lobby was empty. I take the elevator, exit at the second floor, wait for the gutang-khutang. It does not come, the door closes noiselessly, smoothly. Berthe has been at work, or has made sure someone else has. PW's cue has been lubricated out of existence.

But she must have the ears of a cockroach. She is waiting for me. I whistle my way down the corridor. She fixes me with an accusing look. She waits till I stop whistling, then says: 'You know the old man died last night.'

I cease groping for my key. She turns to go and I take a step towards her, my hand still in my trouser pocket. 'Did you know his name?' I ask, but she leaves without answering.

Then Mother said, the part I like best in the last story is about

Grandpa, where he wonders if Grandpa's spirit is really watching him and blessing him, because you know I really told him that, I told him helping an old suffering person who is near death is the most blessed thing to do, because that person will ever after watch over you from heaven, I told him this when he was disgusted with Grandpa's urine-bottle and would not touch it, would not hand it to him even when I was not at home.

Are you sure, said Father, that you really told him this, or you believe you told him because you like the sound of it, you said yourself the other day that he changes and adds and alters things in the stories but he writes it all so beautifully that it seems true, so how can you be sure; this sounds like another theory, said Mother, but I don't care, he says I told him and I believe now I told him, so even if I did not tell him then it does not matter now.

Don't you see, said Father, that you are confusing fiction with facts, fiction does not create facts, fiction can come from facts, it can grow out of facts by compounding, transposing, augmenting, diminishing, or altering them in any way; but you must not confuse cause and effect, you must not confuse what really happened with what the story says happened, you must not loose your grasp on reality, that way madness lies.

Then Mother stopped listening because, as she told Father so often, she was not very fond of theories, and she took out her writing pad and started a letter to her son; Father looked over her shoulder, telling her to say how proud they were of him and were waiting for his next book, he also said, leave a little space for me at the end, I want to write a few lines when I put the address on the envelope.

◆ ◆ ◆

ROHINTON MISTRY was born in Bombay in 1952 and in 1975 moved to Toronto, where with the exception of one year (1986-87) spent in Long Beach, California, he and his wife have lived ever since. While at the University of Toronto, he won two Hart House literary prizes (for 'One Sunday' and 'Auspicious Occasion'), and in 1985 was awarded the *Canadian Fiction* Contributor's Prize. He has just completed a novel, which is set in Bombay. His collection of short stories, *Tales from Firozsha Baag* (Penguin, 1987), was short-listed for the Governor General's Award in 1988.

DAGMAR NOVAK was born in Czechoslovakia and teaches in the department of English at the University of Toronto, where she completed her Ph.D. in English literature in 1985. Her book *The Canadian Novel and the Two World Wars* is forthcoming from McGill-Queen's University Press. She is currently writing a biography of Gabrielle Roy, to be published by Oxford University Press.

Is there anything in your experience that you would say typifies an immigrant experience?

When it happened, I didn't realize it was a Canadian immigrant experience. Being asked when one goes for job interviews, 'Do you have any Canadian experience?' was just a very stupid question, I thought. But later on, I found that it was one way of saying: 'No, there's no job for you.' It's a catch-22 for a new immigrant. They immediately say: 'We're very sorry but we need someone with Canadian experience.' Then I thought perhaps there was something very special about Canadian experience, that if you've done the same kind of work elsewhere, it's not the same thing, according to them.

How long did it take before you discovered that what they were asking had a more subtle or insidious meaning?

My habit of giving people the benefit of the doubt kept getting in the way. It took a while to realize what was going on, just as it took a while to realize what was happening at the bank where I started work. There were so many immigrants working there, of all colours, and it seemed very reassuring. But they were all in the lowest possible salary grade — and predominantly females. Occasionally, a white male would appear in the ranks and in a few weeks be gone. Gone where? In time, it became clear. The higher up the ladder one went, the work force became increasingly white and overwhelmingly male.

Do you think that the values with which you were brought up in India have changed in any way since you came to Canada?

I'd have to say no. It was an easygoing home, although my parents may have preferred stronger religious strictures and observances.

Did your parents emphasize hard work and a sense of having a purpose in life?

Yes, but it didn't strike us as being unusual because it was going on all around us. So, it was just something that parents said, and I'm sure that kids everywhere listen to the things their parents say and probably imagine it's something parents have to do. The way I see it, parents want the same things for their children, no matter what urban culture they belong to or live in, don't they? We all want our children to be successful and the way to success is through hard work. Perhaps the pressures are different in the way the message is pounded in.

In the story 'Swimming Lessons' there's a suggestion of a clash between the old culture of India and the new culture of Canada.

I don't think I really see it as a clash. I see it more as an opportunity to put things in their proper places. If you have a cupboard with a certain amount of space in it, then you have to arrange your belongings in that cupboard the best way you can, given the space. But if you buy a new cupboard you have more space.

Yes, but isn't this rather schizophrenic?

Only if I try to pretend there is just one, where there are two in reality.

Do the cupboards have to be separate?

But they're in the same room, aren't they? And I have the keys to both.

You should write a story called 'The Two Cupboards'. In 'Swimming Lessons' too, though, there is a complex view of the double vision of immigrants — both a looking forward and a yearning backward.

Yes, but I would have to say that it's part of every person's life; it's part of the human condition. No matter where you live, even if you lived in the same village all your life, you would look at the past, at lost moments, lost opportunities, lost loves.

Is this story autobiographical in any way?

Yes and no. Obviously, I came from Bombay to Toronto; I lived in an apartment building. But I don't think this looking forward and yearning backward is restricted to an immigrant. It's a universal phenomenon. We're doing it all the time, all of us, except that here, the two worlds are so far apart geographically that it seems to take on more significance.

So, when I asked you if this is part of the immigrant experience, if it's not an insulting question, it's at least an irritating one. In other words, I'm suggesting that an immigrant writer would have a different experience from one living in his own land.

Yes, but the question has to be asked. It took some time for me to realize that I'm not that different from a person who has lived in Toronto all his life.

Multiculturalism has received a great deal of attention, both positive and negative, in recent years. In your view, is there any difference between the clichés of Canadian multiculturalism and the American melting pot?

They've both become clichés over time. Whatever means they use, the results are the same. Look around us. Canada and the United States: there's racism in both places. Neither cliché is achieving what it's supposed to achieve. The melting pot has not been able to bring everyone together as Americans, by transcending hatred, fear, bigotry, colour prejudice. Multiculturalism is supposed to promote peace and harmony, to foster respect and appreciation for our differences. But it does not. But multiculturalism is also expected to do more than it can and is being blamed where it should not be blamed. It is accused of creating ethnic ghettos, but ethnic ghettos have always existed — inside and outside the melting pot.

Why do you think there's so much resistance to multiculturalism among some Canadians?

Fear, among certain groups, I think.

So, you're saying that prejudice and hatred are the result of fear?

Yes, a misguided fear.

As a writer, does multiculturalism make a difference to you?

I think it makes more of a difference to those around a writer, by creating expectations in the audience, in the critics, in the establishment. I think they feel that when a person arrives here from a different culture, if that person is a writer, he must have some profound observations about the meeting of the two cultures. And he must write about racism. He must write about multiculturalism. He has an area of expertise foisted on him which he may not necessarily want, or which may not really interest him. He may not want to be an expert in race relations.

So, there can be a kind of tyranny associated with multiculturalism?

Yes, the writer may just want to write without any of this agenda of cross-culturalism.

Do you think there is pressure on writers from other countries to conform to certain expectations?

There may be some covert pressure, due to the very existence of those expectations. But I don't think that a writer who allows himself to be pressured is a good writer. If he succumbs to this kind of pressure, he won't write very well. On the other hand, if I want to write about something that is very close to my heart, and then there are pressures on me — if my life is threatened because I want to write about those things — then the pressure will not matter. In fact, it might even help me do better. But if a pressure is of a more primary nature, where it forces me to select something which I really don't want to write about, that's different.

Have you ever experienced this kind of pressure?

No, I just imagine it could happen this way. After the publication of my first book, there were people who said they would be very interested to see what I have to say about the Canadian banking establishment. They suggested — jocularly, I hope — that my next book should be about banks.

In 'Swimming Lessons' there seems to be a competition between the parents to understand their son, to see, in effect, which one of them understands him better through his work.

Yes, the father wants to know his son through his mind: he thinks he will reach his heart through his mind. But the mother takes a more heart-to-heart approach with her son. I think it suggests the way in which each views the world.

There is also in this story a specific kind of portrait of family life. What are some of the differences in the ways in which Canadian and Indian children are raised?

Perhaps the relationships between parents and children are universal. But the way in which the relationships manifest themselves are different. In India, children have to respond to their parents in a certain way, in an open, almost stylized show of respect. Perhaps that's missing here. And I guess from there we can go on to grandparents — the way they are shunted off to old people's homes here just doesn't happen there. But I think that the casual parent-child relationships in North American have their positive side. A child in America would find it easier to write to his parents than the protagonist does in that story. There is a dark side to Indian parent-child relationships.

How do you respond in your writing to the potential dangers of stereotyping an ethnic group in order to show cultural difference?

I've never really had any trouble with that so far, because the characters live in my mind so completely before the writing commences that stereotyping isn't a danger. They're quite well formed, with their own idiosyncrasies. It might be a problem if what a writer is writing about is not really familiar to him. A person has to know certain things before he can be honest about them. And if he does not, no matter how honest he is, the picture will be incomplete. I suppose, too, a writer has to come very close to his material and then move back.

Can you say something about the potential dangers of sentimentality and nostalgia in writing? Do you consciously think about this kind of thing as you write?

I think it's like adding salt to your food. You know after a while that with this much salt the food will taste just right — no more, no less. It's not a very conscious thing. But salt is a bad example: adding salt is a very conscious act. If you're going to put on a sweater, you don't have to think too much about it. When you are cold, you just reach for a sweater and put it on. It's very basic.

I heard John Irving say that it is important for him as a writer to feel detached in some way from what goes on around him. He feels a need to be lonely. For him, loneliness leads to creativity.

I don't think there's any choice in this for a writer. Loneliness, or rather solitude, is a necessary condition. A writer has no choice about his detachment either. At times, I wonder, though, if one writes because one is lonely or if one is alone because one is a writer?

What do you see as the future for Canadian writers of other than British or French ethnic backgrounds? Do you foresee a time when there will no longer be a need to explain differences among us?

Everything may be accepted but the reader will always be curious; that's why he or she reads, and for the reader, the book is the story plus the writer, I think. He or she will want to know both. But if, as we've said, prejudice stems from fear, the only thing that can cast out fear is education. But not education as we know it. That's not education; it's more the processing of children with the least inconvenience to society. Education is respect for humanity, essentially a turning away from fear.

And, of course, some parents are in no position to teach their children.

Or the parents are in a very good position to teach and perpetuate their own prejudice. But racism is not just a North American evil. In India, for example, the tall, wheat-complexioned North Indian Hindu of Aryan descent feels superior to the short, dark-skinned South Indian Hindu of Dravidian descent. And even within the same religion, the hierarchy of castes and sub-castes leads to a maze of prejudice and attitudes which is quite bewildering. Of course, worst of all, the politicians on both sides of the globe are always willing and eager to exploit these irrational feelings and fears. It's one more similarity shared by my old country and new.

Earlier you said that children take to racism easily.

Yes, so easily that maybe it's a response to something very basic inside all of us.

Perhaps it's a need to feel superior in some way?

Yes, but if you have something to feel really good about, something genuine, whatever the reason, then you wouldn't have to rely on artificial or spurious reasons of race and colour.

But the economic and political climate now in Canada isn't conducive to the promotion of fairness and equality among people, is it?

I think that, even if there were no multiculturalism policy, people who are against it would find other reasons for speaking out against those of other backgrounds. Perhaps the multiculturalism concept is offering those bigots and racists a sounding board—at worst, it's doing that. At best, it could be in some way spreading the message that all races, all cultures are to be respected. That's what the goal is and by constantly reiterating it, the bigots and racists are told that it is not fashionable to be very open about racism, that we do not look upon it kindly. So, it keeps a lid on and we do not have the sort of blatancy that is seen in the States. But perhaps that's equally bad— or worse—because it transforms those tendencies in Canada into something more subtle, something more difficult to identify.

DIONNE BRAND b. 1953

Blossom
Priestess of Oya, Goddess of winds, storms and waterfalls

Blossom's was jumping tonight. Oya and Shango and God and spirit and ordinary people was chanting and singing and jumping the place down. Blossom's was a obeah house and speakeasy on Vaughan Road. People didn't come for the cheap liquor Blossom sell, though as night wear on, on any given night, Blossom, in she waters, would tilt the bottle a little in your favour. No, it wasn't the cheap liquor, even if you could drink it all night long till morning. It was the feel of the place. The cheap light revolving over the bar, the red shag covering the wall against which Blossom always sit, a line of beer, along the window-sill behind, as long as she ample arms spread out over the back of a wooden bench. And, the candles glowing bright on the shrine of Oya, Blossom's mother Goddess.

This was Blossom's most successful endeavour since coming to Canada. Every once in a while, under she breath, she curse the day she come to Toronto from Oropuche, Trinidad. But nothing, not even snarky white people could keep Blossom under. When she first come it was to babysit some snot-nosed children on Oriole Parkway. She did meet a man, in a club on Henry Street in Port-of-Spain, who promise she to take care of she, if she ever was in Toronto. When Blossom reach, the man disappear and through the one other person she know in Toronto she get the work on Oriole.

Well Blossom decide long that she did never mean for this kinda work, steady cleaning up after white people, and that is when she decide to take a course in secretarial at night. Is there she meet Peg and Betty, who she did know from home, and Fancy Girl. And for two good years they all try to type; but their heart wasn't in it. So they switch to carpentry and upholstering. Fancy Girl swear that they could make a good business because she father was a joiner and white people was paying a lot of money for old-looking furniture. They all went along with this until Peg say she need to make some fast money because, where they was going to find white people who like old furniture, and who was going to buy old furniture from Black women anyway. That is when Fancy Girl come up with the pyramid scheme.

They was to put everybody name on a piece of paper, everybody was to find five people to put on the list and that five would find five and so on. Everybody on the list would send the first person one hundred dollars. In the end everybody was to get thousands of dollars in the mail and only invest one hundred, unless the pyramid break. Fancy Girl name was first and so the pyramid start. Lo and behold, Fancy Girl leave town saying she going to Montreal for a weekend and it was the last they ever see she. The pyramid bust up and they discover that Fancy Girl pick up ten thousand dollars clean. Blossom had to hide for months from people on the pyramid and she swear to Peg that, if she every see Fancy Girl Munroe again, dog eat she supper.

Well now is five years since Blossom in Canada and nothing ain't breaking. She leave the people on Oriole for some others on Balmoral. The white man boss-man was a doctor. Since the day she reach, he eyeing she, eyeing she. Blossom just mark this down in she head and making sure she ain't in no room alone with he. Now one day, it so happen that she in the basement doing the washing and who come down there but he, playing like if he looking for something. She watching him from the corner of she eye and, sure as the day, he make a grab for she. Blossom know a few things, so she grab on to he little finger and start to squeeze it back till he face change all colour from white to black and he had to scream out. Blossom sheself start to scream like all hell, until the wife and children run downstairs too.

It ain't have cuss, Blossom ain't cuss that day. The wife face red and shame and then she start to watch Blossom cut eye. Well look at my cross nah Lord, Blossom think, here this dog trying to abuse me and she watching *me* cut eye! Me! a church-going woman! A craziness fly up in Blossom head and she start to go mad on them in the house. She flinging things left right and centre and cussing big word. Blossom fly right off the handle, until they send for the police for Blossom. She didn't care. They couldn't make she hush. It don't have no dignity in white man feeling you up! So she cuss out the police too, when they come, and tell them to serve and protect she, like they supposed to do and lock up the so-and-so. The doctor keep saying to the police, 'Oh this is so embarrassing. She's crazy, she's crazy.' And Blossom tell him, 'You ain't see crazy yet.' She run and dash all the people clothes in the swimming pool and shouting, 'Make me a weapon in thine hand, oh Lord!' Blossom grab on to the doctor neck, dragging him, to drown him. It take two police to unlatch Blossom from the man red neck, yes. And how the police get Blossom to leave is a wonder; but she wouldn't leave without she pay, and in cash money too besides, she tell them. Anyhow, the police get Blossom to leave the house; and they must be 'fraid Blossom too, so they let she off down the street and tell she to go home.

The next day Blossom show up on Balmoral with a placard saying the Dr So-and-So was a white rapist; and Peg and Betty bring a Black Power flag and the three of them parade in front of that man house whole day. Well is now this doctor know that he mess with the wrong woman, because when he reach home that evening, Blossom and Peg and Betty bang on he car, singing, 'We Shall Not be Moved' and chanting, 'Doctor So-and-So is a Rapist'. They reach into the car and, well, rough up the doctor—grabbing he tie and threatening to cut off he balls. Not a soul ain't come outside, but you never see so much drapes and curtain moving and swaying up and down Balmoral. Police come again, but they tell Doctor So-and-So that the sidewalk is public property and as long as Blossom and them keep moving they wasn't committing no crime. Well, when they hear that, Blossom and them start to laugh and clap and sing 'We Shall Overcome'. That night, at Peg house, they laugh and they eat and they drink and dance and laugh more, remembering the doctor face when they was banging on he car. The next day Blossom hear from the Guyanese girl working next door that the whole family on Balmoral, Doctor, wife, children, cat, and dog, gone to Florida.

After that, Blossom decide to do day work here and day work there, so that no white man would be over she and she was figuring on a way to save money to do she own business.

Blossom start up with Victor one night in a dance. It ain't have no reason that she could say why she hook up with him except that in a dance one night, before Fancy Girl take off, when Peg and Betty and Fancy Girl was in they dance days, she suddenly look around and all three was jack up in a corner with some man. They was grinding down the Trinidad Club and there was Blossom, alone at the table, playing she was groovin' to the music.

Alone. Well, keeping up sheself, working, working and keeping the spirits up in this cold place all the time . . . Is not until all of a sudden one moment, you does see youself. Something tell she to stop and witness the scene. And then Blossom decide to get a man. All she girl pals had one, and Blossom decide to get one too. It sadden she a little to see she riding partners all off to the side so. After all, every weekend they used to fête and insult man when they come to ask them to dance. They would fête all night in the middle of the floor and get tight on southern comfort. Then they would hobble down the steps out of the club on Church or 'Room at the Top', high heels squeezing and waist in pain, and hail a taxi home to one house or the other. By the time the taxi reach wherever they was going, shoes would be in hand and stockings off and a lot of groaning and description of foot pain would hit the door. And comparing notes on which man look so good and which man had a hard on, they would cook, bake, and salt fish, in the morning and laugh about the night before. If is one thing with Blossom, Peg and Betty and Fancy Girl, they like to have a good time. The world didn't mean for sorrow; and suffering don't suit nobody face, Blossom say.

So when she see girl-days done and everybody else straighten up and get man, Blossom decide to get a man too. The first, first man that pass Blossom eyes after deciding was Victor and Blossom decide on him. It wasn't the first man Blossom had, but it was the first one she decide to keep. It ain't have no special reason either; is just when Victor appear, Blossom get a idea to fall in love. Well, then start a long line of misery the likes of which Blossom never see before and never intend to see again. The only reason that the misery last so long is because Blossom was a stubborn woman and when she decide something, she decide. It wasn't even that Blossom really like Victor because whenever she sit down to count he attributes, the man was really lacking in kindness and had a streak of meanness when it come to woman. But she figure like and love not the same thing. So Blossom married to Victor that same summer, in the Pentecostal Church. Victor wanted to live together, but Blossom say she wouldn't be able to go to church no more if she living in sin and if Victor want any honey from she, it have to be with God blessing.

The wedding night, Victor disappear. He show up in a dance, in he white wedding suit and Blossom ain't see him till Monday morning. So Blossom take a sign from this and start to watch Victor because she wasn't a hasty woman by nature. He come when he want, he go when he want and vex when she ain't there. He don't bring much money. Blossom still working day work and every night of the week Victor have friends over drinking Blossom liquor. But Blossom love Victor, so she put up with this type of behaviour for a good few years; because love supposed to be hard and if it ain't hard, it ain't sweet, they say. You have to bear with man, she mother used to say, and besides, Blossom couldn't grudge Victor he good time. Living wasn't just for slaving and it seem that in this society the harder you work, the less you have. Judge not lest ye be judged; this sermon Blossom would give to Peg and Betty anytime they contradict Victor. And anyway, Blossom have she desires and Victor have more than reputation between he legs.

So life go on as it supposed to go on, until Blossom decide not to go to work one day. That time, they was living on Vaughan Road and Blossom wake up feeling like a old woman. Just tired. Something tell she to stay home and figure out she life; because a thirty-six year old woman shouldn't feel so old and tired. She look at she face in the mirror and figure that she look like a old woman too. Ten years she here now, and nothing shaking, just getting older and older, watching white people live. She, sheself living underneath all the time. She didn't even feel like living with Victor anymore. All the sugar gone outa the thing. Victor had one scheme after another, poor thing. Everything gone a little sour.

She was looking out the window, toward the bus stop on Vaughan Road, thinking this. Looking at people going to work like they does do every morning. It make she even more tired to watch them. Today she was supposed to go to a house on Roselawn. Three bathrooms to clean, two living rooms, basement, laundry—God knows what else. Fifty dollars. She look at she short fingers, still water-laden from the day before, then look at the bus stop again. No, no. Not today. Not this woman. In the bedroom, she watch Victor lying in the bed, face peaceful as ever, young like a baby. Passing into the kitchen shaking she head, she think, 'Victor you ain't ready for the Lord yet.'

Blossom must be was sitting at the kitchen table for a hour or so when Victor get up. She hear him bathe, dress and come out to the kitchen. 'Ah, ah, you still here? Is ten o'clock you know!' She didn't answer. 'Girl, you ain't going to work today, or what?' She didn't answer. 'You is a happy woman yes, Blossom. Anyway,' as he put he coat on, 'I have to meet a fella.' Something just fly up in Blossom head and she reach for the bread knife on the table. 'Victor, just go and don't come back, you hear me?' waving the knife. 'Girl you crazy or what?' Victor edged toward the door, 'What happen to you this morning?'

Next thing Blossom know, she running Victor down Vaughan Road screaming and waving the bread knife. She hear somebody screaming loud, loud. At first she didn't know who it is, and is then she realize that the scream was coming from she and she couldn't stop it. She dress in she nightie alone and screaming in the middle of the road. So it went on and on and on until it turn into cry and Blossom just cry and cry and cry and then she start to walk. That day Blossom walk. And walk and cry, until she was so exhausted that she find she way home and went to sleep.

She wake up the next morning, feeling shaky and something like spiritual. She was frightened, in case the crying come back again. The apartment was empty. She had the feeling that she was holding she body around she heart, holding sheself together, tight, tight. She get dressed and went to the Pentecostal Church where she get married and sit there till evening.

For two weeks this is all Blossom do. As soon as she feel the crying welling up inside she and turning to a scream, she get dressed and go to the Pentecost. After two weeks, another feeling come; one as if Blossom dip she whole head in water and come up gasping. She heart would pump fast as if she going to die and then the feeling, washed and gasping. During these weeks she could drink nothing but water. When she try to eat bread, something reach inside of she throat and spit it out. Two weeks more and Blossom hair turn white all over. Then she start to speak in tongues that she didn't ever learn, but she understand. At night, in Blossom cry dreams, she feel sheself flying round the earth and raging around the world and then, not just this earth, but earth deep in the blackness beyond sky. There, sky become further than sky and further than dream. She dream so much farther than she ever go in a dream, that she was awake. Blossom see volcano erupt and mountain fall down two feet away and she ain't get touch. She come to the place where legahoo and lajabless is not even dog and where soucouyant, the fireball, burn up in the bigger fire of an infinite sun, where none of the ordinary spirit Blossom know is nothing. She come to the place where pestilence mount good, good heart and good heart bust for joy. The place bright one minute and dark the next. The place big one minute, so big Blossom standing in a hole and the blackness rising up like long shafts above she and widening out into a yellow and red desert as far as she could see; the place small, next minute, as a pin head and

only Blossom heart what shrink small, small, small, could fit in the
world of it. Then she feel as if she don't have no hand, no foot
and she don't need them. Sometimes, she crawling like mapeepee
snake; sometimes she walking tall, tall, like a moco jumbie through
desert and darkness, desert and darkness, upside down and
sideways.

In the mornings, Blossom feel she body beating up and breaking
up on a hard mud ground and she, weeping as if she mourning and
as if somebody borning. And talking in tongues, the tongues saying
the name, Oya. The name sound through Blossom into every layer
of she skin, she flesh — like sugar and seasoning. Blossom body come
hard like steel and supple like water, when she say Oya. Oya. This
Oya was a big spirit Blossom know from home.

One night, Oya hold Blossom and bring she through the most
terrifying dream in she life. In the dream, Oya make Blossom look
at Black people suffering. The face of Black people suffering was so
old and hoary that Blossom nearly dead. And is so she vomit. She
skin wither under Suffering look; and she feel hungry and thirsty as
nobody ever feel before. Pain dry out Blossom soul, until it turn to
nothing. Blossom so 'fraid she dead that she takes she last ball of
spit, and stone Suffering. Suffering jump up so fast and grab the stone,
Blossom shocked, because she did think Suffering was decrepit.
Then Suffering head for Blossom with such a speed that Blossom
fingernails and hairs fall out. Blossom start to dry away, and melt
away, until it only had one grain of she left. And Suffering still
descending. Blossom scream for Oya and Oya didn't come and Suffering keep coming. Blossom was never a woman to stop, even before
she start to dream. So she roll and dance she grain-self into a hate
so hard, she chisel sheself into a sharp hot prickle and fly in Suffering
face. Suffering howl like a beast and back back. Blossom spin and
chew on that nut of hate, right in Suffering eyeball. The more Blossom
spin and dance, the more Suffering back back; the more Suffering
back back, the bigger Blossom get, until Blossom was Oya with she
warrior knife, advancing. In the cold light of Suffering, with Oya hot
and advancing, Suffering slam a door and disappear. Blossom climb
into Oya lovely womb of strength and fearlessness. Full of joy when
Oya show she the warrior dance where heart and blood burst open.
Freeness, Oya call that dance; and the colour of the dance was red
and it was a dance to dance high up in the air. In this dance Oya had
such a sweet laugh, it make she black skin shake and it full up
Blossom and shake she too.

Each night Blossom grow more into Oya. Blossom singing, singing for Oya to come,
'Oya arriwo Oya, Oya arriwo Oya, Oya kauako arriwo, Arripiti O Oya.'
Each night Blossom learn a new piece of Oya and finally, it come to she. She had the power to see and the power to fight; she had the power to feel pain and the power to heal. For life was nothing as it could be taken away any minute; what was earthly was fleeting; what could be done was joy and it have no beauty in suffering.
'Oya O Ologbo O de, Ma yak ba Ma Who! leh, Oya O Ologo O de, Ma yak ba Ma Who! leh, Oya Oh de arriwo, Oya Oh de cumale.'
From that day, Blossom dress in yellow and red from head to foot, the colour of joy and the colour of war against suffering. She head wrap in a long yellow cloth; she body wrap in red. She become a obeah woman, spiritual mother and priestess of Oya, Yuroba Goddess-warrior of winds, storms, and waterfalls. It was Oya who run Victor out and it was Oya who plague the doctor and laugh and drink afterwards. It was Oya who well up the tears inside Blossom and who spit the bread out of Blossom mouth.
Quite here, Oya did search for Blossom. Quite here, she find she.
Black people on Vaughan Road recognized Blossom as gifted and powerful by she carriage and the fierce look in she eyes. She fill she rooms with compelling powder and reliance smoke, drink rum and spit it in the corners, for the spirits who would enter Blossom obeah house in the night. Little by little people begin to find out that Blossom was the priestess of Oya, the Goddess. Is through Oya, that Blossom reach prosperity.
'Oya arriwo Oya, Oya arriwo Oya, Oya kauako arriwo, Arripiti O Oya'
Each night Oya would enter Blossom, rumbling and violent like thunder and chant heroically and dance, slowly and majestically, she warrior dance against suffering. To see Oya dancing on one leg all night, a calabash holding a candle on she head, was to see beauty. She fierce warrior face frighten unbelievers. Then she would drink nothing but good liquor, blowing mouthfuls on the gathering, granting favours to the believers for an offering.
The offerings come fast and plentiful. Where people was desperate, Blossom, as Oya, received food as offering, boxes of candles and sweet oil. Blossom send to Trinidad for calabash gourds and herbs for healing, guided by Oya in the mixing and administering.
When Oya enter Blossom, she talk in old African tongues and she

body was part water and part tree. Oya thrash about taking Blossom body up to the ceiling and right through the walls. Oya knife slash the gullets of white men and Oya pitch the world around itself. Some nights, she voice sound as if it was coming from a deep well; and some nights, only if you had the power to hear air, could you listen to Oya.

Blossom fame as a obeah woman spread all over, but only among those who had to know. Those who see the hoary face of Suffering and feel he vibrant slap could come to dance with Oya — Oya freeness dance.

'Oya O Ologbo O de, Ma yak ba Ma Who! leh, Oya O Ologo O de, Ma yak ba Ma Who! leh, Oya Oh de arriwo, Oya Oh de cumale.'

Since Oya reach, Blossom live peaceful. Is so, Blossom start in the speakeasy business. In the day time, Blossom sleep, exhausted and full of Oya warrior dance and laughing. She would wake up in the afternoon to prepare the shrine for Oya entrance.

On the nights that Oya didn't come, Blossom sell liquor and wait for she, sitting against the window.

DIONNE BRAND was born in 1953 in the Caribbean and has lived in Toronto for twenty years. She studied English and philosophy at the University of Toronto and is currently doing post-graduate work at the Ontario Institute for Studies in Education. Her short stories have been published in *Sans Souci and Other Stories* (Stratford: Williams-Wallace, 1988) and have appeared in *Stories by Canadian Women* (Oxford University Press). Her published poetry includes *Winter Epigrams and Epigrams to Ernesto Cardenal in Defense of Claudia* (Toronto: Williams-Wallace, 1983) and *Chronicles of the Hostile Sun* (Toronto: Williams-Wallace, 1984). She is co-author of *Rivers Have Sources Trees Have Roots — Speaking of Racism.*

DAGMAR NOVAK was born in Czechoslovakia and teaches in the English department at the University of Toronto, where she completed her doctorate in English literature in 1985. Her book *The Canadian Novel and the Two World Wars* is forthcoming from McGill-Queen's University Press. She is currently writing a biography of Gabrielle Roy for Oxford University Press.

You've lived in Canada for many years — in fact, since you were seventeen. In your first years here, what were the positive as well as the negative aspects of being an immigrant?

Basically, I really didn't think of myself as an immigrant *per se*. Yes, I came from another country, but I didn't think that the worlds were that far apart, and I knew that the problems that I would have would not stem from my being an immigrant, but would stem from my being black. If I had been white, within a generation my family would have been assimilated. I could escape being an immigrant, but along with the black people who have lived in this country for three centuries, I would not escape my race at any point. Racism was the focus of my encounter with Canada, not immigrancy.

In your short story 'Blossom' there is a definite feeling of separateness between black and white. Indeed, there is a distrust and hatred of whites. Can you comment on Blossom's alienation and her refusal to assimilate?

I think that Blossom's distrust of whites is not based on some personal craziness of hers. It's based on historical practice. It is based on historical events which place her as a black woman in the world at this point in time. Her distrust of whites is not personal paranoia: it has something to do with the social conditions that she finds herself in. She finds herself in a city of whites, where her relation to them is one of subordination. She works for them; they exploit her labour through her race; they oppress her through sexual harassment. The whites in the story are not Blossom's only antagonists, though whites might read the story that way. Blossom also frees herself of an exploiting husband. What Blossom hates is suffering and the suffering of black peoples.

Is there something in 'Blossom' that is universal?

I'm sure there might be, but when I start to write a story, I never begin from what might be universal. In fact, I'm wary of appeals to universality. It seems to me that only works written by writers who are not white are called upon to prove or provide universality. White literature is never called upon to commit itself in this way, but all other literature must abandon its specific projects to fit into the understanding of white literature as the expression of white sensibilities. White critics have a preoccupation with rationalizing, homogenizing meanings into white cultural codes which are, of course, loaded with historical relations of power. Universal, therefore, means white. In that context, I do not care about what is universal. I write about what is specific.

Despite the fact that you've lived in Canada for years, would you say that your racial background has affected your writing in Canada?

Yes. I've heard other writers talk about being on the margins of Canadian writing. I find myself in the middle of black writing. I'm in the centre of black writing, and those are the sensibilities that I check to figure out something that's truthful. I write out of a literature, a genre, a tradition, and that tradition is the tradition of black writing. And whether that black writing comes from the United States as African American writing or African Caribbean writing or African writing from the continent, it's in that tradition that I work. I grew up under a colonial system of education, where I read English literature, and I liked it because I love words. But within that writing, there was never my presence. I was absent from that writing. That writing was predicated on imperial history and imperial aspirations — British or American. That imperial history included black slavery. It included the decimation of native peoples. And if the literature nurtured on this is presented to you as great art and you are absent, or the forms or shapes in which you are included are derided, then you know that this literature means to erase you or to kill you. Then you write yourself.

In 'Blossom' it seems to me that the past is alive in an almost mystical way.

Yes, each time I write, I find that I've got to go back. I have to go back five hundred years to come back again. Blossom had to go back to come back again to make everything beautiful, to understand anything about the world that she was living in. She had to dig into that past of hers which she retained; she becomes an Obeah woman because that was one of the things that black people in the Americas managed to retain, some sense of a past that is not a past controlled by those things that seem to control her now. I think that one of the reasons why we have been able to survive in the Americas, as a people, has been because of what we have been able to hold and preserve. You just have to look at black culture today and, despite the real hardship that we continue to suffer, you also have to look at things like the music that we make or the literature that we write. So, there is an antagonistic discourse that we continually engage in — in order to keep alive.

Of course, there are anti-discriminatory laws, but it seems as if there is no real spirit behind those laws.

It's also not even individual; it's within institutions. I came here in 1970 and went to find a job. I talked on the phone to the person about the job, and the guy was very enthusiastic on the phone. And I went there and I saw consternation on his face — and the job wasn't there. When I got back home, I called and the job was there. Every black person can tell you a similar story.

What does this do to you? What kind of effect does it have?

Personally, you have to develop an armour to deal with it. Collectively, what you do is organize against it. Because, you see, you can't deal with racism on your own — because you will go crazy. What you do is what black communities have done since we landed on these shores.

But how do you change people's minds, their hearts?

I don't think it's up to black people to change white sensibilities. I think it is up to white people to do that. I think that racism is not our problem. I think it's a white problem. I think we can fight against it. I think it's our job to fight for good laws, to fight for equality, but in terms of doing things like changing white attitudes, white people have to do that work.

For you as a writer, has multiculturalism — as an official Canadian policy — had any benefits, or any detrimental effects?

I think what it does essentially is to compartmentalize us into little cultural groups who have dances and different foods and Caribana. But it doesn't address real power.

Real power?

Real power — which is economic power and political power. I think multiculturalism makes the Canadian population think they're doing really nice things: isn't it nice that we can accept 'these' people? But 'these' people remain 'these' people. You know, I've been living in this country for twenty years. I am sure there's a guy who emigrated from England five years ago who feels more of this country than I. And I'm sure that there's a black person who has lived here for 150 years and feels like me.

What effect does this kind of segregation have on people in the arts?

It has never stopped us from writing or playing music or singing. I think for a lot of black artists it's a question of survival, the survival of a culture. So we cannot really depend on the Canada Council or the Ontario Arts Council or the Ministry of Multiculturalism. The black community cannot depend upon, cannot trust these institutions to maintain or nurture our cultural expression in Canada. Those institutions should be asking themselves what it is precisely that they maintain and nurture, if particular communities are not funded or are underfunded. And they should be asking themselves: what is Canadian culture? There are other literary organizations in this country, such as the Writers' Union and PEN, who seem to feel that you can quantify culture into six per cent of this and two per cent of that. These demographic figures are trotted out in hasty self-defence to deny charges of racism. This approach assumes that the contradictions of Canadian culture can be handled by putting them into discrete and isolated packages. Further, it assumes the ongoing dominance of white culture as justifiable and having no responsibility to change its fundamental stance.

But it must make people alien or angry or bitter?

Not really, because, you see, these institutions are a reflection of the culture in which we live. So that it's not something that only happens to us when we write to the Arts Council or the Canada Council. It's something that has happened to us every day on the street. So we're really wise about these things, because they've been happening for years and years and years.

I noticed that in 'Blossom' you portrayed two distinct worlds, the world of the whites and the world of the non-whites. Is this your sense of the divisions within Canadian society?

Of course. It isn't just my sense. There are reservations in this country; there are job ghettos for people of colour. And yes, those things have been marked out by institutions that have grown out of the building of this nation. In the end, we're all responsible for changing that.

How difficult is it to avoid the potential danger of stereotyping a racial group in order to show cultural differences?

Fundamentally, I work against stereotyping. My writing is directed against stereotypes and so I am bound to show complexity in the characters I produce. I am not trying to 'show cultural differences' in my writing; I am not even trying to portray a 'racial group'. What you read into the text so far as that is concerned depends on your stance, your location. The question presumes a reader who is located somewhere else. The white reader may perceive cultural difference, but I am merely writing myself.

Couldn't there also be a danger in showing black men and women as always being the victims of prejudice?

Danger for whom? Racism is a fact in our lives and it is not in our interest to pretend that it does not exist. But that fact has never overwhelmed us and it is certainly not all that we live or all that I write about. I don't think that there's any more danger in it for me, in trying to look at black life, my life, than there was for James Joyce in looking at Irish life.

It seems to me that there's a great deal of anger in Blossom's life. Do you see this as being a force in her transformation?

But she also has a buoyancy. She never thinks of dying. Her anger moves her. You can be angry about silences and injustice. Those are pretty good things to be angry about. And if that anger can then move you, I think it's the real answer. In this culture, one tends to think that anger is destructive. Anger is not an emotion that's only distinguished by destructiveness. To me, it's a more complex emotion. In fact, Blossom is one of the least angry of my characters. She is a woman of mighty resilience and quick action. And this brings me to another point. I'm also wary of the word 'anger' as a description for every emotion of a black character in a black work. White critics tend to describe black emotion as either angry or sad, no matter what else is going on in the text, no matter how many other emotions they are confronted by in the characters in that text. Blossom is also joyful, resigned, peaceful, excited, fearful, confused, hurt, sexual, remorseful, euphoric. . . . But the cultural codes which the critic uses to identify black characters are white cultural codes which see blacks in general as either angry in general or sad in general!

What do you see as the future for Canadian writers who are not white?

I think that we are probably the new wave of Canadian writing. Twenty years ago there was a national wave of Canadian writing which set itself up against American writing and the deluge of American culture in Canada. We are the new wave of Canadian writing. We will write about the internal contradictions.

What do you think about whites who write about native life?

I think I can say categorically that whites cannot write about native life.

Should not?

Should not. Yes, should not and cannot—not at this point in history at any rate, not in the absence of native writers having the opportunity, the possiblity, and the material resources for writing about native life and having that work published and read. History has been weighted against native people in this country and weighted toward whites; this is an obvious truth for native writers. Native peoples do not need white writers to interpret their lives for them. The distortions of native life in interpretations by white writers are far too numerous and destructive to mention. If any white writer feels that he has the right to interpret native life, the shame of those distortions should make him pause, blush, and halt in his tracks. No amount of liberal good will can erase this. If anything, white writers should ponder what in their collective psyche makes them want to write about native life. Why do they need the power to do this? Why do they remain in a past of white conquest and appropriation? Why are they bent on perpetuating stereotypes, instead of breaking with that history? Now, that would make some good reading, but it would take a little more work and thinking.

JANICE KULYK KEEFER b. 1953

Mrs Mucharski and The Princess

1

'Pretty lady have pretty baby,' were Mrs Mucharski's first words to
Laurie on her triumphal return from the hospital. They seemed to
print the necessary ceremonial flourish over the confused joy of the
occasion, shaping the moment as delicately and permanently as the
pink kid-leather frames in which Vic, a few weeks later, enclosed the
first photographs of Laurie and the baby on the hospital steps.

It was not only that she had spoken perfect truths—for neither
camera nor film could make out mother and daughter as anything
other than pretty figures in pretty-coloured clothes—but also that
Mrs Mucharski's accent had somehow rarefied the triteness of the
compliment, so that she seemed to be performing an incantation or
rendering some magical phrase out of an old folksong. R's trilled, a's
lolled, v's huffed; together they summoned images from opulently
illustrated editions of Russian fairy-tales. Laurie assumed that the
housekeeper, with her Slavic cheekbones and tongue, had issued
from the Eastern European hodgepodge: Czech, Bulgarian, Polish,
Ukrainian, Hungarian—it didn't much matter which. She was foreign
and intricately so, independent from her employers both in the shape
and tone of her speech, so that when Mrs Mucharski spoke it was,
for all her drab clothes and spare face—which had certainly never
been pretty—as if she were addressing her equals.

Perhaps, Sheila had hinted, the woman was an ex-princess or at
least of noble blood, fallen from good fortune after some natural or
historical disaster, and forced to work for her bread like a hard-luck
heroine in a fairy-tale. It had been Sheila, ever the indispensable
sister-in-law (married for the second time to a Lebanese computer-
salesman who claimed descent from a royal house) who had suggested Mrs Mucharski when the pediatric nurse the agency had
engaged fell through.

'It's a blessing in disguise, Laurie,' Sheila had urged. 'Whatever do you want a nurse for—you can manage all the care for the baby yourself, that's child's play' (Sheila had four of her own) 'as long as you've got help in the house. You know, for cooking, cleaning, laundry, all the drudge work. And Mrs Mucharski's a gem—a pearl, positive. She's not just a peasant from off the boat, with sweaty armpits and a moustache: she's a lady. And she's honest as the day— of how many Portuguese or Vietnamese people can you say that? She *works*, she doesn't just laze around and chitter-chatter. And she's not expensive, either, especially compared with what you'd have to pay for a pediatric nurse—'

The money, Laurie had interrupted, would be no problem. Vic insisted on the best, and, as Sheila would know, he could afford to get it. This was not just random bitchery; Laurie had, more than a trifle guiltily, wanted someone who could look after the prospective baby for a few hours every day, so that she could escape downtown once in a while; shop, meet friends for lunch, unwind and unbond a bit after her pregnancy. Sheila would have clucked at this, nattered about La Lèche (she still had a two year old tugging at her breasts) and how money was just no substitute for mother-love—so Laurie had deflected her by lighting a little flare of sibling rivalry and had then pounced with: 'But if this Mrs Mucharski is so good, then why isn't she registered with one of the big agencies? It's not that I don't trust your judgement, Sheila, but after all, where a newborn baby is concerned. . . .'

'That's not her style,' Sheila had squealed. 'She's a classy house-keeper, believe me; she likes people to come to her—and she's choosy. Look, Laurie, she may not *want* to work for you at all: *she* doesn't need the best that money can buy. Some of us plain poor people make do very well without—oh, what the hell, I want to help you out. She's not with an agency, I guess, because—I've never asked her straight out, she's not that type of person—because there might be some slight problem with immigration.' Here Sheila's voice had gone all sweet and snaky through the telephone coils. 'Not that there's anything fishy—she's straight as a ruler, is Mrs Mucharski, and she's been in Canada—oh, for years and years, but—well, it seems that she just never did the proper bureaucratic things when she arrived—you know, all that kaboodle with red and pink and blue tape. Besides, she's sensitive about her age—I mean, God knows how old she is, you can't just tot her up as if she were rouged to the hilt and dyed her hair gentian violet. Fifty-five, sixty-five—who knows? But she can do things, Laurie; why, you'll be just astounded' – Sheila blew the vowels of the word in and out as if they were a blob of bubblegum – 'at the things she'll do for you.'

And so she'd come – the very day after Vic had driven a carefully breathing Laurie into the maternity hospital – and stayed. By the time Vic had brought Laurie home, Mrs Mucharski had transcended Sheila's gushes. It was not an easy house to care for, Laurie had run through a baker's dozen of different cleaning women in the year they'd lived there, and all of them put together hadn't managed to accomplish what Mrs Mucharski had in that one week. Walls had been washed, curtains brushed, even mending attended to: the heap of scarcely worn clothing Laurie had thrown into a cardboard box to give to St-Vincent de Paul had all been sorted, salvaged and put neatly into drawers.

The ivory-and-turquoise Chinese carpets had not merely been vacuumed, but first washed, combed, and plumed somehow, so that you'd swear no one ever could have walked on them. If you could work enchantments with linseed oil and flannel cloths, Ajax and Windex and bleach, then Mrs Mucharski was some sort of good fairy out of a story book, though with her humped fingers and hooked back she looked much more like a wicked witch, webbed in by some white magic. Perhaps this would explain why, after nursing the baby (for at the eleventh hour Laurie had been converted by La Lèche) and putting her down to sleep in the wicker bassinet that had once been her own, Laurie should feel Mrs Mucharski's sharply angled face and grave, strange voice shuttle in and out the weave of her own dreams, that first night home.

2

During the first week of Mrs Mucharski's stay Laurie held court in the mid-mornings and late afternoons. Neighbours, acquaintances from the pre-natal classes she'd attended, friends from work, themselves either babyless or unremarried or both, would stop by to see the baby and to gossip with Laurie in her upstairs sitting-room, dabbling stockinged toes in the plush ivory carpeting, sipping hot, fragrant teas out of porcelain cups, tearing large bites out of the breads and cakes and buns with which the housekeeper had laden the tea tray. For ever since Mrs Mucharski's arrival the kitchen air had hummed with the warm spice of baking: poppy-seed strudels, shining braids of golden bread, small pastries plumped with cheese or meat crowded each other on the larder shelves. And as they watched the crooked, neat, old woman come and go, her eyes never meeting any curious glance, her hair braided into a tight steel-coloured band across the top of her head, Laurie's visitors would nod their heads and whisper about the treasure she had found, and then about her good luck in general. Such a baby, such a husband, such a house, such a housekeeper, what fabulous luck: she was like some princess at the end of a fairy-tale. But Laurie would only laugh, or smile and shake her head so that her lovely hair fell into her great coffee-coloured eyes. And if, in her fluted tea-gown, with her peaceful, bassinetted baby and her sitting-room jungling with hot-house flowers she was complacent in her happiness, who could blame her? For what is happiness but a talent for luxuriating in your own given circumstances: circumstances which, Laurie's whole attitude declared, had flocked to her as naturally as birds to a broad-branched tree at evening.

So there she sat on top of her kingdom, like a candied cherry on a peak of flushed meringue, while those of her friends who'd brought their babies scorched their tongues on her tea, remembering their entropic houses heaped with unwashed, milk-stiff nightgowns and souring baby things, while their own infants fretted, mewled, popped out in nervous rashes and spat up over their shabby jeans. And the bare-wombed ex-colleagues from the small, expensive shop for which Laurie had been a buyer cooed over the baby's bonnets and smocked nightdresses, and told Laurie that she looked like an ad for Ivory Snow. And Laurie just looked prettily down at the reflection quivering in her full tea-cup, or rang the brass bell for Mrs Mucharski to come up the stairs with a fresh pot or another plate of delicious things for her guests.

At last, however, everyone who could possibly want to see the baby had come and gone, without ever following up on their promises to return, or to invite Laurie to their own, less happy houses. Only Sheila kept dropping by, with two or more of her over-fed, contrary children and warnings about how this honeymoon phase of newborn bliss would last no longer than a pair of stockings. After four such visits Laurie instructed Mrs Mucharski to tell Sheila that she was resting any time she called, or that the doctor had forbidden visits from anyone with small, snuffling children. And the housekeeper, for all that Sheila had been her good angel in getting her this job,

did just as she was told. Somewhat non-plussed, Laurie added this
to the list of things she was finding out about Mrs Mucharski: that
her loyalties were strictly professional and temporary, like the jobs
she did.

She actually knew very little about the woman, in spite of the fact
that, as her visitors failed and the weather tapered into endless
fine, autumnal rain, Laurie spent all her days indoors with only the
housekeeper and an increasingly wakeful baby to distract her. One
afternoon she'd sat rocking her daughter in a pale blue-velvet chair,
watching Mrs Mucharski expertly unhook, wash and polish the
prisms of the Orrefors chandelier that Vic had brought back from
his last business trip abroad. She noticed how the woman's eyes
tightened each time she picked up a fragment of the crystal, so clear
and slippery-cool it seemed to turn to water in her hands. She saw
the small, purplish mole over Mrs Mucharski's left eyebrow quiver
as she knit her forehead at her work; she noticed how her lips
seemed to make involuntary tremblings, as if she were praying to
herself. Laurie asked various unpatterned questions that were
answered as tersely as possible.

'Have you any children, Mrs Mucharski?'
'No.'
'Is your husband living?'
'No.'
'What country do you come from?'
'I Canadian, now. Canada my country.'
'Have you lived here long?'
'Yes.'

And finally, with more irritation than concern, 'Mrs Mucharski, you
work too hard—don't you ever sit down and rest for a bit? Sit down
now and relax, and just let yourself be for a minute.' But the woman
had kept her silence until, having reassembled the chandelier and
skilfully rehung it, she turned to Laurie, saying in the odd, encrusted
accent, 'No, lady. Once I be sit down do nothing, I start think, start
and no finish. And then I be finish, too.' She'd looked Laurie in the
eyes with her own—not large, not beautiful but precise, judging eyes
that rode the slant of her cheekbones, lodging in her face the way a
night light settles into a room, illuminating odd patches of ceiling,
throwing up soft, distorted shadows. And though Laurie had been
opening her mouth to say something, Mrs Mucharski turned away
from her, taking her polishing cloths and the small step-ladder on

which she had been standing, leaving Laurie to the darkening ruin of the afternoon.

3

Whatever it was Mrs Mucharski refused to let herself think, Laurie wasn't likely to find out. It had happened at any rate, over there, in that country the housekeeper would not name, that place where history went on—real history, the kind that was someone else's nightmare. When Laurie talked with a certain kind of stranger— hairdressers, or cleaning ladies—she wanted small, clear, coloured bits of information about their lives, certainly no black pools that might muddy her own bright reflection.

Once or twice, she had wondered what it would be like to have everything you possessed wrenched from you, as she supposed had happened to Mrs Mucharski all those years ago. House, family, even your language—all gone, for good. But she hadn't a very generous imagination, it stretched no larger than the soft warm smallness of her own skin. Mrs Mucharski would not talk, Laurie would ask no more questions, and their silence would be a clean, snowy Switzer- land between them, permitting a sure neutrality of emotion. For Mrs Mucharski no more demanded pity from anyone than she exercised grudges against those who possessed what she presumably had lost. She went about her endless, infinitesimal tasks with the impersonal fidelity of a verger in some large church. While Laurie flitted in and out of the rooms of her house, the woman kept to her work: the cleaning, baking, polishing, and putting-away that sent a hum of well-tempered domesticity through the household air. And if Mrs Mucharski never asked to hold or rock the baby; if she never stopped over the bassinet to watch the ferocious soundness of her sleep or to the place a finger in the passionate grip of the baby's toylike hand, it was, perhaps, only that never having had children she didn't like babies. Lots of people were like that; Laurie didn't mind.

So that when things started to go wrong it wasn't as if Mrs Muchar- ski had somehow witched the house, disordering the baby's routine or souring Laurie's milk. Yet it was at her that Laurie snapped one morning when, with nothing to look forward to all day but a baby to feed and change and bathe, she had lain spread-eagled over the brass-bound double bed, pressing reddened eyes into the comforter. Her stitches still twisted painfully when she bent down, her belly hadn't yet lost its pregnant puffiness, and her breasts, which once had been as small and snowy as apples, were now long, darkened with railroading veins, the nipples puckered. They hurt her as she hiccoughed short, hard sobs, and then they began to leak warm driblets of milk through the cups of her nursing brassiere, past her peignoir and into the comforter. Sitting up, she fished her reflection from the floor-length mirror that hung across the wall from the bed. She wanted other images, that easy icon of new motherhood that had been beamed at her from every magazine cover, every ad for baby oil: some sixteen-year-old model simulating maternity with a downy-diapered baby who would toddle off and let her be once the photography was finished. To be fresh, untouched, still virgin, somehow; free to create and float appearances without always that anchor of small, vulnerable, all-demanding flesh she'd thought to have shed as she had the rubber plate of after-birth in the delivery-room.

All the mirror gave her back was her own blubbered face, the damp patches making twin bull's-eyes of her breasts, and — Mrs Mucharski's slight, hooked figure, laden now with armfuls of floaty stuff resembling clouds that had spun through rainbows. 'Lady,' she was saying, 'lady, your things, I be washing two, three times, try clean. . . .' The flounced and ribboned things were the nightgowns Laurie'd taken into hospital with her — stupidly, for they'd all been scarred by ugly thick stains from the blood clots and discharge she had passed after the birth. She flushed and took the things from Mrs Mucharski's arms, she crammed them into an open drawer and shoved it shut, ripping one of the peignoirs as she did so. It shamed her to have had this old woman handle her things, her very blood. To have had her see her things unclean like that was an intimacy she could not bear, and so she turned petulant, shouting, 'Get out, go away — and leave my things alone. I don't want you to touch my things ever again; do you understand?'

Mrs Mucharski nodded, but her eyes seemed to hook into Laurie's face; when she walked out she left a mustiness of disapproval behind. Laurie stood up, and threw a pillow at the shadows the old woman had made. Why should that sour-faced witch be judging her with those small, hard eyes? Who did she think she was — whose house did she think this was? And she pushed her head into the comforter again, choking on her sobs; it was all Mrs Mucharski's fault; if they had got the nurse, the lady the agency had lined up for them, she would be free now, she'd have someone with whom to leave the baby—she could go out, downtown, see her friends, live as she'd used to. . . . She would show them all: she'd wean the baby, fire Mrs Mucharski, hire a proper nurse. . . .

But then the house would fall to pieces, and Vic would complain; and the baby was hers—she didn't want to give it up to some paid stranger. So Laurie had risen from the bed, washed her face, dressed, and taken the baby outside, avoiding Mrs Mucharski as if the woman really were a witch who'd walked into their house from some ogre-ridden fairy-tale instead of from the city bus. Jumpy, nervy, she found it difficult to push the high-wheeled, bouncy carriage straight along the sidewalk. Instead of lying back like a little oyster in a flounced shell the baby whimpered, screw-faced, in the frilled sleeping-suit Laurie had dressed her in. Above her head the baggy clouds kept threatening rain; she saw a few steel pins dance off the hood of the baby-carriage and so she turned back in the direction of her house. Never before had she felt quite so leaden at the thought of reaching her front steps, the fluted columns, the fake Georgian portico, the glossy shutters that were nailed against the brick and which, even if they could have moved, would never have shut flush together. All those were not even unique in their prosperous pretence: every fourth house along the new-developed block had features parallel, and just as false. They'd moved here because of the baby—Vic wanted three children close together—because of the baby, this baby crying raucously as Laurie fumbled with the catch of the carriage hood, getting the lace of the sleeping-suit entangled with the wingbolt in the process. Incompetent, useless—she wouldn't have made it even as a nanny, she despaired, feeling the hot prick of tears under her eyelids. At last she got the baby free, just as the rain gushed down.

It seemed as if her key unlocked some stranger's house; the reflections of newly polished brass and copper, the pristine arrange-ment of the furniture threw foreign gleams and shadows over her memory of how things used to be inside the house—her house—before Mrs Mucharski had arrived. Everything had changed so—the breezy calm with which she'd first assumed responsibility for the baby while in hospital, the regal control she had assumed to have over the running of the house. Such unexplained, disastrous differences—what could these be but a counter-spell to her accustomed happiness, her certain luck? This would be the reason why the baby, instead of nuzzling blindly toward Laurie's breasts and latching on to the warm jets of milk, had now begun to pull away and squirm, or send up a baffled cry after a few furious sucks. This would explain why, if she did feed well, she would in half-an-hour's time shudder awake, her chin a-quiver and her tiny legs drawn up. Fretting, starting at the least irregular noise, whining unless she were carried up against Laurie's shoulder, her head crooning into the hollow just below the collarbone, the baby had begun to keep poor Laurie up half the night and all the day.

Throughout that first distempered week Vic tried to spell her off and on but he hadn't enough time; he was working late these nights on a big project for which his company had just contracted, and that he couldn't afford to neglect. When Laurie complained of lines and shadows under her eyes, of taut nerves, and listless boredom, stuck at home all day and night with a whining baby, he'd barked at her: 'What else have you got to do besides look after the baby and yourself? Mrs Mucharski runs the house, I pay the bills, you nurse the baby. Look, she's not a doll, of course she'll cry some of the time, all you've got to do is mother her, so go on — what are you, unnatural or something?'

Over the telephone the doctor had impatiently collapsed Laurie's inquiries as to baby-tranquillizers as if they were so many tottery bowling-pins. 'Colic,' he'd diagnosed, 'colic pure and simple. It comes on suddenly like that, in the third or fourth week — it'll last maybe two or three months and then disappear as magically as it came. You'll just have to cope — the way your mother did with you, and hers with her. Get a sitter in, from time to time, to give yourself a break.' But Vic's reproach had armoured Laurie; when he'd returned one lunchtime from yet another business trip, with a dozen cream-coloured roses, tickets to a play and an offer from Sheila to babysit if they couldn't engage a sitter from the agency, Laurie had hurled the roses at him, thorns and all, and locked herself into the bathroom of the master bedroom while Vic explained the intricacies of post-partum depression through the keyhole. And all the time the baby kept up a siren-wail of discontent, until Vic had had to break off his suasions and go pace the upper landing to a slow, womb-tempo with his fractious daughter in his arms and his wife sobbing into the dry Jacuzzi at the hopelessness of it all: what sitter would be able to stand more than half an hour of that unceasing, plangent misery? Finally Vic had paced the child to silence and put her delicately into the bassinet, terrified of shattering the fragile shell of her sleep. And then he'd padded down the stairs, closed the front door silently behind him and returned an hour later with a year's hoard of Similac in the back of the car.

Perhaps it was because he advanced upon her with a tin and bottle opener as if they were a bayonet that Laurie shouted when she really could have laughed; perhaps it was because she'd hardly slept the night before that she grabbed the Similac out of her husband's hands and threw it at the ceramic tiles of their bathroom floor, from where it bounced up into the giant mirror over the vanity, slashing it into a hundred scintillant ribbons. And then they both began to scream, so single-mindedly that neither heard the baby waking up and joining in.

'How dare you! How dare you interfere with the way I nurse my baby! She's *mine* to feed; I have nothing else to do, remember? You leave us alone —'

'Leave you alone to starve her? What kind of a mother are you if you don't even know your baby's starving? The doctor —'

'Screw the doctor — he wouldn't even come and look at —'

'Of course he wouldn't pay a house call just to hold the hand of some spoiled suburban —'

'You're the one — you're the one who wanted to come to these stupid suburbs. Remember those three kids you wanted to have, "close together"?'

'I remember — and I wish right now that we'd never . . .'

'Don't say it, don't, Vic.'

As is the way of such things, they'd frightened each other into arms so tight and quick they almost squeezed themselves breathless. Laurie made little, whimpering sounds as Vic kissed the top of her head and the quivering domes of her eyelids, and it was another ten minutes before either was quiet enough for Vic to loose his arms and say, 'We'd better get Mrs Mucharski in to sweep up all that glass. . . .'

But when they looked for her Mrs Mucharski was nowhere to be found — neither in the kitchen, nor in the laundry-room, nor in the slightly stuffy, somewhat damp bedroom that had been prepared for her in the basement of the house. Suddenly terrified, Laurie gripped her husband's arm and whispered, 'Vic — oh, Vic — the baby? What if she's gone, and kidnapped the baby? It's been known to happen — and she never liked the poor little thing, and —'

Vic told her not to be an idiot, but, all the same, he raced ahead of her up the stairs to the top floor where the baby had her small and separate room. They opened the door, but froze on the threshold like a pair of children discovered in flagrant misdeed. For there, in the old, curly-maple platform rocker that Vic had had specially refinished for his wife, sat Mrs Mucharski, her steel-coloured hair woven into a tight crown upon her head, her sturdy, shabby shoes rooted deeply in the carpet-fluff, her fine, hard eyes enclosing the face of their little daughter, to whom she was feeding milk out of a baby-bottle, while chanting some low, deep song that had no words, just a soothing throb: ay-yah-ah; ay-yah-ah. And it was not until the whole bottle had been finished, and the baby's eyes were closing in a gassy smile at some bright image on the undersides of her eyelids that Mrs Mucharski rose, brought the baby over to Laurie's limp arms and surrendered her, saying, 'This baby hungry; be cry, no can sleep.' And she walked more in stateliness than arrogance away from them, down the corridor and stairs to some empty portion of the house.

When Vic had showered—after picking up the slivered glass off the ceramic tiles—and dressed, and returned to work; when Laurie had bathed, penitently dressed in one of the few matronly smocks she possessed, and come downstairs to the kitchen, it seemed as if nothing had really happened. Mrs Mucharski was at the worktable, kneading dough. Laurie listened to the sounds of the woman's hands slapping and shaping the pale damp-looking mass. Then, angry at her own awkwardness, she walked a little too quickly to Mrs Mucharski's side, so that she bumped into the table, and caused the woman to leave off her kneading for a moment, just to absorb the shock. Into that freed space, Laurie plunged.

'She was hungry; she's sleeping beautifully now. I guess I haven't enough milk of my own for her. They say that often happens, when you're upset or tired. The books say that—you know—?'

'You know nothing.'

The words went into Laurie like a bee's sting: barbed, so that each blundering attempt to pull it out only makes new points of pain. That pain was wholly foreign, inexplicable; why should this woman, come in to do the cleaning and thus to spare Laurie fatigue and fuss, possess the power to cause sharp, even if small, suffering? Yet, staring into the woman's face, seeing the way the skin puckered about the eye-sockets, and how her own image gaped in the distorting mirrors of Mrs Mucharski's eyes, Laurie seemed to be tugging slow words out of flesh that had scarred and hardened over.

'I be having twin babies; girl and boy. I be in camp; no food, no water, nothing; filthy everywhere, filth and empty, dead, every-thing. I be have'—and here she dropped her eyes to the kitchen counter, as if searching for something; she finally picked up a paring knife. 'I be skin, bone, no more fat on me than this knife, but I feed my children, I make milk from my body, for giving to my babies—' She stopped, all of a sudden, as if someone had seized the knife from her and begun to trace her backbone with it. The knife had simply dropped from her hands, which she had involuntarily stretched open as if to feel her way past some obstacle, in some obscurity.

Laurie gave another tug: 'What camp, Mrs Mucharski, where?'

'Far away—not in your country. Labour camp. Prison camp. No understand, lady.'

'And your babies, Mrs Mucharski? What happened to your little girl and boy?' Laurie had to ask, had to determine the facts, had to pull and tug to get free from that first sting. Mrs Mucharski did not look at her; instead she stopped her kneading and put floury hands up to her head—a gesture that seemed as if it should end in her fastening a strand of hair, but which finished with her putting her hands over her ears.

'I have no babies, no babies, none.' She looked up at Laurie, still covering her ears. 'I have—nothing. You understand, lady, you understand, now?'

And then, as if her throat were a machine-gun she had loaded, which kept spattering long after Laurie had quit the room:

'No babies; none, none, none—'

She told Vic, that night, something of what had happened, but couldn't make him understand what had upset her so. 'Poor old woman,' he'd said—or something like that. And when, before going to sleep in the big, brass-bound bed, she'd pulled at his arm to say 'But, really—you don't think all that happened, do you? It's not true—the way she said it?' he only rubbed her hand briefly, muttering, 'How can I tell? Look, it's ancient history, and another lifetime altogether. Besides, it's none of our business. Go to sleep, Laurie, you need your rest.'

But before she could get to sleep, Laurie heard the baby crying: she got out of bed without turning on the lights, not wanting to wake her husband. Feeling her way along the corridor and up the stairs she crept to where the night lamp was shining in her baby's room.

Carefully, slowly, steadily as she moved, it seemed a long, long way off, that small light at the very end of the landing. As she came nearer, though, it seemed to split into two gleams, two eyes inside a lantern that was no lantern but a skull, a bone cage lengthening link by link into an entire skeleton. It was a woman's skeleton—inside the rib-cage were two small, skeleton babies, clinging to the ribs with fingers no thicker than a hair, and nuzzling at the space between the bones. And the skeleton-woman was putting her arms out to Laurie, whether to brace herself against, or to embrace her, she didn't know; for now there were her husband's arms round her instead, and his hands stroking the thick, toffee-coloured hair from her eyes, and his voice saying soothing, comforting things that had no meaning but which made handles for her to grab while she told him her nightmare.

'She's not real, is she? Is she?' Laurie kept repeating, her face pressed into her husband's shoulder. 'Because if she is real, then how can I be, too? And in the stories it's the old woman, the witch, who goes up the chimney or dances in red-hot shoes till she dies, so that everyone else can keep on happily, ever-after—' And Vic kept crooning, 'Of course not, of course; you're all right, it's just hormones, ancient history—she'll go tomorrow, we don't need her anymore, we'll tell her tomorrow—'

But in the morning it was Mrs Mucharski who stood in the front hall with her cracked vinyl bag, her eyes impassive as she told them she was leaving. She folded five weeks' wages into her small handbag, refusing Vic's offer of a drive to the bus stop. She would walk, she said—she preferred to walk.

From an upstairs window, holding her baby snug in her arms, Laurie watched Mrs Mucharski leave the shelter of the porch and walk down the steps, along the sidewalk and round a corner, until she disappeared. The image of her flickered just for a moment, then vanished, as if it had been no more than a blade of shadow on a windy day.

JANICE KULYK KEEFER was born in 1952 in Toronto and grew up in an 'Anglo' suburb. In a sense, however, like her interviewer, Jars Balan, she also grew up in the Ukrainian community, attending St Vladimir Orthodox Cathedral, spending summers at the Kiev church camp near Oakville, involved in the Canadian Ukrainian Youth Association. She was a member of a choir that toured Canada in 1968 as part of the fiftieth anniversary celebrations of the Ukrainian Orthodox Church. She attended the University of Toronto, receiving a B.A. in English, and the University of Sussex, where she earned an M.A. and Ph.D. She has taught at the University of Sussex, Université Sainte-Anne in Nova Scotia, and the University of Prince Edward Island. Her works include *The Paris-Napoli Express* (Ottawa: Oberon Press, 1986), *White of the Lesser Angels* (Charlottetown: Ragweed Press, 1986), *Transfigurations* (Charlottetown: Ragweed Press, 1987), *Constellations* (Toronto: Random House, 1988), *Travelling Ladies* (Toronto: Random House, 1990), and two books of criticism: *Under Eastern Eyes: A Critical Reading of Maritime Fiction* (Toronto: University of Toronto Press, 1987) and *Reading Mavis Gallant* (Toronto: Oxford University Press, 1989).

JARS BALAN is a Toronto-born poet, author, translator, editor, independent scholar, and freelance writer. A resident of Edmonton since 1975, he is a specialist on Ukrainian visual poetry and the history of Ukrainian writing in Canada. He is the author of *Salt and Braided Bread: Ukrainian Life in Canada* (1984) and the editor of *Identifications: Ethnicity and Writing in Canada* (1982). He also co-edited (with Yuri Klynovy) *Yarmarok: Ukrainian Writing in Canada Since the Second World War* (1987), the first English-language anthology of its kind. His translation of Lina Kostenko's book of children's poetry, *The Lilac King*, is to be issued shortly by Veselka Publishers of Kiev.

What was your initial reaction to doing an interview on multiculturalism and writing in Canada?

It was positive, although I was thinking it's funny: if I had been approached maybe even five years earlier, I probably would have said no.

Why's that?

Well, five years ago I wasn't published, and I think I've always been quite definite on the fact that I wanted to get published simply as a writer, a Canadian writer, rather than as an 'ethnic' writer, because I think it's the unfortunate tendency still to marginalize the ethnic, to see it as something colourful and peripheral. You trot it out for your multicultural festivals, but you don't treat those writers as central. Also, five years ago I had just moved to rural Nova Scotia, having studied in Great Britain and spent some time in France. I was really coming back almost as an immigrant, because I left Canada wanting desperately to get away, to live overseas. I had gone through Canadian high school and completed an undergraduate degree at the U of T without ever really reading more than a token number of books that were Canadian, never mind Ukrainian. So when I came back after those seven or eight years in Europe I decided that I simply had to start reading Canadian literature, to find out where I was. It was really as though I were a foreigner, coming to a new place, since my whole attitude was different, and my sense of who I was and what I wanted to do had changed. But part of the reason I wanted to get out of Canada, I suspect, had to do with wanting to get away from my own background, feeling very ambiguous about being 'multicultural' — though that word didn't really exist, as far as I knew it, when I left back in 1974.

Well, as a political policy it had only been declared in 1971.

Right, it hadn't percolated through public consciousness, and it certainly hadn't reached me as a positive thing. I think if I had heard of it I probably laughed at it, as a lot of people did, because it was perceived as simplistic or trivializing.

Yet, multiculturalism has become an issue not only in Canada but in Britain, where there is a concern about writers from minority backgrounds, not to mention in the United States and Australia.

That's very true. It was funny coming back to the British Isles after ten years away, and reading in the papers about the problems Britain currently faces as a multiracial and multicultural society, particularly the former. I couldn't help thinking: God, they've got a lot to learn from Canada. So ten years later and back in Canada, my feelings had swung completely around from the dubious ones that I first had on leaving Europe. In a sense I thought that I was leaving my heart in Europe, because I also felt — having a mother who had been born in Eastern Europe — that my going back at least in the general direction of where she came from was a kind of romanticized return to some form of homeland. It was part of that whole thing of wanting to reject your roots, reject being Canadian, because at that point — in the early seventies—I was fairly ignorant. I was discouraged at the university from reading Canadian writing, and encouraged to read American or British. And so I was really quite patronizing in my attitude toward my own culture.

How did you feel about being Ukrainian at that time?

Well, when I was at the U of T I didn't want to have anything to do with things like the Ukrainian Students' Club, because I had very ambivalent responses to growing up Ukrainian Canadian, or Canadian Ukrainian, however you want to call it. My ambivalence stemmed from various reasons, some of which had to do with my own feelings as a woman and the traditional place of women in the Ukrainian Canadian culture as I experienced it, and also it had to do with what I perceived as a defensive narrowness among Canadian Ukrainians. There was a general refusal to acknowledge the validity of other cultures, a kind of banding together so that any criticism was perceived as a betrayal or disloyalty, rather than simply an attempt to air alternatives, to bring up questions. So I wanted to put all that behind me and to go to study English in England, and perhaps to adopt a whole new identity.

In many ways your escape from Canada seems a typically Canadian thing to have done. It's certainly a route that other Canadian writers have taken, only to return disabused of some of their illusions and with a fresh perspective on the country. Do you feel that it was something you had to do, an avenue you had to exhaust, and that in the back of your mind you had something else that you were wanting to write about and were working towards?

In my case, I went to Europe primarily because I had a scholarship to do postgraduate work in English. If I had not wanted to write, I probably would have stayed on in Europe, because even though I hadn't really read Canadian literature, I had a kind of gut instinct that I had to go back to Canada and to write about what I'd experienced at home and abroad and to explore who I was through my relationship to people and places I had known since childhood. It's true that, for me, the subject I want to deal with, what I am working towards, is my own experience growing up in a Canadian Ukrainian milieu— particularly those summers at the church camp, Kiev, which—in my imagination, at least—was like a re-creation of a little Ukrainian village. All sorts of things have sprung to my mind about the creative possibilities of using that whole world of exiles, of displaced persons — it strikes me as a very interesting idea for a novel.

You've spoken about the ambivalence you had towards your Ukrainian identity. Could you elaborate on this?

When I was growing up, I was fascinated by it, in that it made me different, unique, but I was also aware of feeling very vulnerable about it because I was living in a very WASP neighbourhood. I mean, when I compare my experiences to those that, say, Jamaican or Pakistani immigrants must have, I have nothing to be traumatized about. Nevertheless, as an over-sensitive kid, I remember feeling humiliated because people would not be able to pronounce the name Kulyk, or would make fun of it; or being embarrassed at having to go off to Ukrainian school and make excuses to my neighbourhood friends that I wasn't really going off to Bathurst Street to sit in a room and memorize the tributaries of the Dnieper River, that I was going to Girl Guides.

I also grew up with the fact that my mother's experience as an immigrant in Canada was a very painful one, for psychological as well as economic reasons, since she encountered a degree of Anglo-Saxon arrogance. For instance, she was made, as a girl of fourteen, to go into a kindergarten class to learn English. She had lost a language, a whole way of being, having grown up in a small village, and suddenly she found herself catapulted into Metropolitan Toronto. It was a huge adjustment to make, and I think she's always felt an instinctive insecurity about being an immigrant and living in a milieu which was domineeringly White Anglo-Saxon Protestant. So I was aware of her defensiveness and her feelings of vulnerability. That came through very strongly in my own childhood — that if you were 'ethnic', if you were an immigrant, if you were different in this sense, it was a stigma; there were people who made fun of you or even despised you.

Yet your mother speaks virtually unaccented English.

Well, afterwards, when I tried to analyse my mother's experience as an immigrant, I thought: here is a woman who is trilingual — she speaks Ukrainian, she speaks Polish, English, and a bit of Russian, and *she* was made to feel inferior? For immigrants of her generation, if you couldn't speak English you were immediately made to feel somehow subnormal, or cretinous. And there was my mother's sister, who upon graduating from medical school was invited to practise in Toronto's Medical Arts Building on the condition that she change her last name to an Anglo-Saxon one. That was the 1950s. All those stories came through very strongly in my childhood, and would tie up with my own sense of being taunted on the school ground and teased about my last name, because it wasn't chic or colourful then to be an immigrant or ethnic—that came much later.

You actually came from a 'mixed marriage' of sorts, in that your father was born here and your mother was an immigrant. What did you get that was different from the two of them?

I think I got a lot more from my mother's side of the family, possibly because the experience of being an immigrant—of getting a toe-hold in Toronto, of moving up from a rooming-house to owning a house of your own—was so much more dramatic to me. Possibly also because the women in my family are quite verbal, and my father tends to be sort of a strong, silent type: he doesn't talk about himself very much. And I didn't know my paternal grandmother at all as well as I knew my maternal grandmother. So what I got was the experience of her, of my aunt, and my mother: a very, very rich sense of what their lives had been like in a village that had then been part of Poland and which is now part of Ukraine. My maternal grandfather had been half-Polish and half-Ukrainian, while my grandmother was Ukrainian, and she'd tell me how people used to be prevented from speaking or reading Ukrainian in her village, and how my mother and her sister had to go to a Polish school She would also tell wonderful stories, vivid stories, some of which were actually quite terrible. All of these were somehow more interesting—and real—than my own life in the suburbs of Toronto. So that made me feel extraordinarily privileged; it gave me something to counterpose against the feeling that I was the same as everybody else; I had a profound need to feel different, special. I really think, looking back, that I lived in two worlds: the world of WASP west-end Toronto, and my world, which was not quite a fantasy world but which was connected to an Old Country which I knew only from stories, not personal experience.

Would it be fair to say that what was once a source of conflict, tension, and anxiety is now a source of inspiration for you?

Yes, though inspiration doesn't necessarily mean celebration. I feel ready to face what's problematic in my background, rather than simply to run away from it or to exchange it for something that I perceived as established, risk-free—like the culture of England, which was so far removed, so pure as it were, and something in which I was not implicated, whereas I am obviously implicated in being of Ukrainian descent, with all its controversial historical ramifications. I can see where my writing has been directly fed by my 'ethnicity', to use that as an umbrella term, by those stories my grandmother told me as a child, and by being part of a Ukrainian community. But to me, it's all so complicated, politically as well as culturally, and I can now understand why, when I was much younger, I was unable to handle it all.

Multiculturalism is a word that has all kinds of connotations attached to it, and especially a lot of political rhetoric surrounding it. Do you have a personal understanding of it, a personal vision of what you would like to see multiculturalism mean?

I would like it to have a central and not marginal impact. I define Canada as a nation of immigrants, and I do not see it as the 'two solitudes' icon Hugh MacLennan offered us. In fact, I much prefer to use the term 'multiculturalism' rather than 'ethnic'—which to me has all sorts of negative connotations. Usually it's WASPs who use it when they try to do anthropology on different groups and who see Slavs as tribal peoples, whereas if you're Anglo-Saxon you belong to Western 'civilization'. Multiculturalism is ultimately a means of preserving a variety of linguistic-cultural heritages, in contrast to the melting-pot reduction of the United States. It can develop forms of openness and tolerance, which necessitate the asking of questions, the airing of griefs, the opening up of locked histories—histories of bad relations between different racial or ethnic groups. What I don't want to see multiculturalism become is the Caravan idea that's trotted out for a week every summer, creating a phoney vision of ethnic harmony, so that a Pole can visit the Kiev or Odessa pavilion or the Tel Aviv pavilion, and everyone is all jolly and happy together. I can see there is some value in that celebration of ethnicity, though it has probably become quite touristic now. But it seems to me that if one doesn't use multiculturalism as a means of exploring the tensions between ethnic cultures and heritages, discussing the politics as well as the aesthetics of ethnicity, then one risks trivializing the whole concept and making it something that is really of no use to a writer or creative artist.

NEIL BISSOONDATH b. 1955

Dancing

I was nothing more than a maid back home in Trinidad, just a ordinary fifty-dollar-a-month maid. I didn't have no uniform but I did get off early Saturdays. I didn't work Sundays, except when they had a party. Then I'd go and wash up the dishes and the boss'd give me a few dollars extra.

My house, if you could call it a house, wasn't nothing more than a two-room shack, well, in truth, a one-room shack with a big cupboard I did use as a bedroom. With one medium-size person in there you couldn't find room to squeeze in a cockaroach. The place wasn't no big thing to look at, you understand. A rusty galvanize roof that leak every time it rain, wood walls I decorate with some calendars and my palm-leaf from the Palm Sunday service. In one corner I did have a old table with a couple of chairs. In the opposite corner, under the window, my kitchen, with a small gas stove and a big bowl for washing dishes. I didn't have pipes in my house, so every morning I had to fetch water from a standpipe around the corner, one bucket for the kitchen bowl, one for the little bathroom behind the house. And, except for the latrine next to the bathroom, that was it, the whole calabash. No big thing. But the place was always clean though, and had enough space for me.

It was in a back trace, behind a big, two-storey house belonging to a Indian doctor-fella. The land was his and he always telling me in a half-jokey kind of way that he going to tear down my house and put up a orchid garden. But he didn't mean it, in truth. He wasn't a too-too bad fella. He did throw a poojah from time to time and as soon as the prayers stop and the conch shell stop blowing, Kali the yardboy always bring me a plate of food from the doc.

The first of every month the doc and the yardboy did walk around with spray pumps on their back, spraying-spraying. The drains was white with poison afterward, but I never had no trouble with mosquito or fly or even silverfish. So the doc wasn't a bad neighbour, although I ain't fooling myself, I well know he was just helping himself and I was getting the droppings. People like that in Trinidad, you know, don't let the poojah food fool you. You could be deading in his front yard in the middle of the night and doc not coming out the house. I count three people dead outside his house and their family calling-calling and the doc never even so much as show his face. We wasn't friends, the doc and me. I tell him 'Mornin' and he tell me 'Mornin' and that was that.

I worked for a Indian family for seven, eight years. Nice people. Not like the doc. Good people. And that's another thing. Down there Black people have Indian maid and Indian people have Black maid. White people does mix them up, it don't matter to them. Black people say, Black people don't know how to work. Indian people say, Indian people always thiefing-thiefing. Me, I did always work for Indian people. They have a way of treating you that make you feel you was part of the family. Like every Christmas, Mum—I did call the missus that, just like her children—Mum give me a cake she make with her own two hand. It did always have white icing all over it, and a lot of red cherry. They was the kind of people who never mind if I wanted to ketch some TV after I finish my work. I'd drag up a kitchen chair behind them in the living room, drinking coffee to try to keep the eyes open. And sometimes when I get too tired the boss did drive me home. Understand my meaning clear, though. They was good people, but strick. They'd fire you in two-twos if you not careful with your work.

Nice people, as I say, but the money . . . Fifty dollars a month can't hardly buy shoe polish for a centipede. I talked to the pastor about it and he tell me ask for a raise. All they gimme is ten dollars more, so I went back to the pastor. You know what he say? 'Why don't you become a secketary, Sister James? Go to secketerial school down in Port of Spain.' Well, I start to laugh. I say, 'Pastor, you good for the soul but you ain't so hot when it come to the stomach.' Well, I never! Me, who hardly know how to read and write, you could see me as one of them prim an proper secketaries in a nice air-condition office? Please take this lettah, Miss James. Bring me that file, Miss James. Just like on TV! I learn fast-fast servant job was the only work for somebody like me.

That was life in Trinidad.

Then I get a letter from my sister Annie up in Toronto. She didn't write too often but when she set her mind to it she could almost turn out a whole book. She talk on and on bout Caribana, and she send some pictures she cut out from the newspaper. It look so strange to see Trinidadians in Carnival costumes dancing and jumping in them big, wide streets. Then she go on bout all the money she was making and how easy her life was. I don't mind saying that make me cry, but the tears dry up fast-fast. She write how Canadians racialist as hell. She say they hate black people for so and she tell me bout a ad on TV showing a black girl eating a banana pudding. Why they give banana to the Black? Annie say is because they think she look like a monkey. I couldn't bring myself to understand how people so bad. Annie say they jump out of the stomach like that. I telling you, man, is a terrible thing how people born racialist.

Anyways, Annie ask me to come up to Canada and live with she. She wanted to sponsor me and say she could help me find a job in two-twos. First I think, No way. Then, later that night in bed, I take a good look at myself. I had thirty years, my little shack and sixty dollars a month. Annie was making five times that Canadian, ten times that Trinidadian. I did always believe, since I was a little girl, that I'd get pregnant one day and catch a man, like most of the women around me. But the Lord never mean for me to make baby. I don't mind saying I try good and hard but it just wasn't in the cards. I thought, No man, no child, a shack, a servant job, sixty dollars a month. What my life was going to be like when I reach sixty? I think hard all night and all next day, and for a whole week.

After the Sunday service, I told the pastor bout Annie's letter. Quick-quick he say, 'Go, Sister James, it is God's doing. He has answered your prayers.'

I didn't bother to tell him that I didn't pray to God for help. I figure he already have His hands full with people like the doc.

Then it jump into my head to go ask the doc what to do. He was always flying off to New York and Toronto. So I thought he could give me more practical advices.

I went to see him that morning self. He was in the garden just behind the high iron gate watering the anthuriums. Kali the yardboy was shovelling leftover manure back into a half-empty cocoa bag. I remember the manure did have a strong-strong smell because they did just finish spreading it on the flowers beds.

The doc was talking to himself. He say, 'A very table masterpiece of gardening.' Or something like that. That was the doc. A couple of times when I was walking home I hear him talking to his friends and it was big and fancy words, if you please. But when he talk to me or

Kali or we kind of people, he did start talking like us quick-quick. Maybe he think we going to like him more. Or maybe he think we doesn't understand good English. I always want to tell him that we not chilren, we grow up too. But why bother?

I knock on the gate.

The doc look up and say, 'Mornin, Miss Sheila.'

'Mornin, doctor.'

'Went to church this morning, Miss Sheila?'

'Yes, doctor.'

'Nice anthuriums, not so?'

'Very nice anthuriums, doctor. Is not everybody could grow them flowers like you.'

He shake his shoulders as if to say, That ain't no news. Then he say, 'Is hard work but they pretty for spite, you don't think so?'

I remember the day a dog dig up one of the anthuriums and the doc take a hoe to the poor animal and break his head in two. There was blood all over the place and the dog drop down stone dead. The owner start to kick up a fuss and the doc call the police to cart the man off to jail. But that was just life in Trinidad and I didn't say nothing. But ever since then those pink, heart-shape flowers remind me of that dog, as if the plants pick up some of the blood and the shape of the heart. It was after that the doc put up the brick fence with broken bottles all along the top and a heavy iron gate.

I say, 'Doctor, I want to ask you for some advices.'

He say, 'I not working now, Miss Sheila, come back tomorrow during office hours.'

'I not sick, doctor, is about another business.' But still he turn away from me, all the time spraying-spraying with the hose.

Kali stop shovelling and say something to the doc.

The doc say, 'What is this I hearing? Miss Sheila? You thinking bout leaving Trinidad?'

Kali start to laugh. I see the doc wanted to laugh too. He turn off the hose and drop it on the ground. He walk over to the gate. He say, 'Is true, Miss Sheila?'

'Yes, doctor.' And I get a strange feeling, as if somebody ketch me thiefing something.

'Canada?'

'Yes, doctor.'

'Toronto?'

'Yes, doctor.'

'So what you want to know, Miss Sheila?'

'I can't make up my mind, doctor. I don't know if to go or if to stay.'

'And you want my advice?'

'I grateful for any help you could give me, doctor.'

He start rubbing the dirt from his hands and he stand there, thinking-thinking. Then he lean against the gate and say, 'Miss Sheila, I going to tell you something I don't say very often because people don't like to hear the truth. They does get vex. But you know, Miss Sheila, people on this island too damn uppity for their own good. They lazy and they good-for-nothing. They don't like to work. And they so damn uppity they think they go to Canada or the States and life easy. Well, it not easy. It very, very hard and you have to work your ass off to get anywhere. Miss Sheila, what you could do? Eh? Tell me. I admire you for wanting to improve your life but what you think you going to do in Canada? You let some damn stupid uppity people put a damn stupid idea in your head and you ready to run off and lose everything you have. Your house, your job, everything. And why? Because of uppitiness. Don't think you going to be able to buy house up in Canada, you know. So, I advise you not to go, Miss Sheila. The grass never greener on the other side.' He stop talking and take a cigarette from his shirt pocket and light it.

I didn't know what to say. I was confuse. I say, 'Thanks doctor. Good day, doctor,' and start walking to my house. Before I even take two steps, I hear Kali say, 'Them nigs think the world is for them and them alone.'

And he and the doc start to laugh.

There I was, hands hurting like hell from suitcase and boxes and bags and I couldn't find the door handle. My head was still full of cotton wool from the plane and my stomach was bawling its head off for food. I just wanted to turn right round and say, 'Take me back. The doc was right. I ain't going to be able to live in a place where doors ain't have no handle.' But then a man in a uniform motion me to keep walking, as if he want me to bounce straight into the door. Well, if it have one thing I fraid is policeman, so I start to walk and, Lord, like the Red Sea parting for Moses, the door open by itself.

This make me feel good. I feel as if I get back at the customs man who did ask me all kind of nasty questions like, 'You have any rum? Whisky? Plants? Food?' as if I look like one of them smugglers that does fly between Trinidad and Venezuela. I thought, I bet the doors don't open like that for him!

As I walk through the door I start feeling dizzy-dizzy. Everything look cloudy-cloudy, as if the building was just going to fade away or melt. I was so frighten I start to think I dreaming, like it wasn't me walking there at all but somebody else. It was almost like looking at a film in a cinema.

Then I hear a voice talking to me inside my head. It say, Sheila James, maid, of Mikey Trace, Trinidad, here you is, a big woman, walking in Toronto airport and you frighten. Why?

I force myself to look around. I see faces, faces, faces. All round me, faces. Some looking at me, some looking past me, and some even looking through me. I start feeling like a flowers vase on a table.

Then all of a sudden the cloudiness disappear and I see all the faces plain-plain. They was mostly white. My chest tighten up and I couldn't hardly breathe. I was surrounded by tourists. And not one of them was wearing a straw hat.

I hear another voice calling me, 'Sheila! Sheila!' I look around but didn't see nobody, only all these strange faces. I start feeling small-small, like a douen. Suddenly it jump into my head to run headlong through the crowd but it was as if somebody did nail my foot to the floor: I couldn't move. Again like in a dream. A bad dream.

And then, bam!, like magic, I see all these black faces running toward me, pushing the tourists out of the way, almost fighting with one another to get to me first. I recognize Annie. She shout, 'Sheila!' Then I see my brother Sylvester, and others I didn't know. Annie grab on to me and hug me tight-tight. Sylvester take my bags and give them to somebody else, then he start hugging me too. Somebody pat me on the back. I felt safe again. It was almost like being back in Trinidad.

Sylvester and the others drop Annie and me off at her flat in Vaughan Road. Annie was a little vex with Syl because he didn't want to stay and talk but I tell her I was tired and she let him go off to his party.

Annie boil up some water for tea and we sit down in the tiny living room to talk. I notice how old Annie was looking. Her face was heavy, it full-out in two years. And the skin under her eyes was dark-dark as if all her tiredness settle there. Like dust. Maybe it was the light. It always dark in Annie's apartment, even in the day. The windows small-small, and she does keep on only one light at a time. To save on the hydro bill, she say.

She ask me about friends and the neighbours and the pastor. It didn't have much family left in Trinidad to talk about. She ask about the doc. I tell she about his advices. She choops loud-loud and say, 'Indian people bad for so, eh, child.'

She ask about Georgie, our father's outside-child. I say, 'Georgie run into some trouble with the police, girl. He get drunk one evening and beat up a fella and almost kill him.'

She say, 'That boy bad since he small. So, what they do with him?'

'Nothing. The police charge him and they was going to take him to court. But you know how things does work in Trinidad. Georgie give a police friend some money. Every time they call him up for trial, the sergeant tell the judge, We can't find the file on this case, Me Lud, and finally the judge get fed up and throw the charge out. You know, he even bawl out the poor sergeant.'

Annie laugh and shake her head. She say, 'Good old Georgie. What he doing now?'

'The usual. Nothing at all. He looking after his papers for coming up here. Next year, probably.'

Annie yawn and ask me if I hungry.

I say no, I did aready eat on the plane: my stomach was tight-tight.

'You don't want some cake? I make it just for you.'

I say no again, and she remember I did never eat much, even as a baby.

'Anyways,' she say quietly, 'I really glad you here now, girl. At last. Is about time.'

What to say? I shake my head and close my eyes. I try to smile. 'I really don't know, Annie girl. I still ain't too sure I doing the right thing. Everything so strange.'

Annie listen to me and her face become serious-serious, like the pastor during sermon. But then she smile and say, 'It have a lot of things for you to learn, and it ain't going to be easy, but you doing the best thing by coming here, believe me.'

But it was too soon. With every minute passing, I was believing the doc was righter.

Annie take my hand in hers. I notice how much bigger hers was, and how much rings she was wearing. Just like our mother, a big woman with hands that make you feel like a little child again when she touch you.

She say, 'Listen, Sheila,' and I hear our mother talking. Sad-sad. From far away. And I think, Is because all of us leave her, she dead long time but now everybody gone, nobody in Trinidad, and who

going to clean her grave and light her candles on All Saints? I close
my eyes again, so Annie wouldn't see the tears.
     She squeeze my hand and say, 'Sheila? You awright? You want
some more tea?'
     She let go my hand, pick up my cup, and went into the kitchen.
She say, 'But, eh, eh, the tea cold already. Nothing does stay hot for
long in this place.' She run the water and put the kettle on the stove.
When she come back in the living room I did aready dry my eyes.
She hand me a piece of cake on a saucer, sponge cake, I think, and
sit down next to me.
     She take a bite from her piece. 'You know, chile,' she say chewing
wide-wide, 'Toronto is a strange place. It have people here from all
over the world—Italian, Greek, Chinee, Japanee, and some people
you and me never even hear bout before. You does see a lot of old
Italian women, and some not so old, running round in black dress
looking like beetle. And Indians walking round with turban on their
head. All of them doing as if they still in Rome or Calcutta.' She stop
and take another bite of the cake. 'Well, girl, us West Indians just
like them. Everybody here to make money, them and us.' She watch
me straight in the eye. 'Tell me, you ketch what I saying?'
     I say, 'Yes, Annie,' but in truth I was thinking bout the grave and
the grass and the candles left over from last year and how lonely our
mother was feeling.
     'Is true most of them here to stay,' she continue, 'but don't forget
they doesn't have a tropical island to go back to.' And she laugh, but
in a false way, as if is a thing she say many times before. She look at
my cake still lying on the saucer, and then at me, but she didn't say
nothing. 'Anyways,' she say, finishing off her piece, 'you see how I
still talking after two years. After two years, girl, you understanding
what I saying?'
     'So I mustn't forget how to talk. Then what? You want me to go
dance shango and sing calypso in the street?'
     'I don't think you ketch what I saying,' Annie say. She put the
saucer down on the floor, lean forwards and rub her eyes, thinking
hard-hard. 'What I mean is . . . you mustn't think you can become
Canajun. You have to become West Indian.'
     'What you mean, become West Indian?'
     'I mean, remain West Indian.'
     I think, Our mother born, live, dead, and bury in Trinidad. And
again I see her grave. I choops, but soft-soft.

Annie says, 'But eh, eh, why you choopsing for, girl?'

'How I going to change, eh?' I almost shout. 'I's a Trinidadian. I born there and my passport say I from there. So how the hell I going to forget?' I was good and vex.

She shake her head slow-slow and say, 'You still ain't ketch on. Look, Canajuns like to go to the islands for two weeks every year to enjoy the sun and the beach and the calypso. But is a different thing if we try to bring the calypso here. Then they doesn't want to hear it. So they always down on we for one reason or another. Us West Indians have to stick together, Sheila. Is the onliest way.' Again her face remind me of the pastor in the middle of a hot sermon. You does feel his eyes heavy on you even though he looking at fifty-sixty people.

My head start to hurt. I say, 'But it sound like if all-you fraid for so, like if all-you hiding from the other people here.'

I think that make she want to give up. I could be stubborn when I want. Her voice sound tired-tired when she say, 'Girl, you have so much to learn. Remember the ad I tell you bout in my letter, the one with the little girl eating the banana pudding?'

'Yes. On the plane I tell a fella what you say and he start laughing. He say is the most ridiculous thing he ever hear.'

Annie lean back and groan loud-loud. 'Oh Gawd, how it still have fools like that fella walking around?'

'The fella was coloured, like us.'

'Even worser. One of we own people. And the word is black, not coloured.'

It almost look to me like if Annie was enjoying what she was saying. And I meet a lot of people like that in my time, people who like to moan and groan and make others feel sorry for them. But I didn't say nothing.

All the time shaking her head, Annie say, 'Anyways, look eh, girl, you going to learn in time. But lemme tell you one thing, and listen to me good. You must stick with your own, don't think that any honky ever going to accept you as one of them. If you want friends, they going to have to be West Indian. Syl tell me so when I first come up to Toronto and is true. I doesn't even try to talk to white people now. I ain't have the time or use for racialists.'

I was really tired out by that point so I just say, 'Okay, Annie, whatever you say. You and Syl must know what you talking bout.'

'Yeah, but you going to see for yourself,' she say, yawning wide-

wide. 'But anyways, enough for tonight.' She get up, then suddenly she clap her hands and smile. 'Oh Gawd, girl, I so happy you here. At last.' She laugh. And I laugh, in a way. She pluck off her wig and say, 'Come, let we go to bed, you must be tired out.'

Before stretching out on the sofa, I finish off my cake. To make Annie happy.

Next morning Annie take me downtown in the subway. It wasn't a nice day. The snow was grey and the sky was grey. The wind cut right through the coat Annie give me and freeze out the last little bit of Trinidad heat I had left in me.

I don't mind saying I was frighten like hell the first time in the subway. Annie, really playing it up like tourist guide, say, 'They does call it the chube in Englan but here we does say subway.' I was amaze at the speed, and I kept looking at the wall flying past on both sides and wondering how I ever going to learn to use this thing. I kept comparing it to the twenty-cent taxi ride to Port of Spain, with the driver blowing horn and passing cars zoom-zoom. The wind use to be so strong you couldn't even spit out the window. But the subway though! The speed! But I couldn't tell Annie that. When she ask me what I think of it, I just shake my head and pretend it was no big thing. To tell the truth woulda make me look like a real chupidy. Annie wasn't too happy bout that. A little vex, she say, 'You have to learn to use it, you can't take taxi here.'

I doesn't remember a lot from my first time in Yonge Street. Just buildings, cars, white faces, grey snow. Everything was confuse. It was too much. The morning before I was still in my little shack in Mikey Trace, having a last tea with the neighbours — not the doc, of course, but he send Kali over with twenty Canadian dollars as a present — and this morning I was walking bold-bold in Toronto.

Too much.

We walk around a lot that day. We look at stores, we look at shops. She show me massage parlours and strip bars with pictures of naked women outside. In one corner I see something that give me a shock. White men bending their back over fork and pickaxe, digging a hole in the street. They was sweating and dirty and tired. Is hard to admit now, but I feel shame for them and I think, But they crazy or what? In Trinidad you never see white people doing that kinda work and it never jump into my head before that white people did do that kinda work. Is only when I see that Annie didn't pay no attention to them that I see my shame. I turn away from them fast-fast.

By the end of the day my foot was hurting real terrible and my right shoe was pinching me like a crab. Finally we got on the subway again and I was glad to be able to rest my bones, even with all kinda iron-face people around me. We stop at a new station and Syl was waiting for us in his car.

It was a fast drive. Syl did always have a heavy foot on the gas pedal. I remember trees without leaf, big buildings, a long bridge, the longest I ever see, longer than the Caroni bridge or any other bridge in Trinidad. By the way, that was one of the first things I notice, how big and long everything was. And when somebody tell me that you could put Trinidad into Lake Untarryo over eight times, my head start to spin. It have something very frightening in that.

Finally we got to Syl place, a high grey, washout apartment building. The paint was peeling and the balconies was rusty for so. I say, 'Is the ghetto?' I was showing off. I wanted to use one of the words I pick up from a Trinidad neighbour with a sister in New York. But Syl and Annie just laugh and shake their heads.

Annie point to a low building across the street. 'They does call that the Untarryo Science Centre.'

'What they does keep in there?' I ask.

Annie say, 'I hear they does keep all kinda scientific things, but I really don't know for sure.'

'You never go see for yourself?' I ask.

Syl cut in with 'And waste good money to see nonsense?' He laugh short-short and tell Annie to stop showing me chupidness.

We went in the building and Syl call the elevator. That was my first time in a elevator but I used to seeing the prim an proper secketaries going into one on TV, pushing a button, nothing moving and they come out somewhere else. Is a funny thing, but you ever notice that elevators doesn't move on TV? Is as if the rest of the building does do the moving up and down.

I look at Syl and I say, 'Eh, eh, boy Syl, it look like you grow a little. You ain't find so, Annie? He not looking taller?' Annie didn't reply but Syl blush and close his eyes, just like when he was a little boy. He did always like to hear people say he grow a little because he don't like being shorter than his sisters. He like to say he grow up short because we did jump over his head when he small, but I doesn't believe that. 'And I see you still like your fancy clothes.' He was wearing a red shirt which hold him tight-tight at the waist and green pants as tight as a skin on a coocoomber. I notice his shoes did have four-inch heels and I realize that was why he was looking taller, but

I didn't mention it. Syl have a short temper when it come to his shortness and his fanciness. I didn't talk about his beard neither. Annie tell me he was growing it for three months and it still look as if he didn't shave yesterday.

We get off at the eight storey and walk down a long-long corridor. Same door after same door after same door. Annie say, 'I could never live in a highrise. It remind me of a funeral home, with coffin pile on coffin.' We turn a corner and I hear the music, a calypso from two or three carnivals back.

Syl didn't have a big apartment, only one bedroom. All the furniture was push to one side, so the floor was free for dancing. The stereo was on the couch, with a pile of records on the floor next to it. There was a table in one corner with glasses and ice and drinks on it.

Somebody shout from the kitchen, drowning out the calypso, 'Syl, is you, man? Where the hell you keeping the rum?'

Syl say, 'You finish the first bottle already?'

The voice say, 'Long time, man. You know I doesn't wait around.'

Syl say, 'Leave it for now, man, come meet my sister Sheila.'

Annie, vex, say, 'Fitzie hand go break if he don't have a drink in it always.'

A big black man wearing a pink shirt-jac come out from the kitchen. Syl say, 'This is Fitzie. He with the tourist office up here.'

A pile of people follow Fitzie from the kitchen and more came out of the bedroom. Syl wasn't finish introducing me when the buzzer buzz and more people arrive. The record finish and somebody put on another one. People start to dance. A man smelling of rum grab on to my waist and start to move. It was a old song, stale. I didn't feel like dancing. I push the man away and went to get some Coke. The Coke didn't taste right, it was different from the one in Trinidad, sweeter and with more bubbles. It make me burp. Fitzie pat me on the back.

The front door open, a crowd of people rush in dancing and singing with the record before they even get inside properly. I couldn't believe so much people was going to fit in such a small room. Somebody turn up the music even louder. Syl give up trying to tell me people's names. It didn't matter. The music was pushing my brain around inside my head, I couldn't think straight, couldn't hardly even stand up straight. Fitzie say to me, 'Is just like being back home in Trinidad, not so?'

I ask Annie where the bathroom was and I went in there and start to cry even before I close the door.

I don't know how long I stay in the bathroom. I kept looking in the mirror and asking myself what the hell I was doing in this country. I was missing my little shack. I wanted to jump on a plane back home right away, before the doc could break down the shack and put up his orchid garden. It was probably too late, the doc wasn't a man to wait around, but all I wanted was that shack and my little bedroom. I kept seeing the pastor saying goodbye, and the neighbours toting away the bed and dishes, the palm-leaf on the floor, the calendars in the rubbish.

Somebody pound on the door and I hear Annie saying, 'Sheila, you awright? Sheila, girl, talk to me.'

I hear Fitzie say, 'Maybe she sick. You know, the change of water does affect a lot of people.'

I wipe my eyes and unlock the door. A man push in, looking desperate, and Annie pull me out fast-fast. She say, 'What happen? You feeling sick?'

I shake my head and say, 'No, is awright. Is only that it have too much people in here. But don't worry, I awright now.'

'You want to go home?'

Fitzie say, 'I'll drive you.'

'No, really, I awright now.'

We went back to the living room. It was dark. People was dancing.

West Indians always ready for a party to start but never ready for it to end. It didn't take long before the air in the apartment was use up. Everybody was breathing everybody else stale air, the place stinking like a rubbish dump. Curry, rum, whisky, smoke, ganja and cigarette both. And the record player still blasting out old Sparrow calypso.

I start to sweat like cheese on a hot day. Somehow people find enough room to form a line and they manage to move together, just like Carnival day in Frederick Street, stamping and shuffling, stamping and shuffling, and shouting their head off. Syl, in the middle of the line, grab on to my arm and pull me in. I feel as if I didn't have no strength left, I just moving with the line, Syl pulling me back and pushing me forwards.

Finally the song end and the line break up, everybody heaving for air, some people just falling to the floor with tiredness. I couldn't breathe. It was like trying to pull in warm soup through my nose. I push through the crowd to a open window. A group of people was standing in front of it, drinking and smoking.

Fitzie was talking. 'These people can't even prononks names right. They does say *Young* Street when everybody who know what is what know is plain an obvious is really *Yon-zhe*. Like in French. But that is what does happen when you ain't got a culcheer to call your own, you does lose your language, you does forget how to talk.'

A young man with hair frizzy and puff-out like a half-use scouring pad say, 'At least we have calypso and steelband.'

'And limbo.'

'And reggae.'

'And callaloo.'

Fitzie spot me listening. 'Eh, eh, Sheila man,' he say, 'but you making yourself scarce tonight. All-you know Sheila, Syl sister?'

Everybody say hello.

Fitzie ask me how it going and I say it very hot in here.

The young man with the scouring pad hair laugh and say, 'Just like Trinidad.'

Everybody laugh.

Fitzie say, 'Yeah, man, just like home.'

The young man say, 'Is the warmth I does miss, and I not talking only about the sun but people too. Man, I remember Trinidad people always leave their doors open day and night, and you could walk in at any time without calling first. Canajuns not like that. Doors shut up tight, eyes cold and hands in pocket. They's not a welcoming people.'

I was going to tell them bout the doc, with the big house and the fence and broken bottles. I wanted to say even me did always keep my shack shut up because if you have nothing worth thiefing, people will still thief it, just for spite. But I didn't want to talk, I just wanted to breathe. Besides, Syl done tell me he don't like people talking at his fetes. He only like to see people dancing and eating and drinking. Seeing people sitting around and talking does make him vex. He say is not a Trinidadian thing to do.

I manage to get to the windowsill and I look out at the city. The lights! I never see so much lights before, yellow and white and red, line after line of lights, stretching far-far away in the distance, as if they have no end. That was what Port of Spain did look like from the Lady Young lookout at night, only it was smaller and it come to an end at the sea, where you could see the ships sitting in the docks. But after looking at this, I don't think I could admire Port of Spain

again. This does make you dizzy, it does fill your eye till you can't
take any more.

Fitzie the Tourist Board man say, 'You looking at the lights?'

'Yes.'

'They nice. But can't compare with the Lady Young though.'

I didn't say nothing. I felt ashame, but I couldn't say why.
He ask me to dance. Reggae music was playing. I not too partial
to reggae. It does sound like the same thing over and over again if
they playing 'Rasta Man' or 'White Christmas'. So I say no, next song.
He grab my arm rough-rough and pull me. I say, 'Okay, okay, I give
up.' Then he hold me tight-tight against him, so that I smell his
cologne and his sweat and his rum and his cigarettes and he start
moving, pushing his thigh up between my legs. I try to pull away but
he was holding on too tight, doing all the moving for the two of us.

About halfway through the song somebody start shouting for Syl.
The front door was open and a white man was standing just outside
in the corridor. My heart start to beat hard-hard. The voice call for
Syl again. Fitzie stop moving and loosen his grip on me. Everybody
else stop dancing. They was just standing there, some still holding
on, staring through the door. All the talking stop. The music was
pounding through the room. A cold draft of air from the window hit
my back and make Fitzie hands feel hot-hot on me.

I take a long, hard look at the white man. His face was a greyish
whiteish colour, like a wax candle, and all crease up. He was pudgy
like a baby. He was standing hands on hips trying to look relaxed
but only looking not-too-comfortable. I think his hair was brown.

Fitzie say, 'I bet I know what that son-of-a-bitch want.'

Annie come up to me, put her arm around my shoulder.

The man take a step closer to the door, as if he want to come in.
I feel Fitzie tense up, but it seem to me the man was only trying to
get a better look inside.

Fitzie say, 'Like he looking in a zoo, or what?'

Then Syl appear at the door, shorter than the man but wider,
tougher looking. Syl say loud-loud, 'What you want here?'

I couldn't hear what the man was saying but I see his lips moving.

Syl lean on the door frame, shaking his head. Then he choops
loud-loud.

The man take a step backward, waving his hands around in the
air.

The song came to an end, the turntable click off. I could hear myself breathing.

Syl choops again and say, 'You call the cops and I go take you and them to the Untarryo Human Right Commission. Is trouble you want, is trouble you go get.'

The man put his hands in his pants pockets and open his mouth but before he could talk somebody else push himself between Syl and the man. It was a short, fat Indian fella by the name of Ram. He did arrive at the party drunk. A white girl was with him, drunk too. Annie tell me she wasn't his wife, she was his girlfriend. His wife was home pregnant and vomiting half the time.

Ram say, 'What going on here, Syl boy?'

Syl say, 'This son-of-a-bitch say the music too loud. He complaining. He say he going to call the police.'

Ram say, 'The music too loud?'

The man say, 'I just want it turned down. I don't want to have to call the police.'

Ram laugh loud-loud, put his arm around Syl shoulder and say, 'Syl, boy, the music too loud. It disturbing the neighbours. So what we going to do bout this?'

'Ram, boy, it have only one thing to do, yes.'

'Yes, boy Syl, only one thing.'

Ram put his hand to his nose, blow twice, rub the cold between his fingers and then wipe his fingers clean on the white man's sweater.

The white man pull back and push Ram away. Then he turn grey-grey and rush off, leaving Syl and Ram in the door.

I start to feel sick.

Ram and Syl, laughing hard-hard, hug on to each other.

The young man with the scouring pad hair run to the door and shout down the corridor, 'Blasted racialist honky!'

Fitzie run up to Syl and Ram shouting, 'Well done, man, well done. All-you really show that son-of-a-bitch.'

The young man say, 'Nice going, man, you really know how to handle them.'

Annie say, 'Good, good.'

Suddenly everybody was laughing. A few people start to clap.

Syl take a rum bottle and drink long and hard. He fill his mouth till a little bit run down his chin. Ram shout, 'Leave some for me, man,' grab the bottle and take a mouthful, too.

Syl spot me and call me over. I was finding it hard to smile but I try anyways. He put his hand on my shoulder and Annie put her arm around my waist. Syl eyes was red like blood and he couldn't talk right. After some mumbling and stumbling, he manage to say, 'Sheila, girl, you see what just happen there? Remember it, remember it good. Is the first time you run into something like that but it ain't going to be the last. You see how I handle him? You think you could do that? Eh? You think you could do that?'

I didn't know what to say. I was feeling I didn't want to treat nobody like that and I didn't know if I could. Finally I just say, 'Yes, Syl,' without knowing myself what I mean.

Ram say, 'Screw all of them.'

I say, 'Maybe we should go back home?'

Annie say, 'But it early still, girl.'

I say, 'No, I mean Trinidad.' Our mother's grave, and the grass and the candles was in my head again.

Syl dig his fingers into my shoulder. 'Never let me hear you saying that again. Don't think it! We have every right to be here. They owe us. And we going to collect, you hear me?'

I say, 'Syl, I ain't come here to fight.' I start crying.

Annie say rough-rough, 'Don't do that,' and it wasn't my Annie, it wasn't Annie like our mother, it was a different Annie.

Then Syl grab me and shout, 'Somebody put on the music. Turn it up loud-loud. For everybody to hear! This whole damn building! Come, girl, dance. Dance like you never dance before.'

And I dance.

I dance an dance an dance.

I dance like I never dance before.

NEIL BISSOONDATH, born in Trinidad in 1955, is of East Indian origin. He lived in Trinidad until the age of eighteen, when he came to Canada to study French at York University. He received his B.A. there in 1977, and studied advanced writing at the Banff School of Fine Arts. He taught English and French as a second language from 1977 to 1985 in Toronto, and has been a full-time writer since 1985. He was awarded the McClelland and Stewart Award for fiction in 1986 for the story 'Dancing', which has been anthologized and adapted for radio. Bissoondath divides his time between Toronto and Montreal, and is just finishing a second collection of short stories. His published works are *Digging Up the Mountains* (Toronto: Macmillan, 1985); and *A Casual Brutality* (Toronto: Macmillan, 1988).

ARUNA SRIVASTAVA teaches in the English department at the University of British Columbia. She was born in Canada of Indian and Scottish parents. Her areas of teaching and research interest include postcolonial literature and theory and feminist theory.

Have you experienced racial prejudice, either as a person or a writer?

Definitely not as a writer. As a person, there is an incident that I used and expanded on in the novel *A Casual Brutality*, when the young man knocks at the door and asks, 'Where's ya nigger?' I'm told I've been extremely lucky, but I can't believe that for over sixteen years I've been simply so lucky. My feeling is that there are times that racial problems are exaggerated.

Do you think it's true that Canada is not a particularly racist country?

I think every country is racist, unless it is a country that has only one race living in it. But Canada is less racist than most countries I can think of. I think we're far less racist than the States.

What about Bharati Mukherjee's feelings about racism in Canada?

Bharati and I have had our disagreements over that; I don't know what she's talking about quite frankly. She says that she prefers the United States because there everything is up front. An American doesn't like you because of the colour of your skin, you will know it, whereas in Canada people will smile and be polite and not let you know it. And therefore Canada is a more racist country. I would much rather have a racist behave in the Canadian way: smile and be polite. They don't have to like me or do anything nice for me, but I know they are not going to hit me over the head. Canadians, even when they are racist, realize that it's not a nice thing to be.

But is it then logical to say that Canada is a country in which we don't have to worry about racism any more?

No, we always have to worry about racism, as we do with any social problem, but I don't think it's one that's out of hand. One thing we have to keep in perspective is that when a new group arrives, historically they have always had problems which, as they've settled in and become part of the landscape, have disappeared. In the mid-seventies in Toronto there was a bit of a problem with people of East Indian background, but that was soon taken care of. What always impressed me about Toronto was that people — police, civic authorities — always jumped in to solve a problem before it got out of hand. I'm fearful of people over-reacting: screaming racism simply because the two people involved happen to be of different races or different colours. Whenever there's a problem in Toronto between the police and a black man, it's always claimed to be racism. I'm afraid of people overusing the word. I got tired of the screams of racism. I'm very wary of that because there are truly racial incidents — but if you cry wolf often enough, people will not pay attention anymore, and racism is such a powerful charge, it's got to be reserved for when it clearly is needed.

What do you think of the concept of multiculturalism? Is there a real difference between Canada and the United States in their approach to multiculturalism?

I think there is something — and here, strangely enough, Bharati and I agree. The US approach seems to be much more relaxed; their relaxation is a form of absorption, whereas what we end up doing is creating division between groups, so that we end up — all through high-mindedness — with a kind of gentle cultural, ethnic, Canadian apartheid. What I'd like to see is a mingling of the two: not quite absorption, but not quite division either. I would be more comfortable knowing that I was a Canadian, and not an ethnic, not a Trinidadian Canadian or a West Indian Canadian; I don't know what those things mean anyway. To be called a Trinidadian Canadian to me conjures a picture of someone who, in March or April, whenever they have the carnival in Toronto, dresses up in a costume to jump and dance in the streets, while drinking illegally. That has nothing to do with me.

And you don't think there's any value to the assertion of ethnic identity?

I'm really wary of it.

Are you saying that people really should be absorbed?

No, I'm saying that on a certain level one should do everything one can to fit in with the society at large. It doesn't mean that at home you should change your habits or change your way of living, your religious and cultural beliefs, the foods you enjoy eating — that's fine. Those are yours; there's no reason to get rid of them. But I don't think we should expect the greater society to adjust to our ways; I think that's calling for a kind of anarchy because there are simply so many groups. There has to be an across-the-board standard of what it is to be Canadian. And that's where immigrants have to make a certain adjustment, just as society has to make an adjustment too. But sometimes I think we ask the society to go too far.

My argument would be that perhaps the assertion of ethnic or group identity does help the larger Canadian society change.

How?

Visibility, I suppose, although the underside of that is ghettoization.

Precisely.

People can lock themselves in their ethnic communities, but I'm not sure that that entirely has to be the case.

I think we're talking about the same thing here: people looking for a kind of medium ground. I've seen the ghettoization occur: people who arrive and find themselves living in their little ethnic community, never engaging with society. That's what I think has to be avoided, because a person ends up in a way caged by their cultural baggage. I know too many people from the Caribbean who insist on living here as if they were still back there, and then resenting being told that there are certain ways of doing things here.

How do you feel about any of the changes in immigration and

*refugee policy? Do you feel that Canada has to protect itself against
an influx of immigrants or refugees through these laws?*

No. I think we could be doing a lot more than we are. My feeling is
that we need more immigrants. But part of the problem is that the
immigration law is a mess. Immigration should be opened up, but it
has to be cleaned up first. I have a hard time with the entire question,
because while I think we should be doing more, it's obvious that
there are hundreds of millions of refugees out there, and we cannot
accept everyone, so criteria have to be established. The first category,
the one of political persecution, is rather strangely applied. There
were Trinidadians arriving by the thousands a few months ago, and
claiming refugee status. Now they're not people in political danger;
they're not from South America or Central America, with the mass
killing, the torture that's going on there. And so under the UN definition of a refugee, they didn't qualify. That's fine, I understand that,
yet at the same time I also know what's happening in Trinidad;
people are not looking at viable futures. There are people who are
having a hard time finding food to feed their children, and I have to
ask myself, aren't lives in danger here? They're not political, but
they're economic, and isn't their claim to a future as strong as the
political one? The political one may be more direct, and maybe it
takes one bullet to kill you, whereas you starve to death over a period
of months, but in the end, they're heading towards the same thing.
I have a hard time with that, because most of the refugees at this
point, I suppose, are economic refugees. What do we do? It's a moral
decision. I don't think there's any one answer.

What do you think about projects such as this book?

From what I understand of the concept of this book, it sounds like
a useful one. It's a question of ideas and visions—where we are,
where we're going, where we've come from, and that's what's missing in multiculturalism: ideas. The multicultural projects that I object
to are the so-called cultural ones, the dancing and singing. They're
Disneyland. Yet that's what multiculturalism means to most people,
that's where it's most valuable to the politicians.

*One of the dangers in identifying writers by their ethnic identity,
in a project such as this, is the criteria for selection. Are there other
constituencies being ignored?*

Well, that's part of the entire problem with multiculturalism. It doesn't need to be celebrated, it needs to be examined as broadly, as widely as possible. The questioning has to be done from every possible angle.

With your views on multiculturalism, how do you feel about biculturalism?

I'm all for it; I'm for bilingualism.

And you don't think there's a contradiction there?

No I don't, because—and this is not to ignore the native question—but we have to look at the political reality of the two founding cultures, French and English. That is the basic identity of this country. And until we've settled that, we're tilting at windmills trying to build anything else. Part of it too is that multiculturalism has created a resistance to the acceptance of French in Canada. A lot of work has to be done with francophones, getting them to accept English Canada. A lot also has to be done with English Canada, getting them to accept what's going on in Quebec. But Ontario will eventually declare itself bilingual; there are services already, which is a nice change. With the new sign law here [in Quebec]—it's a ridiculous issue, but it got a lot of people upset—there's some wonderful political manipulation going on: forget about unemployment folks; let's talk about signs. And then the news media in English Canada reporting on the demonstrations and all the rest of it—exaggerated. Quebec has got its demands and a lot of them are legitimate. I'm uncomfortable with many of them at the same time, because I think there are basic questions of human rights there. Yet at the same time I understand their concerns, which will be answered only when English Canada fully accepts the French fact, and until that happens Quebec is going to come dangerously close to overriding human rights. They have to, because they see a lot of English Canada as being opposed to their own existence.

I'd like to turn to your writing now. One of the criticisms made of A Casual Brutality *is that it has little sense of history. Do you think there is too much attention paid to the ills of colonialism and imperialism in post-colonial writing? Do you think it's something we have to get away from?*

It's not that too much attention is paid to it, but attention has to be paid to other things too at this point. I'm tired of people blaming all of their problems on what the British did, the French did, the Spanish did. That ignores the fact that we've had a generation or two when they weren't there. You've had these very educated classes from your own country stealing. *They're* the ones who have created the torture, the refugees, and so we have to move beyond that. It's simply not enough to blame colonialism for everything. That's my irritation.

Edward Said calls this the 'politics of blame'. Do you have any thoughts about what's possible, in order to get beyond blame?

The problem with blaming colonialism for everything is that it allows you to reject all responsibility for yourself. What is needed is extremely urgent self-examination, a look at who you are today. Forget why you are this way: it may not even be important, because it's too late in the day. You've got to say, 'This is the way we are. This is why things aren't working. If we want to make things work, then this how we've got to change.' That's a very simplistic way of looking at it, but I think that's the kind of attitude that has to start appearing. I know some people in the Caribbean who have attempted to do that, and have found themselves stalled: economists, sociologists, who have started to question, in order to serve the future. But that is not appreciated, because it is a betrayal. I have been accused of this occasionally—that there is no screaming and tearing of hair because of what the British did. It's suddenly 'who are we, and why are we doing this to ourselves?' That's a no-no. There are people who seem to be so comfortable feeling themselves to be victims of others, and it's probably hard to give that up, because it's so comfortable. But it has to be done.

The story called 'Dancing' has drawn the charge of inverse racism. How do you respond to that?

This is a story that says: not only whites are racist. The fact is that non-whites can also be racist. And that's what the story is about. A story can't contain everything; it's not meant to satisfy every ideologue or every political point of view.

Perhaps it makes many white readers feel uncomfortable to see themselves portrayed in such a way.

Maybe one day I'll write a story with nice white people. There are people who view characters as representative of the larger community and that is absolute nonsense. If they want to believe that characters represent their race or culture, then don't come to me. I write about individuals.

A feminist reader, however, might look at one of your female characters and say, 'Where is the understanding of the woman's situation?'

In 'Dancing', Sheila is a very sympathetic person. But that's the problem of reading literature politically. That to me is a mistake. Literature is literature; it's not politics. There's always political content in good writing, but if you bring a political vision to a novel and you begin reading it looking for political brownie points, you're being unfair to the writer and yourself, and you're not fully open to the role of fiction. Fiction is not, and it must not be, propaganda.

What's your next project?

I'm very close to finishing a new collection of stories. There are fewer Caribbean stories, and some of the stories explore people and experiences totally alien to mine: there's a story in the new collection that deals with an old Jewish man. But, generally, the themes of displacement and immigration are there still.

YESHIM TERNAR b. 1956

Ajax Là-Bas = translate ?

Saliha Samson sits on one of the empty washing machines in the basement and lights a cigarette. There are three loads of wash in the machines. The wash cycle takes 35 minutes; the drying cycle another 25. The French couple who employ her are very nice people. They leave for work early in the morning, as soon as she arrives at 8:30. They trust her with everything. They know she is a conscientious worker, that she doesn't slack off like some of the other cleaning women.

Madame Rivest tells Saliha to eat whatever she wants from the refrigerator. She always leaves some change in the ceramic vase on the telephone table just in case Saliha needs to get extra detergent, cigarettes, or whatever. Madame Rivest knows she likes to snack on strawberry and blueberry yoghurt, so she always makes sure there is some in the refrigerator for her. This morning she has told her she hasn't done her weekly shopping yet, so she is leaving some money for Saliha especially to buy fruit yoghurt.

Now that's a nice gesture! I wish everyone were like that, thinks Saliha as she takes a deep puff from her cigarette. The Rivests live a long ways off from where she lives. She has to take the 80 bus from Park Extension, then the metro at Place des Arts to Berri, and then change metros at Berri to go to Longueuil; afterwards she has to take yet another bus to come here. But the trip is worth it because some of the people she works for close to home treat her so badly that she'd rather lose an hour on the way and work for Madame and Monsieur Rivest. That's a lot easier than working for the two old spinsters on upper Querbes.

Saliha notices the unbalanced load signal flash on one of the washers, and gets off the machine she is sitting on to straighten things out. As she untangles the heavy blue cotton velour bedspread from the black rotor blades of the washing machine, she thinks it was lucky she decided to take this cigarette break in the basement because if she had gone straight upstairs to continue her vacuuming, she would have lost an extra 25 minutes by having to wait for this load after all the others were completed. That would have thrown her schedule off perhaps by an hour because she would have had to take the elevator up and down twice more and delay other tasks in the meantime. That's how cleaning jobs are. You have to plan what you're going to do and how, and in what order. Otherwise. . . . Well, the machine starts churning again and she jumps back on the machine she was sitting on before to finish her cigarette.

She has her period again. It's crazy, she thinks. Madame Rivest calls her every two weeks. And every other time she has to work for Madame Rivest, she gets her period. It's either the first day or the second day of her period when she has to make that long trip to come here. I've never had any luck with periods, thinks Saliha as she massages her back with her left hand. Saliha's dream is to be able to lie in bed the whole day when she gets her period. But it never works that way.

The first time she had her period when she was eleven, she was in Istanbul then, she ran to up her mom to announce it. Her mother slapped her. 'Why did you do that?' Saliha asked. 'So that you won't lose your wits.' Saliha went to her room and cried less for the mess of blood than for the fact that she was getting too old to play hopscotch. That was fifteen years ago. Saliha cannot remember when she stopped playing hopscotch, but it was at least a year after she got her first period.

Some things in life are like that. First they come to you like big worries, and you spend days and nights worrying about them, but they have the life span and personality of a soap bubble. They grow and grow like a wart in one's heart and just when you're sure they are big and strong and will never go away, they pop out of your life not even leaving a rind, not even a speck of dust, but the dry flake of a single detergent grain.

Canadians are funny, thinks Saliha. They have detergents and lotions and soaps for everything. Everything has its own cleanser here. And every cleanser has its own name. Like Mr Clean. But Mr Clean is also M. Net. Wisk! What a strange way to call your laundry detergent. And Ajax. Particularly Ajax. George, the Greek *dépanneur* at Park Ex, told her Ajax was a Greek hero. Old heroes live on as detergents in Canada. Saliha smiles at her own joke. She thinks she should write this to her mom.

The wash is done in one of the machines. She opens a dryer and transfers the load there. Just as she starts the dryer, the other two machines go off. So she puts these loads in the dryers too, and feeds quarters to the machines. It's time to go up and vacuum the Rivests' bedroom, she decides.

She goes up on the elevator, happy that no one else is on it. She hates to be seen in her work clothes. She is wearing a pink cotton jumper, a navy blue shirt with the sleeves rolled up underneath that, and knee socks and her red moccasins. She had tied a Turkish scarf on her head with a knot in the back to keep her hair away from her face. Madame Rivest says she looks like a school girl like that. But Saliha feels uneasy in her work clothes. After all, it is hard to resign herself to being a cleaning woman on the sly in Canada.

As she is vacuuming the Rivests' bedroom, she remembers her friend Frederiki's warning. Frederiki told her to be careful most when she is vacuuming because when you have the vacuum on full blast, you can't hear if someone is approaching from the back. Frederiki said she knows a couple of cases of rape that happened when the cleaning woman was vacuuming and the old geezer tip-toed and caught the cleaning woman and forced her on the bed . . . Saliha shivers at the thought. She drops the vacuum cleaner and goes to check if she locked both locks on the door. Not that M. Rivest would do anything like that. He has two married daughters, but you never know who might have keys to the apartment.

On her way back from the door, walking through the living room, Saliha checks the time on the mantel clock that she guesses comes from Spain. The clock is set in a gold and black lacework metal fan that reminds one of the Spanish flamenco dancers. The Rivests appear to be well-travelled people. Scattered about the apartment there are several photographs of Madame and M. Rivest, in silver-rimmed frames, from various countries. The one on the side table next to the loveseat in the living room looks like it was taken in Spain. Madame Rivest, looking several years younger, is smiling in front of a white-washed Mediterranean-type house with red garde-nias blooming in clay pots along the window sill. She is slightly tanned. It is a sunny photograph, making Madame Rivest whose face carries many wrinkles from cold Canadian winters look out of place in the country where Saliha assumes the true residents greet the sunshine with less suspicion and distress.

Nevertheless, Madame Rivest smiles in that photograph as all middle-aged tourists do on well-deserved holidays. A straw handbag hangs from her left shoulder, and in her right hand, she holds something like a camera lens cover.

Saliha notes that the dryers must have completed their cycle, so she goes back to the bedroom and quickly finishes off the corners of the room with the special attachment Madame Rivest has taught her to use.

She takes along the yellow plastic laundry basket to carry the wash. She gets unlucky going down. A young housewife and her son step into the elevator on the second floor and ride with her to the main floor. Saliha tries to act oblivious to the woman's presence, but she winks surreptitiously at the little boy. The boy responds with a blank face.

Saliha is relieved when they get out. In the basement she quickly piles all the wash together in the laundry basket and after turning the drums around and feeling around the ridges for a stray sock or handkerchief, she goes up to the Rivests' apartment to sort the clothes. She is folding the towels and the sheets neatly and mechanically when she looks up at the ceiling of the Rivest's bedroom for an instant and starts remembering.

She is back in fourth grade at her elementary school on the Asian side of Istanbul. It was late September, several weeks into the fall term when the school principal had given the all-important Monday morning speech to the whole elementary school population: rows of fidgety kids lined up in twos behind overweight maternal teachers.

They had all finished pledging allegiance to the Turkish nation and Turkish morality. In unison, they had proclaimed the following verses with pride:

'I am Turkish, I am honest, I am industrious. My motto is: to love my inferiors, to respect my superiors, to love my country and my people more than my own life. May my existence be a gift to the existence of the Turkish people.'

It was after the whole schoolyard had fallen silent that the old principal had cleared his throat, adjusted his glasses with a nervous push of the index finger of his right hand, and straightened the arms of his worn navy blue jacket by pulling at the sleeves. He had then solemnly said, more like a poet than the disciplinarian that the Ministry of Education demanded him to be:

'My dear children, today I would like to tell you about your counterparts in America. Little boys and girls your age in America are very different from you in some very important respects. For one, they are often more industrious, and they are better behaved. I felt it was my duty to remind you of this after the very grave accidents your wild running about in the schoolyard during recesses last week has caused. Several of your friends are not at school today because they gashed their heads or sprained their ankles from all the savage games they have been playing. The weather was been very nice. The school year has just begun. Your teachers and I understand that you are all happy to join your friends after the summer holidays, but school is not a place where you come to play unruly games of tag and hide-and-seek. School is a place where you come to learn about the vital skills that you will need for all your lives and where you receive the benefits of civilization. Your counterparts in America understand what school is all about. At recess, they don't run around like you, but make use of their time to practise the knowledge that they learn in the classroom. For example, when they go out into the schoolyard — and let me remind you that not all of them are blessed with a schoolyard such as ours — they examine their surroundings. Look at all the leaves on the ground about you. You have perhaps not noticed them during all your frenzied horseplay. An American child, however, would pick up a leaf, examine it, do research to identify it, and record his observations in his notebook. An American child would do the same for an ant, a worm, or a spider instead of madly crushing it. If you, as young Turks, the adults of the future, learn to do the same, you will help to build a better nation and honour this country that our great Ataturk had offered to you as your most cherished gift.'

With this, the principal ended his speech. Saliha felt she was one of the few who had heard the true message of the principal's words. She looked about and saw, for the first time, the mounds of leaves in the schoolyard and the shady corners teeming with insects. After that day, every dry copper-coloured leaf, every quiet ant bespoke of her new task to pay attention to the world.

Saliha went on to finish her primary school education with distinctions despite some uncomfortable failures in the science class of her fifth year. Then she went to teacher's college to become a primary school teacher. After teaching in remote Anatolian villages where she gained the awe and respect of the peasants, she came to Canada to join her brother who is an auto mechanic in Montreal. She is presently enrolled at Plato College on Park Avenue to learn English and French.

Saliha folds all the towels and linen neatly. She separates Madame Rivest's lingerie from M. Rivest's underwear and pairs up his socks. She puts away all of the clean laundry on the appropriate shelves in the closet and the dresser. She does not neglect to arrange what was already there before she puts away the newly washed clothes.

Everything looks fresh and clean! Only some light dusting remains to be done. Then she will clean the bathroom. First she'll throw away the dirty water in the pail from mopping the floors, then she'll rinse out the cleaning rags and put away all the cleaning materials. Afterwards she'll take her shower and scrub the bathtub clean.

But before she finishes up the remaining tasks, Saliha decides to take a cigarette break on the blue floral patterned armchair in the living room. She makes some fresh coffee in the kitchen, brings her cup over to the living room and lights a cigarette. She unties her scarf and lets her wavy black hair down. As she sips her coffee in between puffs, Saliha goes over her cleaning appointments for the next two weeks. To remember the exact dates, she visualizes the Chrysler calender in her kitchen with pictures of different kimono-clad Japanese geishas for each month.

She has to clean the two spinster sisters on Thursday. She certainly doesn't look forward to that one. They are very messy people. They are also very careful with their money.

Contrary to the Rivests, they always follow her around and check how much detergent and soap she uses. They never offer her much at lunchtime. Not that she would eat what they eat. They always eat some strange food that she is unaccustomed to, things like blood sausage and sauerkraut; topping it off with stale May West cakes they buy at Steinberg or Provigo. Saliha prefers to keep to herself when she works there.

On Friday afternoon, she will clean for the old Czech at Côte des Neiges. He is a kind and quiet man who doesn't demand much from Saliha. He is glad to have a woman clean up once every few weeks. When she is there, Saliha cooks a couple of light dishes for him. He is always grateful for that and gives her an extra two dollars.

Saliha hopes that Eleni will call her on the weekend to confirm a cleaning job next week. Eleni lives close to where Saliha lives in Park Extension. But the best part of working for Eleni is that at the end of the work day when she is done at her hairdressing salon down-stairs, Eleni comes upstairs to have coffee with Saliha and trims her hair and manicures her nails as a gesture of appreciation. Eleni's house is large and demands all of Saliha's energy but the extra reward makes the effort worth it. Eleni expects the cleaning to be done well, but always offers refreshments like Kool-aid and Tang. Last time Saliha worked there, Eleni gave her some of her daughter's old clothes. Saliha hopes she might receive a reasonable sweater next time because she badly needs something a little fashionable for the end of the term party at Plato College.

Sipping the last of her coffee, Saliha rises from the armchair and looks around the living room to plan her dusting strategy. She will do just the outside panels of the display cabinet this time, leaving the silver goblets and British china for the next time. Then she will dust the buffet and the little figurines on top of it, taking care to dust off the folds of the Chinese jade Buddha. She decides not to waste too much time polishing the wood this time as all the wooden surfaces are still sparkling from the last time she did it. The Rivests don't seem to have invited anyone over for dinner in the meantime because the guest sets remain as she last arranged them.

Saliha has just finished drying her hair and changing into her street clothes after her shower when Madame Rivest comes back from work. She greets Saliha in French, glances around the house and shows her approval with many 'Ooh's and 'Wonderful's, stretching her words to make Saliha understand her heart-felt appreciation. Then she says in French that she will call Saliha again next week to confirm their next cleaning date. As she says this, Madame Rivest gestures as if she were dialling and holding on to the receiver of an imaginary telephone.

Of course Saliha can understand everything Madame Rivest is saying without the added gestures, but Madame Rivest is being so kind and helpful that Saliha decides not to use a couple of appropriate French phrases she has recently learned at Plato College.

Madame Rivest goes into her bedroom and comes back out with a sealed white envelope containing Saliha's thirty-five dollars. The Rivests are the only people that put Saliha's earnings in an envelope. They are considerate people.

As Saliha takes the envelope, she says, 'Merci beaucoup, Madame Rivest.' Stepping out the door, she switches the plastic bag containing her work clothes from her right hand to her left hand and extends her right hand to Madame Rivest and says, 'Bonjour, Madame Rivest,' and smiles. These are the first real words she has uttered since she woke up that morning.

In the elevator, going down, Saliha is alone. She checks the contents of the envelope and smiles with satisfaction. Before the elevator reaches the ground floor, Saliha has time to reflect on her day. She has earned enough for the week's food and cigarettes. Last week, she paid the last instalment for her tuition at Plato College. She is tired but life is under control. Her only regret is that she hasn't answered Madame Rivest in longer sentences. But she chases away her regrets with a light shrug and admits the reality.

We come here to speak like them, she thinks; but it will be a long time before they let us practise.

◆ ◆ ◆

YESHIM YASHAR TERNAR was born in Istanbul, Turkey, in 1956. She lived in the United States from 1975 to 1979, and holds a B.A. from Bennington College, Vermont. She moved to Montreal in 1980 and in 1989 completed a doctoral thesis, a critique of orientalism from a feminist perspective, at McGill University. She has previously published in *Canadian Fiction Magazine, Chelsea, Rubicon, Canadian Woman Studies* and *Telling Differences: New English Fiction from Quebec* (Véhicule Press); several of these stories have won prizes. Her book of short fiction, *Lighter in Spirit*, is forthcoming from Williams Wallace Publishers.

LINDA LEITH, publisher and editor of *Matrix* magazine, is a member of the English department of John Abbott College in Ste-Anne de Bellevue, Quebec and the editor of *Telling Differences: New English Fiction from Quebec* (1989), and is the author of *Introducing Hugh MacLennan's Two Solitudes* (forthcoming, ECW Press).

Is there any incident that sums up your experience of Canada?

I recently became a Canadian citizen, and for the first time in my life, I had a chance to vote. The ladies at the table who were checking the list earnestly looked for my name. They were very happy when they found it, and they read it aloud and were pleased when they were able to pronounce it right, and I smiled back. Then one of them asked me, in French, about my name—what nationality is it? And I answered in French, it's Canadian. That's the problem I find being an immigrant in Canada—that you're never accepted totally if your name isn't an identifiably Christian French or English name. That was a difficult moment.

So you have had a sense of ethnic prejudice here?

Of course. There are certain things you always have to deal with, and I'm always going to have to deal with them. But what is prejudice, and what is curiosity, and what is tactless questioning? Often I wonder about those things. I came here as an immigrant with no money in the bank. I didn't come here as an investor. But there are certain factors working in my favour. One is that I'm not identifiably a member of a minority group in that I'm not dark-skinned. I don't have features that are strikingly exotic. They are different, but my features are not the kind that would put a white middle-class person immediately on guard. The other thing in my favour is that I speak English very well, without an accent, and I have gone to graduate school here. I do have certain advantages that allow me to live here facing less prejudice because I can also present certain credentials that are very valuable in this society.

Many of your stories are about people who are displaced, people who are here in Montreal, in Canada, and who are not fully at home here. Saliha in 'Ajax là-bas' is one of these. Displaced as they are, I find these characters have a philosophical acceptance of being different.

The characters I write about reflect the view I have of leaving places and of being displaced. Every crisis is an opportunity for innovation, for change, for growth. After a while, travelling, the carrying of images in one's memory, complemented with an openness to new things, becomes a way of life for the people I write about, and that's the way I live.

Is there any danger of romanticizing the experience of being an immigrant?

I don't think so because I've been through very difficult experiences here. 'Ajax' is based on my own experience house-cleaning, and on those of a very close friend of mine. I try to be very careful about writing about experiences I have in some way understood. Employers normally don't think that their employees have the range of imagination that Saliha has in the story, or they don't think that the cleaning lady may be examining their life from the artifacts that she is left to deal with during the day. I wanted to show the employee as a thinking, imagining, and therefore a fully appreciative human being.

Do you have much to do with other Turkish immigrants?

No, I don't. I have taught English to Turkish refugees. I have always given my telephone number out to people who need an interpreter. In that sense, I don't feel cut off, but I don't really associate with Turkish people on a day-to-day basis. I feel very happy, though, when I see a few people I really like.

You've lived both in the United States and here. Have your experiences as a newcomer in the two countries differed?

The contexts were very different. I went to the States at eighteen to study at Bennington College, which is a very avant-garde university, and I met people, and I went to their homes. I didn't have to look for work, apply for immigrant status — I didn't do any of the things, in other words, that I did in Canada. So I can't really judge on that level. But sometimes, just sometimes, I feel like running away to the States. And maybe I'll take a trip there and visit my friends and I'll feel fine for about a week. But then I'll start getting very anxious and come back to Canada, and I've often cried with relief passing the border into Canada.

So you are aware of a difference.

It's hard to say which country is more hospitable. I know the difference is there, because I have two sisters who are now Americans, and we often compare notes. I think one does get integrated into the American system a lot more easily. The ghettoization occurs not culturally but economically in the States.

And in Canada?

I find that Canadians, especially in Montreal where I live, are much more accepting of different cultural practices, of different ways of dressing, of having trouble with the language. On the other hand, I find more willingness to open up and let a person become a part of society in the United States than here. At some level Americans are more accepting, and at some other level Canadians are. Don't forget that I come to the Canadian multiculturalism and the American melting pot idea with a knowledge of what happened in the Ottoman Empire, which lasted until the 1920s. Their ethnic minorities were regulated in many ways, but they were also allowed their own religious and cultural practices. They were marked, but they were not harassed. They were taxed and given protection. In some ways they were allowed to be very free as long as they accepted that they were now citizens of the Empire. I try to operate with the same understanding. I try to be very cognizant of the fact that I'm always going to be different, that I'm also entitled to be different, and it's fine. Istanbul was a city that welcomed different people, my own ancestors. I approach Montreal the same way. I see Montreal as a great city to reach out to the world from, a city I'll try to understand and learn from, but also add to. I feel that I can change this city in some small way, as much as it will change me.

You've mentioned Canada's multiculturalism. Do you think this policy has done anything for you?

Not really. It hasn't done anything for me personally.

And as a writer?

It's very difficult to say. I can't say I have really benefited from being a Turkish-Canadian writer, no. As a matter of fact, I often feel it is important for me not to talk about that. Often this whole business of multiculturalism has a way of promoting people because of their ethnic origins and not because of the value of the art—in the same way that certain quotas are set for granting money and publishing people from different regions of Canada. I think in the end that kind of attitude promotes a kind of egalitarian mediocrity, and I don't want to be sucked into it.

Do you find it is somehow expected that you will write about Turks in Montreal?

Obviously my Turkish past is going to come into play, but I'm more interested in using what I know to touch a universal chord. So I don't feel pressured. Sometimes I find myself thinking of all the exotica, of all the things people would love to know about—sort of spilling the beans—and I catch myself. I ask myself how much of this is motivated by the desire for instant attention or the desire to rock the boat, and how much of it is really an honest desire to write about a subject that I feel is worth exploring. I inevitably make the choice in favour of writing about something that will sustain my interest. But always the Turkish past comes in.

Do you ever feel you might be better off writing about something that looked more like mainstream Canadian experience?

I think people increasingly want to read about what is not immediately familiar. Therefore I feel lucky. If not now, in the next ten years, I think my Turkish past — which, though it was a difficult past, was one of the greatest gifts I have received in my life — will be much more valuable as an asset for me as a writer. There was a time when I thought: I will never be able to write about Canada or be a good writer in Canada because I'm not from here. I definitely don't think this way any more. I've come to recognize that my difference is a very valuable asset.

How has the fact that you are a woman affected your experience here?

I'm in a very special position, having a name that is not identifiably feminine. Unless people have heard my voice, they are not going to know this is a woman applying for a job or a woman supplying information. I like it that way. I don't like to have my gender a decisive factor in anyone's mind — in the same way that I don't go ahead and say I'm of Turkish origin. Once I appear on the scene as a woman, I don't feel at all discriminated against. I think I'm living in a very good time as a woman; it's a very good time for me to be living as a woman writer.

The position of immigrants in Quebec has been much discussed recently, especially since the television documentary Disparaître *focused on anxieties over the future of Quebec. Some immigrants, particularly members of visible minorities, evidently feel unwelcome here. The magazine* La Parole Métèque *was founded by women who felt excluded from the Québécois feminist milieu. Do you have any such sense?*

This is a very interesting question, and I have to answer this very honestly. I don't lead a very social life. As a writer, I live in a prison of my own making, and I've been able to create a situation in which I can think and write about what I choose. I've also been able to find people I enjoy associating with. I don't associate myself with situations or people that I feel I have to fight to exist among. I know there are situations where I'm not welcome. I know there are people who would be very intrusive and very cutting. I just don't associate with them. I'm not closing my eyes to them, but I feel that, if I can survive and flourish in this city and write what I can write and learn to write even better, somehow, in the long run, that'll be heard, that'll be read, and people whose views are defensive will change. Maybe I'm too much of a dreamer. I guess I'm not fighting battles on every front, and this is one area where I'm not fighting.

What do you think of Canada?

Canada has been a great refuge. I came here to seek refuge, to find a place where I could control my life in some way, flourish, grow. But there are times when I feel that I'm almost living a life of early retirement, that somehow all the great things are happening out there in all the other cities of the world. There is a sense that somehow I'm missing out. That happens because I also know, coming from Istanbul, that people do interact with one another at a much more maddening pace, with much more curiosity and interest in one another than they do here. And I find as a writer that maybe the lack of this is going to be debilitating for me. Sometimes I ask myself what is going to happen to me when I deplete my memories.

Might I suggest that your doubts about Canada and your feeling that real life goes on elsewhere are very Canadian thoughts?

Yes, some people would say so — some of my friends would say so.

So many Canadians have been convinced good writing comes from elsewhere.

This is changing. And I'm now writing at a time when this is changing. I think Canadian writing will be more and more appreciated, because of this questioning and this humorous attitude that we can bring to a lot of issues that Americans just don't see in the same light. I think we're illuminating the reality of living in North America in a different way. In that sense I identify with being a Canadian.

PAUL YEE b. 1956

Prairie Widow

As far as she was concerned, the mourning period was over. She had
wept as any widow would, but more from fear and fury than from
grief. Four days had passed since the funeral, and the café remained
sealed to the townspeople and travellers who frequented it. Only
the rattle of an occasional car or truck and the steady hum of the
refrigerator slipped through the soft slitted grey of the afternoon.
Gum-may Yee sat at one of the dining tables, sifting through the tin
can holding all their important documents. Only the photographs
made sense to her, for she could read little Chinese and even less
English.

She had discovered Gordon's cousin leafing through the box just
before his departure. 'Leave it!' she had shouted, her voice rising
loud and shrill as her face suddenly glared ferocious. 'That box, it's
not yours! His things, I don't want you touching them!'

His intrusion had shaken loose her grim silences. At first, the
raging anger had conquered the fear. Her mind cursed the worm of
a husband who had deserted her in a strange country with children
but without means. Once again she felt betrayed, now to face the
uncertainty and townspeople of Wilding alone. The Yees were the
sole Chinese family there, forty miles over the horizon and down the
highway from the next prairie bus stop. Gum-may knew only a few
words of English. Could she run the café herself? How was she to
raise her two sons? She had already decided to stay.

'Stay?' the cousin had asked incredulously. 'How? You can't speak,
can't write! You're a woman, do you know that?'

She had shaken her head stubbornly. 'Here, it's better.'

'Come out, with the children, to Vancouver,' he had pleaded.
'Come out after the month is full. We have Chinese stores, Chinese
schools, theatres, everything you want. Come out!'

Gum-may had shrugged and looked away. She did not know why
she had instinctively decided to stay. She had not thought out reasons
and procedures. She only knew that she could not leave the café

even though she had never felt at home in Wilding. The townspeople had watched Gordon with distant, guarded eyes for twenty years, suspicious that a wifeless young Oriental might somehow sully the farming settlement. Nor had they changed after Gum-may's arrival in 1950. After business hours, the Yees were left to themselves and their box-like home sank silently into the deep prairie night. Gum-may had learned to wrap the isolation around her like a blanket, sealing in the warmth of a solitary beating heart.

In the days after the funeral, Gum-may had moved about dazedly, cooking for the children with hands that acted of their own accord. Her mind wandered far and near. At moments, all things seemed workable: her sons would start school once again, the two waitresses Kay and Mabel would return, and she would resume baking, cooking, and washing. But at other times, her mind lost its calm. What if the supplies did not come? Suppose there was a fire? Whom would she turn to in case of sudden illness? She detested the idiotic smiling and nodding she used to turn away the banter of customers. Over and over she wondered why she had decided to stay.

She slept soundly and dreamlessly through all the nights as if exhausted from a long journey. This morning, she had awakened late and then stumbled groggily into the kitchen. The boys had already eaten and slipped outside. She saw the empty bowls, the bread bag lying open, and the milk bottle standing uncapped, and was stricken with panic.

'Are you fit to be a mother?' Self disgust had slashed at her. 'Look at you, sleeping like a pig. No brains at all! Are you crazy?' She pictured herself wandering the street, hair dishevelled, and crooning shrill lullabies to herself. The smirking townsfolk walked wide arcs around her. Then she saw a ring of dancing chanting children encircling her sons.

'Crazy lady, *deen-poh*,' they screamed, 'Your mother's a crazy lady!' To possess sons and then lose her mind was an unbearable idea. In terror, Gum-may had darted to the wash basin and splashed cold water onto her face.

For the rest of the morning, she had worked herself furiously. She pulled on a baggy sweater and went out to water and hoe her neglected vegetables. This was her fifth garden in as many years, and the earth continued to send up beans and potatoes despite Gordon's dire predictions. Of course, Gum-may nursed the soil thoroughly with the outhouse offerings once the winter relaxed.

The uneven rows of green formed her only lines of reference over the vast terrain. In China, a river streamed by one side of the village, mountains rolled in the distant north, and castle-like watchtowers had guarded the opposite horizons. Here, she felt adrift in a swaying, unyielding ocean, and she clung to her hoe and shovel as if they were life-preservers.

'Widows are work-mules,' she muttered at the weeds, and she was no exception. The famous Third Lady of an earlier dynasty, when widowed, had laboured late into the night at her weaving. Then she immortalized herself with a scissor slash across the loom to admonish her delinquent son. In front of the devastated threads, she hissed, 'An unschooled man is like an unfinished bolt of cloth — unsaleable, irreparable, and wasted!' Wisdom and drama, it seemed, were incumbent for widowhood, and Gum-may prayed that she could afford both.

Returning to the kitchen, she had started to wash the accumulated piles of dishes. Dull grey sheets of galvanized tin framed the once-white sink. She checked if the lard pail underneath required emptying before cranking the water pump. Beside it stood the sturdy gas stove, the mainstay of their livelihood. This kitchen would be her loom, Gum-may thought, to transform her efforts into food for her sons. It was a pity that she did not possess the pretty face or shapely figure that less dutiful widows exploited. Small eyes on a face too broad glared back when she glanced in the mirror. The rigours of bearing children and enduring Canadian winters had thickened her body.

Gum-may pumped a steady flow of water to rinse the soap away. Perhaps, she thought, she should follow the cousin's advice and move. Her lips tightened as the familiar questions reasserted themselves in her mind. She did not want to move. But had not the widowed mother of the sage Mencius moved three times before satisfying herself? The wise matron had finally settled by the schoolmaster's house where her son could observe studious habits. Mencius had almost become a butcher when the slaughterhouse was located next door.

Of course, Gum-may reminded herself, she would situate her family wherever the advantages for her sons lay. Yet the thought of moving left her cold. Vancouver seemed ten thousand miles away, across oceans and mountains that would claim her life if she ventured away. She dreaded the boarding of trains, the changing of scenery, and the meeting of new faces — and she was not sure why. She had always considered herself quite fearless and brave.

Next, Gum-may had filled the wash bucket to go out to scrub the café floor. On her knees, she pushed the bristle brush with renewed energy, hoping that weariness would displace the unease. In earlier days, she had imagined herself a gentry-woman, presiding over private and public quarters. The two bedrooms ran side by side to the length of the café, connected only at the kitchen. It had been wondrously sinful to lie in bed and listen to the unsuspecting customers eat and chat on the other side of the thin wall.

But the work soon destroyed her imagination. She rose at six to knead bread and doughnuts for the first busload of customers. Day after day, the diners ordered from the same unchanging menu. The plates and glasses were washed and reused every two hours. She and Gordon ate the leftovers, whatever could not be served next day. This was Gum San, the mountains of gold that men in China dreamt about? There were neither mountains in the prairie nor gold in the café kitchen. Gum-may learned to let her mind hum the old tunes carried by opera troupes across the Toisan countryside.

As the floor dried, Gum-may had gone into the bedroom and started to empty Gordon's clothes from the drawers. It was then that she had come across the tin box with the papers and photographs. She carried it into the dining room and opened it curiously. Not much had accumulated: a few letters, some heavy folded documents, their passports. She had never seen the box's contents before.

'Why am I looking through this?' she wondered. 'Me, a woman without schooling.' Even if Gordon had left instructions for her future life, she would have been unable to decipher them. She recognized rows of numbers, but nothing made sense. Every sheet was meaningless until she came to the snapshots at the bottom.

The first photograph brought a fleeting smile to her face. Five Chinese couples stared solemnly out at her. The café's menu board hung behind them, chalk marks grinning off the soda pop company's blackboard. Gum-may cradled her first-born son in the centre. The gathering had marked the full-month celebration of David's birth. She put names to the faces: the men were addressed as 'uncles' and the women as 'elder sisters' or 'sisters-in-law' to establish a simple intimacy quickly among strangers.

It had been the first time that guests had come to the café since Gum-may's arrival in Wilding. Gordon's friends had journeyed from several neighbouring towns, bearing gifts of oranges and red packets of good-luck money. They too were small businessmen, operating laundries and cafés in their own visions of Gum San. The men might meet by chance in Regina or Saskatoon, but contact was otherwise scarce. Yet they greeted one another affectionately as brothers, bound by unspoken aspirations and desperations shaped by a common destiny.

Like Gum-may, the wives had come to Canada only after the immigration laws were changed. After the introductions of the day, the women had eyed each other's newly curled hair and long full dresses with momentary suspicion. But in the kitchen away from the men, they had giggled, touched one another, and talked without restraint. They traded names of home villages and details of travelling to their new homes. They fretted over the Communists in China and laughed at the raised toilets of Canada, wondering how the bowels could possibly move when perched two feet above the ground. Their voices filled the room along with the steam from numerous bowls and pots of tea and tangy ginger-vinegar broth.

For them, every aspect of life here proved a new discovery and they had withdrawn from public sight in their awkwardness. Only when they shared the hurt could they laugh at themselves and look at the world around them. Only then did Canada become real. There were drunks and cheats who never paid their bills, and farmers' wives who refused even to nod at them in passing. Their own husbands gambled and drank, to be sure, and there were whispered tales of less able men gone mad and 'kept' women still waiting. But all things taken, the women celebrated their arrival in Gum San. The men welcomed the helping hand and moved eagerly to water the family tree. Gum-may had basked in the rhythms of village dialects but she had told none of her secrets.

Even then she had feared that Gordon's drinking was excessive. He would pull out the whiskey once the blind was drawn and the front door latched for the night. 'I'm all tired out,' he announced curtly, 'The tendons are all tight.' During the months of pregnancy, it seemed to Gum-may that her husband was greying and shrinking before her very eyes. After a long swallow from the bottle, he sat motionless, eyes clenched shut on his pale and haggard face. Was it liquor that had eased his years alone in this land? Gum-may could not help but wonder who and how many he had slept with. Could he be trying to forget or remember someone?

She had hovered silent and apprehensive, a nervous hand over her growing belly. An unfathomable gulf hung between them. It had been too late after her arrival to test for new intimacies. For the first weeks he had smiled constantly at her, as if to reassure and to encourage her. They had both aged, but separately, in different worlds. She knew nothing about the man who pulled her body into his on the sagging bed. And for either to cast about coyly for new sensations or fresh information seemed unbecoming for their age and a cruel mockery of their situation.

After she had mastered the locations and processes of her new home, silence filled their relationship and drove them apart. Gordon disappeared at night, and came back very late with his clothes reeking of tobacco and more alcohol. Soon she realized that the townsmen had set up a gambling table behind the barber shop. Gum-may consoled herself with the child, but found herself wishing that she had been more attentive when they had first met in their younger and more playful days.

'More playful?' Gum-may jolted back to the present and sneered. What a waste of time to daydream. Youth was a bird spreading its wings; once aloft, it never returned. The next photo she picked up showed a younger, prettier version of her with hair braided into sturdy pigtails. She stood erect behind her seated parents, careful not to stir a wrinkle into her new blouse. She had never visited the photographer's shop in the county seat before. Little did she suspect that the print would be employed by her father to solicit a useful son-in-law.

Gum-may hardly knew her father and trusted him less. She was out in the paddy fields by the time he arose and already asleep when he returned at nights. He was nicknamed Big-gun Ming for his frequent volleys of opinions and plans. But the money-minded advice went to everyone else while he lived off the remittances received from a brother in America. The family fields he rented out, reserving only a small plot for his wife and daughter to tend to.

The announcement of marriage had demolished the sixteen-year-old Gum-may. She expected that her body would ultimately be surrendered to a husband. But already? It seemed that it was only yesterday that she had discovered the supple strength of her body. She was tall and bold, carrying laden baskets to trade at the country marketplace. The pride of filial accomplishment filled her when she slipped the coins into her mother's hand, tendering them as proof of her devotion and ability. She had dared to think the shame of a son-less family could be redeemed by hard work.

Her father had presided loudly at the wedding banquet, toasting all the guests with a ready glass. Gum-may kept her eyes lowered, but on one upward glance, she had caught her father staring at her. The setting sun glinted off his sweaty jowls and his eyes narrowed to squint at her.

'You better do well,' came the silent command. Gordon's family had several men working in Gum San. Gum-may was her parents' only child. No one would fault her if she kept ties to her own family. As for her new husband, he behaved like other returnees from abroad: cocky and confident in talk and movement. He had looked at her and seemed relieved that she resembled the photograph and had not concealed moles, buck teeth or the like from him.

Gum-may had not wanted to lie with Gordon. He had smiled at her with knowing eyes. His pale stocky body smelled sharply sweet when he moved up to her on the bed. Gum-may retreated and looked away. But Gordon knew what to do, he knew what he wanted. She kept her eyes and hands tightly clenched as he eased her legs apart and slid between them. The pain swirled with her fear. Two months later, he departed. Gordon was afraid they might change the immigration laws in his absence and block his re-entry.

Gum-may had not shed tears for him in the two decades that followed. The years of war and hunger swept her thoughts into survival, away from wishful sentimentality. Her own mother died during the invasion, and Gum-may felt her body harden and her gums loosen. There was no aching or dreaming for this distant stranger who had moved painfully inside her. No special quirks to his speech or movements called him to her. She mused that even the scrawny water buffalo was a more intimate companion. When Gum-may did weep, it was for those definitions that Gordon's absence denied her—wife to his needs, mother of his sons, partner to his labour. Gordon's mother had not been overly cruel, taking Gum-may's barrenness as a reassuring sign of her chastity.

Gum-may's hands trembled over the photos. 'Why bring these memories back?' she demanded. 'Forget them! Cast them aside, they're useless. Everything is different now.' She tried to think of the future. The café was a routine she had lived for six years. The customers would return if she acted quickly. She could re-open the doors if Mabel watched the cash register in the front. She could be trusted with the money for she too was a widow. Mabel had sat silently by her side that first night before the relatives had arrived. They both wept: Mabel's tears slid down her round cheeks while Gum-may's wails clawed the air. The boys were huddled in a corner with lost looks on their frightened faces.

The boys' faces leapt up at her from more snapshots. David's eyes resembled hers, small and set close to the nose. John's over-sized ears were a sign of future longevity. In a rare gesture of affection, Gordon had trimmed their hair the night before seeing the photographer. It had been Gum-may's suggestion to send family portraits to their relatives in China. There, she had reasoned, she and the boys might finally receive a measure of appreciation. Her sons testified to her virtue: she had violated no taboos and had produced hardy insurance to guarantee the lineage's future fortunes. In the village, Gum-may's high status would have been confirmed.

But out here, her sons drew no special attention. The town was a closed circle: she spoke to no one and no one came to visit. The boys became dusty treasures that depreciated daily. They played with the twins from across the street, stealing candy and soda pop from the café to trade for wild flowers and limp rodents plucked from the rolling fields. The boys came home with burrs and grass tangled in their hair and gaping holes in their pants. Gum-may looked and sighed.

Gordon glared at them with dulled eyes. He did not speak or play with them. If they angered him, his eyes flashed at Gum-may, and she would scold and discipline them. She had once hoped that the boys might restore some youth in their father or even entice him to stay home. Maybe he would teach them to count and write in Chinese. But Gordon played the cold hard father of Confucian virtue and the boys only became another topic of argument.

'What do I do, that makes you so angry?' she had ventured recently.

Gordon had snapped back, 'I'm not angry! Who says I'm angry?'

She had bit her lip. 'Then why don't you look at the children? Don't you know how to be a father?'

Gordon's eyes had blazed. 'I'm tired, that's what! Don't I do enough? There's rice to eat, the children have clothes. You have money to send home. What more do you want?'

All fighting over money, gambling, and alcohol ended with this standard challenge, 'Are you not satisfied, woman?'

She had been forced to concede that she was indeed not in want, for their joint labours in the café met all their needs well enough. But the futility of these confrontations had slowly given her strength, for they revealed the weaknesses of her husband. She saw that Gordon's despair of life could find no release anywhere.

During the day, Gordon appeared in the kitchen only when fat Mister Martinsen and his friends congregated at the café for their weekly coffee sessions. They hunched around one table for the afternoon, nudging and chortling and welcoming every additional body with a hearty chorus of hullo's. Gordon left them a pot of coffee and a pie and then went behind his counter. Soon he came into the back, searching for odd jobs to do. Gum-may had observed his downcast eyes, but it was some time before she realized that it would take more than a wife and sons to fill the void inside him roused by the camaraderie and confidences of menfolk.

She had watched her husband wipe the grill and strain the soup over and over with deliberate care. This man of hers was like her father, eager to play the word games that men devised for business and merriment. But Gordon was treated like a servant in his own proprietorship and a mute among his peers. The farmers and truck-drivers would never accept him as their equal, yet Gordon had made a commitment to a life in this country.

Gordon had wanted the strangest things in life—things denied him because he was Chinese, because he was a newcomer. Why did he yearn for the impossible? Gum-may wondered. He should have tasted China's starvation and the panic of refugees pursued by soldiers, guns, and bandits. Had life in Canada become too soft, too easy? If he had huddled under the droning airplanes swooping low with bombs, he might have valued life more. If he had touched the clammy darknesses she once battled before awakening, he might have clasped his sons to him.

The door slammed and Gum-may looked up as the boys rushed in. Her hands moved to cover the photographs as if they were delicate shards of a broken bowl being pieced together.

'They want to know if we are moving to Vancouver,' David blurted in a child's clear Toisanese. Gum-may looked at the bright eyes focused on her and answered slowly, 'No, we're staying.'

'Hurrah!' The boys shouted with joy and rushed out. Gum-may stacked the photographs carefully and replaced them in the tin box. She would go through the rest later. Now it was time to prepare dinner.

Yes, they were staying, Gum-may repeated as she turned on the kitchen light. An unusual sense of peace filled her now. Surely she had learned and suffered enough to survive whatever twists heaven might throw at her. Surely her life was not meant to be a continual trek through the doors of strangers to fall under their baneful staring. She felt at once weary and energized: too tired to pack her bags for another move, but more than ready to show everyone her determination to succeed. The pieces of life she had gathered along the road to Gum San made best sense here, within the four walls of this café. She had finally arrived at a place she understood.

◆ ◆ ◆

PAUL YEE was born in Spalding, Saskatchewan, in 1956 and raised in Vancouver, where he received his B.A. and M.A. in history at the University of British Columbia. Currently the Multicultural Co-ordinator of the Archives of Ontario, he has also worked as an editor, curator, scriptwriter, and teacher. In addition to many articles on Canada's Chinese community, he has written *Cityscape: A Walking Tour of Vancouver's Chinatown* (Vancouver: Weller Cartographic Services, 1983) and *Saltwater City: The Chinese in Vancouver, 1886-1986* (Vancouver: Douglas & McIntyre, 1988), which was awarded the Vancouver Book Prize in 1989. His other published work includes *Teach Me to Fly, Skyfighter!* (Toronto: James Lorimer, 1983), *The Curses of Third Uncle* (Toronto: James Lorimer, 1986), *Tales from Gold Mountain: The Chinese in the New World* (Toronto: Groundwood, 1989), and *The Cook Who Knew Everything* (Toronto: Groundwood, forthcoming, 1991).

GEOFF HANCOCK is editor-in-chief of *Canadian Fiction Magazine*. His recent books include *Canadian Writers at Work: Interviews* (1987), *Invisible Fictions: Contemporary Stories from Quebec* (1987), *Published in Canada: the Small Presses* (forthcoming).

Let's start with your background.

I consider myself third-generation Canadian, though I am the first generation of my family to be born here. My grandfather came here in the late nineteenth century and worked on the railway. He returned to China, where my father was born. My father then came over to Canada and ended up in Saskatchewan, where he ran a café. I was born there in the fifties. My parents died when I was young, though. I was raised in Vancouver by a second-generation Chinese aunt who was born in Canada in 1895. My experience benefited from her life as someone who had grown up in Canada.

Do you try to reflect that background in your writing?

Absolutely. When I write I see myself as a voice coming from that particular part of the Chinese community. Today, the Chinese community is largely immigrant, mostly from Hong Kong. The Hong Kong element gives the community a certain vitality, a certain glamour — and lots of media exposure. However, the part I come from — old pioneer and Canadian-born — has a different outlook on life. This was the generation that actually lived through the dark ages of anti-Chinese racism. They don't see themselves as immigrants. They see themselves as Canadians, having earned that right through the railway, the Depression, and World War II. My outlook on life, writing, and Chinese Canadians is tempered by that experience, of coming through those dark ages. I grew up during the time when the Chinese thought they could actually fit into this society. All that exploded after 1967 when Chinese immigration picked up again.

Marshall McLuhan said 'The world is going Oriental.' By that he meant Oriental philosophies and a way of looking at the world, and being in the world, especially in the 1960s.

The sixties were certainly a more open era of liberal thinking. The eighties and nineties have drifted toward conservative values and a narrowing of tolerance. The current backlash and scapegoating of Hong Kong money in Vancouver is disgraceful. The Chinese have been in BC as an obvious presence for over a hundred years. Yet, despite all the gains that have been made, once again anti-Chinese feelings and fears of being 'overwhelmed' are emerging. I'm not convinced that we have seen a real acceptance of things Chinese in Canada.

Have you experienced personal prejudice?

Not directly. I've been walking down a street and someone in a car

PAUL YEE 345

shouts 'ricer' or 'Chink'. That occurs infrequently, though. I don't encounter racism amongst my current circle of friends or in the kind of work I do as an archivist. I haven't been personally victimized by racism, yet I would say that racism has affected the psychology of my generation. We were conscious of not rocking the boat; we were conscious of wanting to fit into Canadian society, to succeed on 'their' terms. To be left out was a symbol of failure.

One of the ways Canadians try to incorporate everybody is the concept of the multicultural mosaic. Do you think the mosaic idea is working, or was it just a vote-getting initiative of the Liberal party who helped bring many people to Canada? Or is it a good idea whose time has not yet arrived?

For me, multiculturalism is one way of looking at the issue of visible minorities. The great divide in Canada is not that there are many cultures here, but that there are many races of people. It's the multi-racial aspect of Canada that is at the core of issues of discrimination: issues of housing, jobs, police violence. It's all related to race as opposed to culture. Canada is going to become more and more multiracial, given the demographic patterns that we have. The question then becomes: how are we going to make sure this works so that we don't have riots in the streets? More blacks, more Asians will come to Canada. What is going to happen? Multiculturalism gives a useful message: it's just one tool to fight racism. It preaches tolerance of various races of people, no matter what they look like. But it's important that this come from the top, as government policy. Racism is at the forefront of all the protests and all the dissatisfactions with the way Canada is developing today. How can we ensure true equality for all?

That means everybody in Canada has to make a psychological adjustment to each other.

That means everybody in Canada has to make a psychological adjust-ment to everybody of *colour*. Though I am third-generation, people still ask me how long I have been in Canada. They marvel at how well I speak English. These are constant reminders that I am still viewed as an outsider from mainstream Canada, even though I was born here, even though I write 'Canadian'.

Yet your book Tales from Gold Mountain *uses Chinese tales and mythology.*

That's a major confusion. When I wrote those tales, I was not writing Chinese mythology. I have not read a great deal of Chinese literature. My stories and tales came very much out of BC's history of industrial capitalism, the labour force, racism, the landscape, and the everyday folk culture that my people brought over here. The stories also came out of reading of Western folklore: Little Red Riding Hood, Hansel and Gretel, Sleeping Beauty. Book reviews have all commented on the Chinese tradition in my work, but I was not writing in a 'Chinese' tradition; I was writing in a Western tradition.

Why was it important to write these stories for children?

I didn't write them for children; I was writing tales for anybody who wanted to read stories. I was writing to make history more accessible to more people. I do have a pedagogical motivation in all my writing. I want to teach things. Adults are resistant. I have certain things I want children today to understand about Chinese people. Children are the future and they ought to recognize what the Chinese have done in Canada. It's the next generation that will change the social fabric of this country.

If an adult audience had been intended, would the texture and content of the stories have changed?

The structure and narrative form of that book would be different. Most of my fiction has been directed at children, so my writing is plot-oriented. I don't write great wads of description. Children enjoy the rapid clip of plot. In children's literature ambivalent endings are unacceptable. Writing for adults gives you more flexibility.

Do you see a danger in stereotyping the Chinese as a group? Your tales are much different from a more documentary kind of realism. Evelyn Lau's Runaway *speaks of the pressures on a young Chinese girl from her family, pressures which forced her into the unsavoury and unhappy life of a teenage runaway.*

I see myself fighting certain kinds of stereotypical roles. Several children's books about the Chinese have been written by non-Chinese. These books are offensive to me; none of them ring true to the experience of growing up as a visible minority. There's a fairly romanticized vision of the kind of identity crises that children of a visible minority go through and how those crises are resolved. In my earlier books, I deal with that issue too, but the resolution is quite different. As a Chinese Canadian writer writing about Chinese Canadian people, I try to be honest and realistic as to their emotional experiences. Chinese Canadians are a prime audience for me because I view literature as a mirror for people to see themselves and their own community. Literature has a mirroring function: this is who we are; this is who we might become. Children who read these other books say: 'This isn't us' and they give up on literature.

Do you think your books are received differently in the so-called 'melting pot' of the United States than in the 'multicultural mosaic' of Canada?

When you look at these two clichés, ask: 'Is racism any less virulent in these two countries, given these two national mythologies?' It's not any less strong in the United States, even though people here say the 'melting pot' is better because it avoids ghettoizing people. Racism is alive and well in the US. Visible minorities are just as visible. Yet, funding for art and culture in recognition of visible differences is just as prominent as in Canada. The National Endowment for the Arts funds Chicano, Asian American, and black arts projects. There's a recognition of the mosaic there, just as there is here.

Did you ever want to write about anything other than your own experience?

No. Writing is empowerment. History is empowerment. I can only write about the things I know best. It's a deliberate attempt to grow, to take what I learned from the community and bring it back into the community. I have a very deliberate motive and mission in writing about the things that I do. First, I want to help the Chinese Canadian community grow spiritually and creatively. It needs to know that it has a history here. Second, Chinese Canadians ought to be exploring various kinds of ways of writing about their experiences here in Canada. We ought to do that now.

Are you part of an ongoing tradition of Chinese Canadian writers?

Or are you reacting against an earlier generation or striking out in original new directions?

I'm certainly not part of an ongoing tradition of writers in Canada. There aren't that many writers. I'm probably more reactive: I'm reacting to a lack of writers, and to the kind of books that do get published about Chinese Canadians. At the same time, I'm pro-active because writing folktales is a deliberate attempt to create mythology as a foundation, as a way of saying we've been here since Day One. Everybody should be writing these kinds of mythologies about Canada because this is the way we become Canadians. This is what we all ultimately share.

Through Canadian Fiction Magazine *I have published three volumes of fiction in translation from the unofficial languages of Canada. It was very difficult to find creative work from the Chinese community, compared to the European communities. Why this difficulty?*

Even in my generation, the first to have gone through university and to enjoy all the advantages of the education system in Canada, we were conservatively raised. Our parental generation taught us to study hard, work hard, get a good job—never to be vulnerable to racism or job discrimination. Writing is not a secure occupation. None of us were encouraged to go into the arts when we did further studies—it was not profitable. Also I see the suppression of our own Chinese Canadian history as a deliberate mistake. Our parental generation wanted to protect and shelter us from the negative parts of our history. They'd say, yes, there was racism, but we don't want you to grow up with a chip on your shoulder. We want you to be equal, and as Canadian as the white kid down the street. What that attitude did was to gut us. It did not give us a soul to write from. We need to go back to recover our history. Our parents protected us. We got piano lessons and hockey so we'd grow up and be accepted. It was a major mistake not to recognize our history. Those years of hardship will give us the power to write. Only recently have we come to reclaim that history in dribs and drabs.

*The First and Founding Nations
Respond*

TOMSON HIGHWAY

TOMSON HIGHWAY was born in 1951 in a tent pitched in a snow bank on his father's trapline on Maria Lake in the northwestern corner of Manitoba. When he was six, he was sent south to the Guy Hill Residential School, a move that tore him from his family, his culture, and his language—as a child he had spoken only Cree, and at school he was forced to learn English. Highway received a B.A. in music from the University of Western Ontario and, after a period as a social worker, he turned to work in the theatre. Currently he is Artistic Director of Native Earth Performing Arts, a theatre company based in Toronto. He has twice received the Dora Mavor Moore Award for Best New Play: first for *The Rez Sisters* (Saskatoon: Fifth House, 1988)—which also won the Floyd S. Chalmers Award for Best Canadian Play and was nominated for a Governor General's Award for Drama—and then for *Dry Lips Oughta Move to Kapuskasing* (Saskatoon: Fifth House, 1989).

ANN WILSON was born in 1956 in Montreal, and moved with her family the following year to Ottawa. Both the maternal and paternal sides of her family have lived in Canada for several generations, although her mother's family has its roots in Scotland, her father's roots in Northern Ireland. She received a B.A. in History and an M.A. and Ph.D. in English from York University. Since 1987, she has taught in the department of drama at the University of Guelph. Currently she is an associate editor of the *Canadian Theatre Review* and of *Essays in Theatre*.

You grew up in northern Manitoba and then, at the age of six, you were sent to a Catholic boarding school in The Pas. In other interviews you have indicated that this meant more than being sent away from your family: it was being pulled from your culture. This violent dislocation of young native children from their families

*and culture has been a means of assimilating them into the domi-
nant white culture. I was wondering at what stage you became
conscious that the point of your schooling was to assimilate you.*

About the age of twenty-three or twenty-four.

*Not when you were a child? How do you remember responding to
being sent away to school?*

It was like entering a wonderland. It was lonely because you were
away from your parents ten months of the year, for many, many
years. The choice, of course, was to quit — but you couldn't — or to
learn as well as possible. So I took everything; I learned everything
possible to the best of my ability. Now I use it in my writing.

What was it like to go back to your family in the summer?

It was fabulous. Just fabulous. My father was a trapper in the winter-
time and a fisherman in the summertime. We didn't actually live on
the reserve; we lived about a hundred miles north of the [Brochet]
Reserve, close to the Northwest Territories and Saskatchewan border. We lived on a different lake every summer. Up there, there are
about 10,000 lakes — and rivers and waterfalls, hills and forests. It is
totally untouched — at least it was then. We lived in tents all summer
long. I started fishing with my dad when I was eleven. We'd get up
at three o'clock in the morning when the sun rose — we were close
to the Arctic Circle — and we'd go until six P.M., six days a week. On
Sundays, we'd go off on picnics and berry-picking expeditions. It was
fantastic, unbelievable — compared to what most kids know today
in downtown Toronto or New York or Los Angeles or Ottawa or
Vancouver. It was like a paradise.

*So you had two months of paradise and then ten months when you
were removed and being assimilated into this other, quite hostile,
culture. What interests me is that, as you admit, you were pretty
successful at giving the appearance of having been assimilated.
You did university work in English and music. On other occasions,
you've talked about going to England, to London, with a man who
had been your music teacher. What was it like to be in London?*

It was fabulous. I was very lucky: I ran into wonderful people, Londoners.
I was taken in and I made wonderful friends. I don't know how much

detail you want me to go into. Being gay gives you a lot of insights into a fantastic world: artists, all kinds of really unusual people. It showed me a world of artists, film and stage actors, architects, designers, models and magazine publishing industry people. It was fantasy land. I saw shows every night: the symphony, the opera, the ballet, theatre — Glenda Jackson, Alec Guinness, Joan Sutherland, Leontyne Price, Artur Rubinstein, and on and on. I saw some of the best artists in the world working and for a twenty-year-old that was astounding.

I think it is astounding for almost any Canadian to go to London because it is such a cultural centre. But if you come from a WASP background, as I do, going to London is like going back to the roots of your culture, like going back to visit the home which your family left a long time ago. But that couldn't have been what it was like for you.

Well, I was considered an exotic creature. I was introduced to people; people liked to show me around, so that's what happened. I got this extra inch. It was beautiful.

It's interesting that roughly a year after you returned from England, you decided not to continue pursuing your career as a classical pianist, although you were launched on a career in music. I'm wondering why the shift in direction? Why move into forms of social work with native Canadians?

It was fabulous to do that [classical music] for a while, but I belong here. I'll always belong here. I might go to Paris for two years or to Tokyo for a year, or whatever, but I'll always live here. I'll die here. I love this place; I love my people — more and more, as the years go on. It's nice to take the occasional excursion into a different world . . .

But you have to keep coming back. I'm curious about why you chose to work in theatre, about why you write plays and not novels.

I have no idea. It's not a rational decision. By sheer luck I fell into it. It happens to work. I'm a very, very lucky individual because I'm making a living at something I absolutely adore. It is just luck.

I don't want to contradict you, but I wonder if it really is 'luck' that you write plays. It seems to me that the Nanabush figure, who

is so important to your work and presumably to you, undergoes
transformations that can be captured wonderfully on stage because
transformation is an important element of theatre. It's hard for me
to imagine Nanabush having the same sort of vitality in a poem or
story that he does on stage.

The best I can do for a rational explanation of why I picked theatre
is because I love beautiful things. And I guess that it's something that
you inherit; it's in your blood or it's not in your blood. But I think
what we've inherited in our family comes from a very strong strain
of the musician and the troubadour, the travelling story-teller.

Your brother, René, is a dancer, isn't he?

Yes, and my grandfather was a musician. It just goes on and on. The
Cree people have a powerful tradition, like the Celtic people in
Ireland, of troubadours. The strength of the tradition in Ireland is so
great that some of the most powerful writers in the English language
are Irish—like James Joyce, Samuel Beckett, George Bernard Shaw.
That tradition of troubadour, of story-telling is also very powerful in
Cree. Like the Celtic tradition, there is a rich mythology in Cree, but
one which is specific to our landscape. We inherited about 10,000
years of a tradition, a literary tradition that happens to be oral. I think
that what we are doing is essentially continuing that tradition, but
taking it one step further, extending it one step over into the three-
dimensional medium of the stage by using sound, music, actors,
costumes and, most important of all, the spoken word. It is still the
oral tradition; that's what I like about it. The spoken word in theatre
is its most distinct quality.

One of the elements of your work is the sense of bridging two
cultures. When I saw The Rez Sisters *and* Dry Lips, *there were native*
people in the audience in Toronto, but a fairly sizeable segment of
that audience was white, so clearly your work has appeal to the
non-native community. Do you think that sort of bridging is an
important element of your work?

Yes, I think that every society is constantly in a state of change, of
transformation, of metamorphosis. I think it is very important that it
continue to be so to prevent the stagnation of our imaginations, our
spirits, our soul. It is bad enough that our bodies and our physical

environment are in danger of stagnating. I think the very fact that British and French and Czechoslovakian, Yugoslavian and Polish, are now living on this continent means that we need a different experience, one that changes any identification, even if by the very nature of the fact that all are called Canadians, Ontarians, Torontonians. Right there, you have Indian names. There is an additional psychic magic that happens there, just as a result of that name. So I think that white culture in Canada is very much changing and transforming as a result of living with native culture; likewise Cree culture, native culture. It is impossible for me to live in a tent for the rest of my life, even though I was born in one; but I don't have any desire whatsoever to live in a tent for the rest of my life. It is nice enough for a couple of weeks in the summer, but I live in downtown Toronto, in a house with a microwave oven, and a piano and a washer and dryer. I take the subway to work. All these are things which I appreciate, but what I really find fascinating about the future of my life, the life of my people, the life of my fellow Canadians is the searching for this new voice, this new identity, this new tradition, this magical transformation that potentially is quite magnificent. It is the combination of the best of both worlds, wherein you take a symphony or a string quartet by Beethoven, study it, utilize the best of what you get from it, the best knowledge you get from that structure of that instrumentation, and apply that structure, utilize it for the telling of Cree myth made contemporary—in downtown Toronto. That kind of stuff—taking the best of both worlds, combining them and coming up with something new—I think that's the most exciting thing.

That's interesting, because one of the things that seems often to underlie policies of multiculturalism is the desire to ghettoize, but you seem to be arguing against that: that there is something very rich that can happen from cultures meeting and combining.

Well, I think that it is inevitable. I can't help but be influenced by the fact that I've seen *Superman* or Joan Collins or *Archie* comic books, or for that matter, that I've heard the works of Beethoven. They are all irreparably, irretrievably, a part of my imagination now. I have absolutely no intention or any way of rejecting them. I'll use them to create something that is from my imagination.

How does that reconcile with the politics of your works? Sometimes they aren't overtly political, but are so by the very fact that, before your plays, native culture rarely had been seen on the 'main' stages of Canada. You are a celebrated artist whose recognition has generated interest in the work of other native artists. There is a politics involved in that. I think that in Canada the recognition by white, Anglo culture of native culture seems, somewhat, to parallel the—albeit sometimes reluctant—recognition by English Canada of French Canada. This has been fraught with tension that seems to be intensifying into open hostility with the discussions about the Meech Lake Accord. How do you think that tension between cultures should be negotiated? Do you think a culture needs legal protection, or would it be better off without it?

I think that we could do with something like that; and I think that it is the hostility which we could do without. I look at countries like Germany, Holland or Denmark, where children grow up speaking three languages fluently and retain them for the rest of their lives. There is a real openness to multilingualism there. What I find very difficult here is the way that people close their minds. I know so many people who speak only one language; to me, that's cultural poverty. I'm not a political person, by any stretch of the imagination, but I suppose, if I were given the chance to create a world, it would be one where multilingualism was accepted as the norm. I find unilingualism sad.

And boring! I wonder what kinds of issues you see yourself pursuing in your work, what directions you see yourself going in?

Well, I'm working on a musical.

Is that a continuation of The Rez Sisters *and* Dry Lips, *which critics see as companion pieces?*

Yes. They were the first two; there are seven altogether. The musical again uses myths and music which I know—everything from Cree mythology to Teutonic myth to Las Vegas to Saskatchewan pow-wow. I'm putting it all together and coming up with a piece of theatre that I hope will be rich, exciting, and unusual.

It sounds as if this piece will merge a range of influences from various cultures.

I love all those cultures.

JACQUES GODBOUT

JACQUES GODBOUT was born in Montreal in 1933. Although best known as a novelist, he is also an important filmmaker and essayist. He has made more than twenty films, both fiction and documentary, including a film on Paul-Emile Borduas in 1963 and one on Hubert Aquin in 1979. A founding editor of *Liberté*, Godbout has long been a respected and important analyst of Quebec culture and society. His *Salut Galarneau!* (Paris: Editions du Seuil, 1967, translated as *Hail Galarneau!* by Alan Brown) has become a classic of the Quebec literature of the 1960s. His other novels (all published by Editions du Seuil, Paris) include *L'Aquarium*, 1962; *Le Couteau sur la table*, 1965; *D'Amour, P.Q.*, 1972; *L'Isle au dragon*, 1976; *Les Têtes à Papineau*, 1981; *Une histoire américaine*, 1986. His essays, untranslated, are collected in *Le Réformiste: textes tranquilles* (Montréal, Quinze, 1975) and *Le Murmure marchand* (Montréal, Boréal, 1984).

SHERRY SIMON is co-director of the Quebec cultural magazine *Spirale* and teaches in the département d'études françaises at Concordia University. She has published *Mapping Literature: The Art and Politics of Translation* (1988) with David Homel and *L'Inscription sociale de la traduction au Québec* (1989). She writes regularly in *Spirale* and other journals on literary theory and cultural issues.

Jacques Godbout, as a kind of literary reporter, you have written several very significant chapters of Quebec's cultural history over the last two and a half decades. Many commentators would agree that one of the most significant changes to have affected Quebec society over the last few years is the increasing pluralization of its population and the consequent pressures on a traditionally defensive sense of collective identity. Have you considered writing the novel which captures the new reality of Quebec's social and cultural pluralism?

I think that I have already written that novel. It's called *Une histoire américaine* [*An American Story*, trans. Yves Lapierre] and in it, especially in the last lines of the novel, there is a vision of a pluri-ethnic Quebec in a Quebec unified by *one* language. Pluri-ethnicity considered as a *diversity* of expressions seems to me a concept which is inappropriate and in fact politicized. It is part of a pluricultural vision of the world which sees each writer as a kind of deputy of his or her cultural group. All these writers would gather in a vast parliament called Quebec — or Canadian or American — literature and these literatures would be nothing more than deliberate exchanges between authors who act as representatives of their various constituencies. This is a vision which hardly corresponds to our reality. In *Une histoire américaine*, at the end, the main character, who is a Québécois, of French-Canadian origin, leaves the United States with a woman from Africa, and returns to Quebec to 'create a planetary generation', to open up to the world, but by remaining themselves and not by creating a kind of cultural shopping centre. I think that multiculturalism is something like those ethnic fast food areas you find in shopping centres of the third generation across Canada. Life, thought, literature would become a bit like these super-cafeterias. When you feel the need for a bit of Italian-ness, you could go out and get the literary equivalent of a pizza. This is a reductive conception of ethnicity, culture and food.

It is interesting to note that this reflection takes place in the context of a novel in which an 'American story' takes the place of the 'American dream'. The experience you relate is basically one of rejection by America. And yet, Quebec remains fascinated by the United States, while English Canada — as shown by the reaction of leftists and intellectuals in the recent free-trade debate — has a much more ambivalent and fearful attitude.

The free-trade debate certainly demonstrated the enormous distance between differing perceptions of the United States. English Canadian intellectuals see the United States as threatening; Québécois intellectuals see it as a land of liberty. I think there is enormous naïveté in both cases. English Canadians don't realize to what extent their political and cultural life is Americanized; outsiders can hardly see any difference. Certainly Canada is less violent, but there are less violent states too, like Vermont. English Canada is simply a non-violent American state. Québécois naïveté consists in seeing the United States as a land of liberty and not seeing to what extent commercial structures are also cultural structures. We imagine, rightly or not, that the French language will safeguard our identity, even if other aspects of our life become Americanized. Perhaps we shouldn't exclude here the fact that Quebec intellectuals were just somewhat amused by the defeat of the Toronto intellectuals who were against free trade — it made up perhaps a little for the defeat of the referendum. But this kind of attitude comes from seeing politics like a tennis game where two partners slug it out face to face. That's not the way things really are.

In a recent book, Pierre Nepveu suggests that we can no longer speak of Quebec literature in national terms, but that perhaps we should now be speaking of 'post-Québécois' literature. Do you agree that what was once recognizable as a coherent body of work has now exploded into fragments? What is the place of minority writers in this context?

Exactly twenty years ago the question Pierre Nepveu would have asked would have been: does Quebec literature exist? The answer today is obvious, if only because of the quantity of the work. By the forties there were writers of course like Gabrielle Roy, Roger Lemelin, Germaine Guèvremont and then Ringuet and all the authors of the *romans de la terre*, but that didn't make for a literature — only books. Among the many, many works that appeared since the 1950s there developed a kind of continuous dialogue. Each new writer was a conductor making music with the same instruments as the others; the colour of the sound was the same — whether in poetry, the novel or the essay. It was a literature of identity, with essentially political themes. With the eighties there are more and more writers, and for the first time there are now three generations writing simultaneously. Obviously there is now a much greater diversity. But there is also certainly a coherence behind this production. My generation discovered colonialism, the next generation discovered feminism, the next generation will find other worlds. And to this diversity will be added the perceptions of a small number of writers born elsewhere. Whether of Haitian or other origin, these writers at first focused on a literature linked to their countries of origin rather than to their immediate surroundings; now it is their Quebec environment which allows them to explore their universe. But these writers are only adding one more dimension to the proliferation which is a very healthy diversification.

Not too long ago there was a controversy in Outremont surround-
ing the Hassidic community which seemed to suggest the possibility
of a more generalized backlash in Quebec against 'outsiders'. Are
you concerned about the climate of intercultural relations in
Quebec?

We have been seeing for some time now reactions of impatience or
fear which are quite simply the product of ignorance. I think that
the problem of difference, of alterity, occurs also in homogeneous
societies. When I began to write, I lived in a homogeneous society;
I began to write precisely because I rejected this homogeneity. I've
often said it: the writer is the black sheep in the family, but it's hard
to be black sheep when there is no flock. All the writers here want
the flock to exist, quite certainly, so that they can be the black sheep.
The unfortunate aspect of the yet unresolved language problem
here — and it is unlikely that it will be resolved soon — is that it keeps
writers and intellectuals from doing their work. The quality of French
in Quebec is in certain milieux quite correct, but in others it's quite
mediocre. The language which is spoken and taught in schools
should be challenged. But how can I talk about the kind of French
which will be taught to immigrants, or the passage from the idiomatic,
spoken language of the past to a more open kind of code, how can
I begin to question these norms when French is not yet a stable and
recognized reality? And even more, how can we approach the normal
intellectual questioning of self in relation to others, of racism and
intercultural relations; how can we engage in a reasonable discussion
of multiculturalism? These questions must wait until we are out of
the mire of the old questions, the flock. Personally, I've had it. I find
it particularly symbolic that Saint-Jean Baptiste — the man with the
sheep — continues to take a leading role in this struggle. The Saint-
Jean Baptiste Society and all the groups associated with the Mouve-
ment Québec français could surely be doing important work in a
mutual education process with immigrants, but this cannot yet be
done when they are still fixed on the question of survival. Just as the
French Canadian Catholic clergy kept us in a state of suffocation by
obliging us to think about sin and the utopian vision of a non-existent
world, English Canadian society is now obliging us, by its laws and
its policies, to focus our attention on a single and sterile issue. We
are still living the legacy of Pierre Elliott Trudeau, who was always —
let us remember — a practising Catholic. And violence is no answer,

even if at times the temptation is strong. Power has become so abstract and symbolic that there is no real target to attack.

Some theoreticians have seen an analogy between feminism and ethnicity, between feminist and minority writing. To a certain extent one could draw comparisons between La vie en rose *and* Vice versa *as magazines which have drawn attention to a new way of seeing and writing about Quebec society. Do you agree with such a comparison? Do you see feminism and the concern for ethnicity as parallel phenomena?*

There is a fundamental difference between feminism and the arrival of immigrants to this country. There have always of course been women here and the questioning of power was inevitable. On the other hand, there has never been the mass arrival of immigrants racially different from the people here. The European immigration caused cultural difficulties which were resolved within a generation or a generation and a half. Italian, Hungarian, Polish minorities within French Canadian society posed few problems. But now you have immigrants from Asia, Africa, the Caribbean, and Latin America who are visibly different, have different religions, different attitudes towards women, etc. and who are arriving in great numbers. And more than half of these immigrants have come as refugees. This causes difficulties in schools and the older teachers feel insecure. I think this is a very complex situation which will certainly preoccupy us for the next twenty-five, thirty years. It is a phenomenon which concerns the human race and the planet. We are so unprepared for this that everything is possible. We may invent a way of integrating these people which will solve all our problems or we may fail miserably. But this has nothing to do with literature. It is a question for sociologists. Of course this will probably change some of the questions which literature will ask, but in the end I think that the essential social questions of today are not terribly different from those of 1958. I am still fighting for the presence of the French language. We are back to square one. My novels could almost be reprinted one after the other for the next twenty years, every three or four years as I wrote them, and they would be as appropriate now as they were then. We're about to start the same story again, with a different cast and with a different musical background, but basically it's the same. The difference is that I won't be alone. This question will also concern the immigrants and refugees who have come here and who will have to take positions on an issue which is clearer now than it was before.

Translated by Sherry Simon

ROBERTSON DAVIES

ROBERTSON DAVIES was born in Thamesville, in western Ontario, in 1913, of Welsh and partly Scottish ancestry on his father's side; his maternal ancestry goes back to eighteenth-century Dutch immigrants. Son of William Rupert Davies, a publisher and later a senator, he was educated at two of Canada's most prestigious schools — Upper Canada College and Queen's University — and went on to study at Oxford University, where he wrote a B.Litt. thesis on Shakespeare's boy actors. During his London years, Davies was associated with the Old Vic theatre company as actor and literary assistant before returning to Canada as literary editor of *Saturday Night*. Editor of the *Peterborough Examiner* for twenty years, he has also taught English at the University of Toronto and was appointed first Master of Massey College in 1962. Davies has not only produced innumerable articles, reviews, essays, books, and plays but has distinguished himself in acting, stage management, teaching, journalism, and academic administration. His works include *The Diary of Samuel Marchbanks* (Toronto: Clarke, Irwin, 1947); *Tempest-Tost* (1951; rpt. Markham, Ont.: Penguin, 1980); *Leaven of Malice* (1954; rpt. Markham, Ont.: Penguin, 1980); *A Mixture of Frailties* (Toronto: Macmillan, 1958); *A Voice from the Attic* (Toronto: McClelland and Stewart, 1960); *Fifth Business* (Toronto: Macmillan, 1970); *The Manticore* (Toronto: Macmillan, 1972); *World of Wonders* (Toronto: Macmillan, 1975); *The Rebel Angels* (Toronto: Macmillan, 1981); *What's Bred in the Bone* (Toronto: Macmillan, 1985); *The Lyre of Orpheus* (Toronto; Macmillan, 1988).

KAARINA KAILO has completed her Ph.D. dissertation on C.G. Jung, feminism, and the primal scene/s of psychoanalytic reader-response criticism at the Centre for Comparative Literature, University of Toronto. A recent immigrant from Finland, she is active in her own ethnic community both as an amateur writer and as a cultural critic. A junior researcher of the Finnish Academy, she has published articles on North American reinterpretations of the Finnish epic *Kalev-*

ala and is working on re-centring the epic's marginalized women and their Greek mythological sisters.

As Master Emeritus of Massey College, University of Toronto, educated at Upper Canada College and Queen's University, as the recipient of endless awards and distinctions, you are regarded as a symbol of the British establishment in Canada.

Why do you suppose that I am British or an establishment figure?

You are Welsh, Dutch, Scottish . . .

And you will be interested to know that, just at the end of the eighteenth century, I had some Red Indian ancestry. What do people mean when they talk about establishment figures? What is it? Tell me.

There is a certain continuity in the dominant white Anglo-Saxon world view that may not be shared by the other ethnic groups — Canadians from, let's say, India. Relatively speaking, I am closer to the establishment myself, for while I am not Anglo-Saxon, I am Nordic.

You just said something that I think is very important. You are Nordic, you are northern. Most of Canada is. And these people who come from distant lands, from many different climates, quite apart from cultural backgrounds, are bound to find this country strange and different because it is a northern country. I think the term 'establishment' is a dangerous one because it suggests bankers sitting somewhere, saying what to do and what not to do.

Not only thematic but stylistic features of literature can be an element of 'establishment'. I am involved in a Finnish amateur creative writing group that has got some assistance from the Secretary of State to publish a collection of immigrant stories.

When you start financing literature that does not find acceptance on its own, then you are in very bad trouble. You see, that is guilty conscience. They are just babying people who cannot manage for themselves. That is not the way Canada was put together. Canada was not put together by people who had to be underwritten and given hand-outs.

But it is a way of encouraging expression of whatever it is to be an ethnic Canadian, of allowing material to be published which is not only of obvious commercial value.

But, you see, this is where a very big split comes between the world that you are talking about as the establishment world, who allegedly have it all, and the new Canadians. *We* had to give up everything when we came here. We came here out of sheer necessity. Nobody paid us to stay Scots or English or Irish or Welsh. I think it is a mistake to continue helping people to stay non-Canadian while they are taking everything Canada has to give them.

Are you not in favour of multicultural encouragement of the arts?

Oh yes I am. But in a Canadian way, not sticking to some country a long way off and refusing to face the fact that you have come to a new country. I know a good many Finns. And the younger people don't want that. It is too bad.

Then we have to decide — and define what is 'Canadian'.

You can define some of these things. Do these people who are so anxious to preserve their Finnish culture, do they say no to the baby bonus, old age pension or unemployment insurance? Now we are talking about solid money. They don't refuse that.

I don't see a contradiction there. I think we can have two kinds of identities. And one of them is a nostalgic one. I am quite aware that there is a kind of ideal self that is . . .

But it has to be maintained artificially with public money!

But who decides about values, what gets sold, published? Who has the power?

The publishers, the majority. Nobody will risk any money. You see, literature depends on what people wish to hear, and if writers wish to say what Finnish people want to hear, they should have stayed in Finland. If it was precious to them to do their Finnish cultural thing, they should have stayed in Finland.

But it is not only Finnish. It is the Finnish experience contributing to whatever the Canadian shared reality is. Do you read 'ethnic' literature?

No. It does not come my way. I think it is distributed by the State department as hand-outs. A very striking example of an author who has come to Canada and who publishes in English and is enormously successful is Joseph Skvorecky, who comes from Czechoslovakia. And Skvorecky has made his name as a North American writer, and is immensely appreciated. That is the way to do it. If he was still writing in Czech it would just be some home industry. [Ed. note: He does write in Czech, but is translated into English.]

What do you think constitutes the truly Canadian myth?

I don't think Canada has really found its dearest and deepest myth — which is going to be the myth of the northland. It is created by our founders and our history, which is very special. But we are different from the United States. You see, the United States was created in a revolution — our country was not. *It* was created in acceptance of often bitter realities. Now that is part of the Canadian myth: the myth of having deep necessity at the root of our nationhood. And the people who came from Ireland, England, Northern Europe often came here because of sheer necessity. There has been great prejudice in the last thirty years or so in the way in which the native population has been treated, but the native population was something quite extraordinary. They were primitive then. And the conflict between them and these — not particularly intellectual — immigrants was a frightful one.

Primitive in what way?

They belonged to the stone age. You cannot mix modern people with stone age people and expect the stone age people to get the best of it, because they won't. Also they were not as numerous as the newcomers, whose technology was rather good. Nowadays, the Indians suffer painfully and their trouble is a horrible one, but I think it is the inevitable impact of modern civilization upon some people who have not advanced beyond the stone age and who are still alive. Mind you, this is something which I think is very often neglected in the consideration of the lot of the native people. They were not all trodden down and they did not all live in squalor. There is always collective guilt when a highly civilized group takes a country from primitive groups. It is just one of the facts of history.

I think they have a very rich alternative philosophy which has not been appreciated.

I think we have to treat them with decency. But we cannot make them do what they do not want to do. I haven't any prejudice whatever against the Indians. As I told you I am part Indian myself, but we can't do something for them if they don't want to.

You have often suggested that Canada's approach to multicultural otherness, particularly in contrast with the supposedly more 'Freudian' melting-pot philosophy of the United States, is similar to the receptive, 'feminine' openness and suspension of dogma in Jungian philosophy and psychology.

I get into great trouble when I talk about it because, in a recent article in *Harper's*, I said what I truly believe in Jungian terms—which they simply couldn't understand and refused to believe: Canada is very much an introverted country because its history made it so. The States is an extroverted country and its revolutionary impulse is carried right on, and they still have the feeling that they are marvellously vital and they project it outwards onto a shadow. Who is the shadow? The shadow is the USSR. We do not have enemies. [For them] the evil is always on the other side. What they don't recognize is that the enemy is within. I honestly think we are more open to the rest of the world than the States is. Because we are introverted, we are a sort of accepting nation, not a projecting nation.

This is how I feel about the issue of multiculturalism: at best, it means accepting and encouraging other ideas regarding the myths of Canada, other kinds of cultural expression.

Yes, well, I have probably overstated my case. I am in favour; I just feel that we have got to have some kind of [system] whereby the people whom we welcome here in a country as rich as ours are all pushing, as we are, towards a great new country, because I think Canada is a very, very important country.

On the other hand, some feel that multiculturalism conceals a subtle tyranny, in the sense that some ethnic groups are really kept from assimilating to the establishment rules and values. Maybe 'the White Anglo-Saxon Protestant Middle-Upper-Class Male World View' is the only one worth adopting in a country where competition is getting tougher and tougher? Divide and conquer, isn't that an aspect of mastery over the ethnics' mysteries?

It might be so here in Ontario, and it is certainly so in Quebec, but I don't think it is so in the West. And you know the composition of the Canadian parliament, look at their names! What a mix their names are! In what groups do you think any sort of cultural apartheid exists, except obviously among the blacks?

The native people, definitely. I think that there is a feeling among the natives, for example, that their system of values is not understood: for example, their idea of being somehow closer to the earth, to the feminine aspects of the planet.

But this is something I insist upon all the time. None of these people ever come to me and talk about that. I would embrace them as people who believe in and understand the values I believe in. Their myths are romanticized and idealized, not sufficiently pulled together. They never offer us much that we can read or hear, to know what their philosophy is. I am not in favour of being exploited by the Indians, which I think we are at the moment: they're working on our Calvinist sense of guilt.

What about the fairly persistent theme in your fiction that the Canadian potential flows backwards towards its origins, for want of cultural recognition and a sufficiently high level of appreciation back home? You suggest one should go to Europe for training and bring it back to Canada.

Exactly, because you are not going to get the kind of training in Canada that you can get in Europe. We must go and get it and bring it home. We won't get it in the United States. One of the things I do very strongly feel is that every young Canadian who can ought to get away from Canada for a while.

Did your experience in Oxford in any way change your views about Canada and how you had internalized its ways and values?

That is what happened with me when I went to Oxford: I realized that Canada was not really the centre of the universe . . . but everything is changing so it isn't so much on the edge any more.

What do you think will happen with free trade? How will it affect the multicultural mix, the mosaic?

Well, I think it is going to be very difficult because already we are hearing criticism and mutterings from the States about the fact that our social programs are creating unfair competition with some of their manufacturing and wages and so forth. If these things are going to be endangered by free trade, free trade is going to cost us much more than it will ever be worth. I am afraid, because one of the things that is going to be hit is our radio and television system, and that is very vital to Canada. I think that the CBC, although everybody abuses it and it costs an awful lot of money, is something we can't afford to be without.

We have discussed the positive aspects of Canada. You write that the 'devil is the unexamined side of life.' In cultural, national terms, in terms of politics and immigration policies, how do you perceive the shadow side of the Canadian mosaic?

I don't know that the mosaic itself isn't directly responsible for the shadow side: the shadow in Canada is our sense of self-righteousness and the sort of intellectual laziness that goes with it. We don't feel we have to work hard enough, think intently and carefully enough; we are not intellectually alert and that is our shadow.

In the Salterton novels you dramatize this kind of self-satisfied littleness of provincial Canadian minds. But how do you define art? Now I realize that defining, for instance, 'good literature' is very hard. My own feeling is that it is 'good' when you activate the reader's own imagination and powers of judgement.

That is exactly it. I think that Canada is at last developing a recognizable intelligentsia. It did not have one before because it was just not big enough, but also the origins of most of our people did not tend towards the intelligentsia. We were not settled by people of education and often of aristocratic background, as America was before the Revolution. We were settled by poor people who had to come here out of naked necessity and they were not the kind of people from whom you produce an intelligentsia, but we are producing one now.

And this is something very strongly on your side. I think those in the intelligentsia are to be found among the new Canadians. To mention only one group that has contributed very greatly to the intelligent appreciation of the arts in Canada, there are the Hungarians. Because of the Revolution, an enormous number of them came here, upper-middle-class people of education and culture at home, and they brought culture with them.

What is the most important aspect of multiculturalism as you see it?

Time, time, time will take care of it. Time will develop it so that what is best in it, we will make use of.

You think the 'other solitudes' will be assimilated?

Not assimilated to the point of being washed out and made to be just like everybody else. But they will feel at home here. And feeling at home is important. But now my grandchildren are so Canadian I have to remind them that they had some Welsh ancestors.

I chose to come to Canada. I could go back but I do feel it has much to offer.

Yes. This is it, you see. You are in Canada by choice and that is a marvellous thing. So many came of bleak necessity. But out of pain comes strength.

CANADIAN MULTICULTURALISM ACT[1]
R.S.C. 1985, Chap. 24 (4th Supp.);
[1988, c. 31, assented to 21st July, 1988]

An Act for the preservation and enhancement of multiculturalism in Canada

[1988, c. 31, assented to 21st July, 1988]

WHEREAS the Constitution of Canada provides that every individual is equal before and under the law and has the right to the equal protection and benefit of the law without discrimination and that everyone has the freedom of conscience, religion, thought, belief, opinion, expression, peaceful assembly and association and guarantees those rights and freedoms equally to male and female persons;

AND WHEREAS the Constitution of Canada recognizes the importance of preserving and enhancing the multicultural heritage of Canadians;

AND WHEREAS the Constitution of Canada recognizes rights of the aboriginal peoples of Canada;

AND WHEREAS the Constitution of Canada and the *Official Languages Act* provide that English and French are the official languages of Canada and neither abrogates or derogates from any rights or privileges acquired or enjoyed with respect to any other language;

AND WHEREAS the *Citizenship Act* provides that all Canadians, whether by birth or by choice, enjoy equal status, are entitled to the same rights, powers and privileges and are subject to the same obligations, duties and liabilities;

AND WHEREAS the *Canadian Human Rights Act* provides that every individual should have an equal opportunity with other individuals to make the life that the individual is able and wishes to have, consistent with the duties and obligations of that individual as a member of society, and, in order to secure that opportunity, establishes the Canadian Human Rights Commission to redress any pro-

---

[1] The text of the Act that follows includes only the English-language section.

scribed discrimination, including discrimination on the basis of race, national or ethnic origin or colour;

AND WHEREAS Canada is a party to the *International Convention on the Elimination of All Forms of Racial Discrimination*, which Convention recognizes that all human beings are equal before the law and are entitled to equal protection of the law against any discrimination and against any incitement to discrimination, and to the *International Covenant on Civil and Political Rights*, which Covenant provides that persons belonging to ethnic, religious or linguistic minorities shall not be denied the right to enjoy their own culture, or profess and practise their own religion or to use their own language;

AND WHEREAS the Government of Canada recognizes the diversity of Canadians as regards race, national or ethnic origin, colour and religion as a fundamental characteristic of Canadian society and is committed to a policy of multiculturalism designed to preserve and enhance the multicultural heritage of Canadians while working to achieve the equality of all Canadians in the economic, social, cultural and political life of Canada;

NOW, THEREFORE, Her Majesty, by and with the advice and consent of the Senate and House of Commons of Canada, enacts as follows:

SHORT TITLE

1. This Act may be cited as the *Canadian Multiculturalism Act*.

INTERPRETATION

2. In this Act,
'federal institution' means any of the following institutions of the Government of Canada:
  (a) a department, board, commission or council, or other body or office, established to perform a governmental function by or pursuant to an Act of Parliament or by or under the authority of the Governor in Council, and
  (b) a departmental corporation or Crown corporation as defined in section 2 of the *Financial Administration Act*,
but does not include
  (c) any institution of the Council or government of the Northwest Territories or the Yukon Territory, or

(d) any Indian band, band council or other body established to perform a governmental function in relation to an Indian band or other group of aboriginal people;

'Minister' means such member of the Queen's Privy Council for Canada as is designated by the Governor in Council as the Minister for the purposes of this Act.

MULTICULTURALISM POLICY OF CANADA

3. (1) It is hereby declared to be the policy of the Government of Canada to

(a) recognize and promote the understanding that multiculturalism reflects the cultural and racial diversity of Canadian society and acknowledges the freedom of all members of Canadian society to preserve, enhance and share their cultural heritage;

(b) recognize and promote the understanding that multiculturalism is a fundamental characteristic of the Canadian heritage and identity and that it provides an invaluable resource in the shaping of Canada's future;

(c) promote the full and equitable participation of individuals and communities of all origins in the continuing evolution and shaping of all aspects of Canadian society and assist them in the elimination of any barrier to such participation;

(d) recognize the existence of communities whose members share a common origin and their historic contribution to Canadian society, and enhance their development;

(e) ensure that all individuals receive equal treatment and equal protection under the law, while respecting and valuing their diversity;

(f) encourage and assist the social, cultural, economic and political institutions of Canada to be both respectful and inclusive of Canada's multicultural character;

(g) promote the understanding and creativity that arise from the interaction between individuals and communities of different origins;

(h) foster the recognition and appreciation of the diverse cultures of Canadian society and promote the reflection and the evolving expressions of those cultures;

(i) preserve and enhance the use of languages other than English and French, while strengthening the status and use of the official languages of Canada; and

(j) advance multiculturalism throughout Canada in harmony with the national commitment to the official languages of Canada.

(2) It is further declared to be the policy of the Government of Canada that all federal institutions shall
  (a) ensure that Canadians of all origins have an equal opportunity to obtain employment and advancement in those institutions;
  (b) promote policies, programs and practices that enhance the ability of individuals and communities of all origins to contribute to the continuing evolution of Canada;
  (c) promote policies, programs and practices that enhance the understanding of and respect for the diversity of the members of Canadian society;
  (d) collect statistical data in order to enable the development of policies, programs and practices that are sensitive and responsive to the multicultural reality of Canada;
  (e) make use, as appropriate, of the language skills and cultural understanding of individuals of all origins; and
  (f) generally, carry on their activities in a manner that is sensitive and responsive to the multicultural reality of Canada.

IMPLEMENTATION OF THE MULTICULTURAL POLICY OF CANADA

4. The Minister, in consultation with other ministers of the Crown, shall encourage and promote a coordinated approach to the implementation of the multiculturalism policy of Canada and may provide advice and assistance in the development and implementation of programs and practices in support of the policy.

5. (1) The Minister shall take such measures as the Minister considers appropriate to implement the multiculturalism policy of Canada and, without limiting the generality of the foregoing, may
  (a) encourage and assist individuals, organizations and institutions to project the multicultural reality of Canada in their activities in Canada and abroad;
  (b) undertake and assist research relating to Canadian multiculturalism and foster scholarship in the field;
  (c) encourage and promote exchanges and cooperation among the diverse communities of Canada;
  (d) encourage and assist the business community, labour organizations, voluntary and other private organizations as well as

public institutions, in ensuring full participation in Canadian society, including the social and economic aspects, of individuals of all origins and their communities, and in promoting respect and appreciation for the multicultural reality of Canada;

(e) encourage the preservation, enhancement, sharing and evolving expression of the multicultural heritage of Canada;

(f) facilitate the acquisition, retention and use of all languages that contribute to the multicultural heritage of Canada;

(g) assist ethno-cultural minority communities to conduct activities with a view to overcoming any discriminatory barrier and, in particular, discrimination based on race or national or ethnic origin;

(h) provide support to individuals, groups or organizations for the purpose of preserving, enhancing and promoting multiculturalism in Canada; and

(i) undertake such other projects or programs in respect of multiculturalism, not by law assigned to any other federal institution, as are designed to promote the multiculturalism policy of Canada.

(2) The Minister may enter into an agreement or arrangement with any province respecting the implementation of the multiculturalism policy of Canada.

(3) The Minister may, with the approval of the Governor in Council, enter into an agreement or arrangement with the government of any foreign state in order to foster the multicultural character of Canada.

6. (1) The ministers of the Crown, other than the Minister, shall, in the execution of their respective mandates, take such measures as they consider appropriate to implement the multiculturalism policy of Canada.

(2) A minister of the Crown, other than the Minister, may enter into an agreement or arrangement with any province respecting the implementation of the multiculturalism policy of Canada.

7. (1) The Minister may establish an advisory committee to advise and assist the Minister on the implementation of this Act and any

other matter relating to multiculturalism and, in consultation with such organizations representing multicultural interests as the Minister deems appropriate, may appoint the members and designate the chairman and other officers of the committee.

(2) Each member of the advisory committee shall be paid such remuneration for the member's services as may be fixed by the Minister and is entitled to be paid the reasonable travel and living expenses incurred by the member while absent from the member's ordinary place of residence in connection with the work of the committee.

(3) The chairman of the advisory committee shall, within four months after the end of each fiscal year, submit to the Minister a report on the activities of the committee for that year and on any other matter relating to the implementation of the multiculturalism policy of Canada that the chairman considers appropriate.

GENERAL

8. The Minister shall cause to be laid before each House of Parliament, not later than the fifth sitting day of that House after January 31 next following the end of each fiscal year, a report on the operation of this Act for that fiscal year.

9. The operation of this Act and any report made pursuant to section 8 shall be reviewed on a permanent basis by such committee of the House, of the Senate or of both Houses of Parliament as may be designated or established for the purpose.